ILLUSTRATED HANDBOOK OF ELECTRONIC TABLES, SYMBOLS, MEASUREMENTS AND VALUES

second edition

ILLUSTRATED HANDBOOK OF ELECTRONIC TABLES, SYMBOLS, MEASUREMENTS AND VALUES

second edition

Raymond H. Ludwig

Prentice-Hall, Inc.
Business and Professional Division
Englewood Cliffs, New Jersey

Prentice-Hall International, Inc., *London*
Prentice-Hall of Australia, Pty. Ltd., *Sydney*
Prentice-Hall Canada Inc., *Toronto*
Prentice-Hall of India Private Ltd., *New Delhi*
Prentice-Hall of Japan, Inc., *Tokyo*
Prentice-Hall of Southeast Asia Pte. Ltd., *Singapore*
Whitehall Books, Ltd., *Wellington, New Zealand*
Editora Prentice-Hall do Brasil Ltda., *Rio de Janeiro*

© 1984 by

Prentice-Hall, Inc.
Englewood Cliffs, N.J.

Editor: George E. Parker

Library of Congress Cataloging in Publication Data

Ludwig, Raymond H.
  Illustrated handbook of electronic tables, symbols,
measurements and values.

  Includes index.
  1. Electronics—Handbooks, manuals, etc. I. Title.
TK7825.L83   1984   621.381'0212   83-17620
ISBN 0-13-450494-1

Printed in the United States of America

To Dawn and Dad

The Increased Value
This Second Edition Offers

All of us have read and studied reference books that dwell on theoretical aspects with only minimum coverage of practical application data (in fact, some let important application data evaporate in mid-paragraph). The second edition of this *Illustrated Handbook* places even greater stress on practical application of both standardized and nonstandardized data, plus theory, rules, secrets, formulas, facts, and other essential application data you need. New facts, formulas, symbols, technical data, hints, secrets . . . and better organization for finding data quickly are but a few of the key areas focused on in this edition.

You will find the following six chapters to be a veritable electronics library, consisting of literally thousands of facts which you and I are expected to know, and apply, often at an instant's notice. Each chapter serves as a hub for important subject matter deemed necessary based upon today's technology. In order to make your daily use of this book more productive, the contents within each chapter are subdivided into specific data sections, each of which is identified by its chapter number plus the special numbering code. The Table of Contents listing, the special chapter indicators throughout the book, along with section and/or subsection reference numbers in the index, will help speed you to the specific data you require.

There are two major similarities, or carryovers, from the first edition. The first similarity is: I continue to speak to you in a language you recognize and understand. The second likeness is the "buffet" approach to knowledge. You still need not reconsume and digest technical data which has no significant value at that particular time. You can skip chapters, or skip around within chapters to focus on what you want, when you want, and as often as needed.

A priceless gold mine of facts concerning the unique language for today's technology is found in Chapter 1. You will find an accumulation of standardized symbols, along with those used in industry, which differ between companies. Each symbol has been identified by popular name and specific reference number. The assigned numbering will yield quicker referencing when desiring information on abbreviation and letter symbols, computer technology abbreviations, mathematical signs and symbols, logic symbols, schematic symbols, semiconductor device packaging and symbols, or vacuum tube symbols.

A quick review, ready reference of all essential facts, and rules for electronic calculation is found in Chapter 2. You will find a host of specific information concerning advanced mathematics, algebra, arithmetic, complex numbers and vectors, geometry, logarithms, and trigonometry.

Chapter 3 has pulled together all of the important rules, laws, characteristics, facts, and formulas concerning admittance, alternating current, antennas, characteristic impedance, circuitry comparison, conductance, decibels, delta and wye circuits, impedance, inductors, magnetism, meters, modulation, motor-generator-alternator, Ohm's Law, oscillators, power, power supplies, reactance, resonance, theorems, time constants, and wavelength-waveguide specifics.

The unprecedented combination of facts, secrets, and applied theory arrangement of Chapter 4, "Technical Assistance Guide—Technology Update" is topically organized. The alphabetical subject matter listing includes capacitors, disks, diodes, FETs, fuses, IC's, op-amps, opto-electronics, resistors, SCR's, transformers, transistors, timers, triacs, vacuum tubes, and zener diodes. In this chapter, it would be best to start at the beginning of whichever of the sixteen subject matter topics selected for reference. By doing so, an all-inclusive, "whole-story account" will be unfolded in a sequential manner, and reveal it all in a "this is the way it is" approach. The "quick find" subject matter identification method, referenced both in the Table of Contents and in the Index, plus special chapter marking used throughout the book, will aid you in data seeking. If, for example, you desire information on Operational Amplifiers, the Index and Table of Contents would suggest section 4.7 (Chapter 4, Part 7). If, more specifically, you desire the noninverting characteristics and data for the Operational Amplifier, then Section 4.7-4 would be suggested. First locate Chapter 4 using the blackened chapter indicators, then follow subsection numbers within Chapter 4 subject matter.

The last two Chapters, 5 and 6, serve as ready reference for those of us who simply forget some broad-range, hard-to-find, time-saving information. Chapter 5 will provide data particulars concerning Alpha, Beta, American Wire Gage, decibels, decimal and millimeter, fractional unit of inch equivalents, gas-filled lamps, miniature lamps, drill and tap and machine screw sizes, etc., radio frequency, cable, plus television channel frequency allocations. Chapter 6 catalogs hundreds of alphabetized conversion factors just for those numerous occasions when this data is of primary importance.

Almost every profession has its own language, symbols, and specialized terminology. This is especially true in electronics. We must know and properly use countless numbers of facts, formulas, tables, rules, component identification characteristics, wire codes, symbols, and meanings . . . blending all of this knowledge with the latest application procedures and techniques.

This second edition of the *Illustrated Handbook of Electronic Tables, Symbols, Measurements and Values* is even easier to use because all related rules, formulas, facts, hints, and secrets are put together in one subject section: resistor data is with resistors, capacitor data with capacitors, etc. This alone will benefit anyone whose experience ranges from one week of electronic training to twenty or more years of experience. It eliminates nice-to-know or impressive data, and tells what you need to know to survive in Electronics . . . what it is, what it is called, what it looks like, how it is tested, how it is numbered, which lead is which, and just what you can rely upon for industry standards.

The practical value offered by this handbook lies in its extraordinary range of important reference data. You will find that it will continue to be one of your most frequently used and important references now . . . and for years to come.

Raymond H. Ludwig

Contents

4 Technical Assistance Guide—Technology Update 242

C
O
N
T
E
N
T
S

1 Directory of Electronic Symbols

Communication between individuals is actually a two-way street because the speaker and listener must talk the same language to avoid any misconceptions. Sometimes what you are trying to convey is known by someone else as being something different and may lead to a communications gap.

The terms, schematic symbols, subscripts, and abbreviations commonly employed in the vast field of electronics make up a specialized language, a language full of possible communication gaps. One reason for this is that the standards governing our language often become modified within an industry, so that each company has its own individual language.

The following eleven sections of Chapter 1 will close any electronic communication gaps that may exist in your language, by quickly and clearly relating standardized data to those meaning the same thing.

To aid you further, all of the illustrations and data have been alphabetized within each particular section.

1.1   ARCHITECTURAL ELECTRICAL/ELECTRONIC SYMBOLS

1.1-1   BUS DUCTS/WIRE WAYS

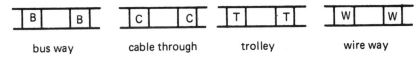

bus way   cable through   trolley   wire way

1.1-2   DISTRIBUTION (UNDERGROUND)

hand hole   man hole

1.1-3   LIGHTING OUTLETS

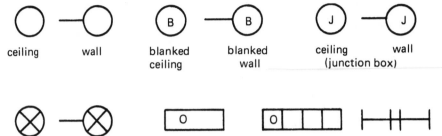

ceiling   wall   blanked ceiling   blanked wall   ceiling (junction box)   wall

exit-ceiling exit-wall
(surface/suspended)

fluorescent (surface) (suspended)

fluorescent (continuous row)

fluorescent-strip (bare lamp)

1.1-4   LIGHTING OUTLETS–RECESSED

ceiling   wall   exit-ceiling   exit-wall   fluorescent

1.1-5   PANEL BOARD / SWITCH BOARD

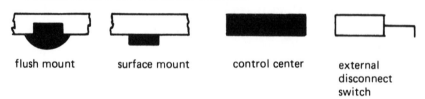

flush mount   surface mount   control center   external disconnect switch

1.1-6   RECEPTACLE OUTLETS

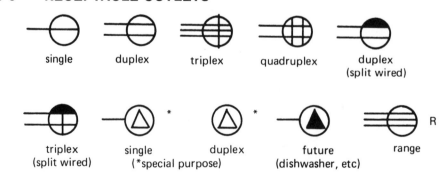

single   duplex   triplex   quadruplex   duplex (split wired)

triplex (split wired)   single (*special purpose)   duplex *   future (dishwasher, etc)   range

1.1-6   RECEPTACLE OUTLETS, continued

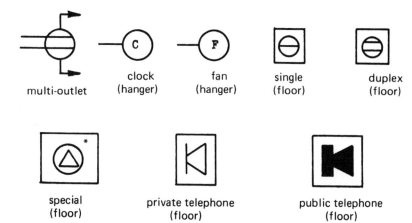

NOTE: GROUNDED OUTLETS HAVE A "G" NEXT TO THE SAME SYMBOLS.

1.1-7   SIGNALING OUTLETS (INDUSTRIAL – COMMERCIAL – INSTITUTIONS)

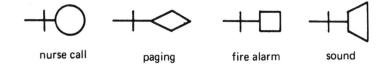

1.1-8   SIGNALING OUTLETS (RESIDENTIAL)

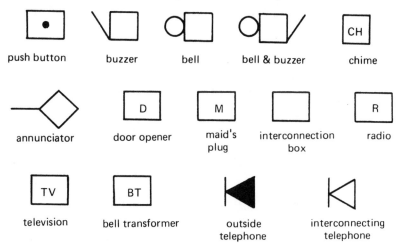

1.1-9   SWITCHES

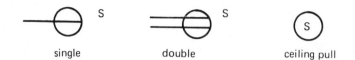

single   double   ceiling pull

NOTE: LETTERS WITH SWITCHES HAVE THE FOLLOWING MEANING:

S	single pole	SL	low voltage
S2	double pole	SD	door
S3	three way	ST	time
S4	four way	SCB	circuit breaker
SK	key operated	SMC	momentary contact
SP	with pilot lamp		

1.1-10   WIRING

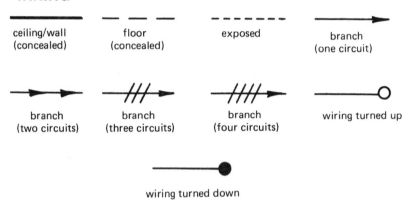

ceiling/wall   floor   exposed   branch
(concealed)   (concealed)   (one circuit)

branch   branch   branch   wiring turned up
(two circuits)   (three circuits) (four circuits)

wiring turned down

1.2   CHASSIS AND INDUSTRIAL WIRING COLOR CODES

Manufacturers of electronic components and devices have for years marked their products with specific color codes which have specific meanings. The trained electronics person can readily identify facts concerning resistors, capacitors, inductors, transistors and even circuitry functions.

Industrial and commercial electronic circuitry wiring have accepted color codes that help us identify circuitry functions. The unfortunate part of identifying circuits solely by wire colors used is that of reliability, because not all manufacturers use accepted colors for specific circuitry connection. The colored wiring assignments listed in this chapter usually can be relied upon, but due caution must be observed when equipment circuitry identification by colors is in doubt. To be safe, verify first and rely second.

Wiring Identification

In wiring harnesses, or in places where wires cannot be easily traced from beginning to end, manufacturers identify each wire circuit by color, by color and number, or simply by number. The resistor color code digit assignment provides quick relationships that are frequently used. To the left of each color listed for the wire colors employed in chassis and industrial wiring assignments, you will find a digit representing that particular color.

1.2-1 COMMERCIAL RADIO–TELEVISION CHASSIS WIRING COLOR CODE

		Digit	Color	Circuitry Function
1.2-1A	**Grounds**	0	Black (solid)	Grounded components and returns
			Black-brown	Identified grounds i.e., filament
			Black-red	Identified grounds i.e., B−
			Black-yellow	Identified grounds i.e., cathode/emitter
			Black-green	Identified grounds i.e., grid/base
1.2-1B	**Heater/Filaments**	1	Brown (solid)	Above or below ground
			Brown-red	Identified purpose i.e., rectifier
			Brown-yellow	Identified purpose
			Brown-green	Identified purpose
			Brown-white	Identified purpose
1.2-1C	**Power Supplies**	2	Red (solid)	Main source, B+
			Red-black	Intermediate source potential
			Red-yellow	Identified source potential
			Red-green	Intermediate source potential
			Red-blue	Intermediate source potential
			Red-white	Identified source
			Red-blue-yellow	Intermediate source potential

		Digit	Color	Circuitry Function
1.2-1D	**Screen Grids**	3	Orange (solid)	Positive potential
1.2-1E	**Cathodes/Emitter**	4	Yellow (solid)	Above and below ground
			Yellow-red	Identified circuit i.e., output
			Yellow-green	Identified circuit i.e., oscillator
1.2-1F	**Control Grids/Bases**	5	Green (solid)	Bias potentials
			Green-red	Identified element
			Green-yellow	Identified element
			Green-white	Identified element
1.2-1G	**Plate/Collector**	6	Blue (solid)	Plate or collector potentials
			Blue-red	Identified element
			Blue-yellow	Identified element
1.2-1H	**Miscellaneous**	7	Violet (solid)	Biases, returns
1.2-1I	**AC Power Source**	8	Gray (solid)	AC power potentials
1.2-1J	**Bias Supply Source**	9	White (solid)	Main source
			White-black	Alternate/offground connection
			White-brown	Intermediate AVC bias
			White-red	Below ground, maximum value
			White-orange	Intermediate fixed value
			White-yellow	Intermediate fixed value
			White-green	Preferred AVC bias
			White-blue	Internal antenna or connection to

1.2-2 INDUSTRIAL WIRING COLOR CODES

Color	Abbreviation	Common Circuit Function
Black	Bk	Line not at ground potential, load, line voltage control
Red	R	Alternating current control, not at ground potential
Yellow	Y	Interlock panel control
Green	Gn	Safety grounding conductor
Blue	Bl	Direct current control
White	W	Grounded neutral conductor

1.3 CIRCUIT ELEMENT SCHEMATIC SYMBOLS

1.3-1 ADJUSTABLE

preset   continuous   non-linear

1.3-2 ALTERNATOR

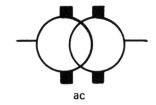

ac

1.3-3 AMPERAGE

DC   AC

1.3-4 AMPLIFIER

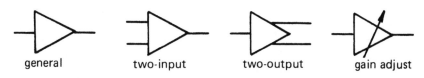

general   two-input   two-output   gain adjust

1.3-4   AMPLIFIER, continued

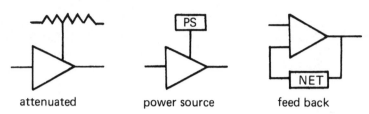

attenuated   power source   feed back

1.3-5   ANTENNA

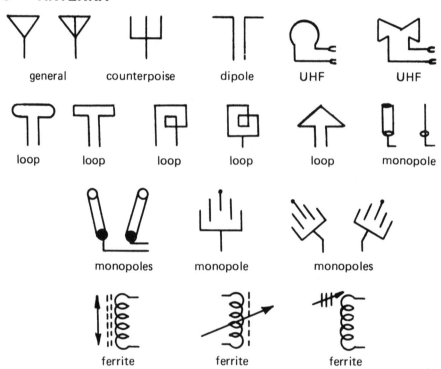

general   counterpoise   dipole   UHF   UHF

loop   loop   loop   loop   loop   monopole

monopoles   monopole   monopoles

ferrite   ferrite   ferrite

1.3-6   ARRESTER –LIGHTNING

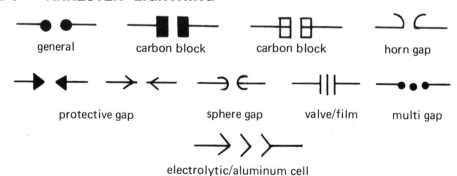

general   carbon block   carbon block   horn gap

protective gap   sphere gap   valve/film   multi gap

electrolytic/aluminum cell

1.3-7 ATTENUATOR

general/balanced   unbalanced   fixed

1.3-8 AUDIBLE SIGNALING DEVICE

bell   buzzer   bell & buzzer   speaker
siren
horn

telegraph sounder

1.3-9 BRAKE, CLUTCH

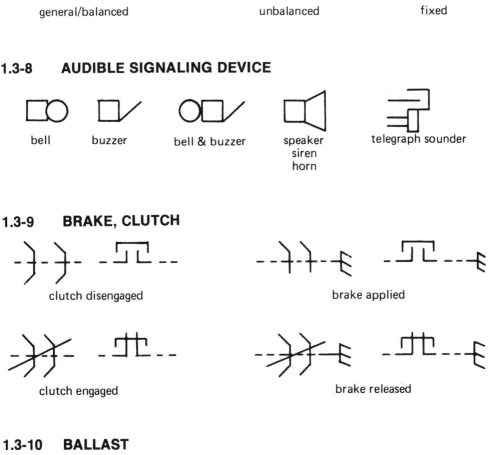

clutch disengaged   brake applied

clutch engaged   brake released

1.3-10 BALLAST

1.3-11 BATTERY

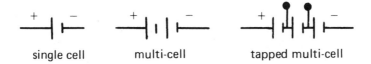

single cell   multi-cell   tapped multi-cell

1.3-12 CAPACITOR –FIXED

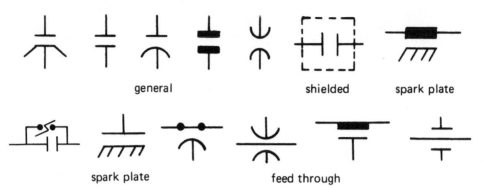

general   shielded   spark plate

spark plate   feed through

1.3-13 CAPACITOR –ELECTROLYTIC

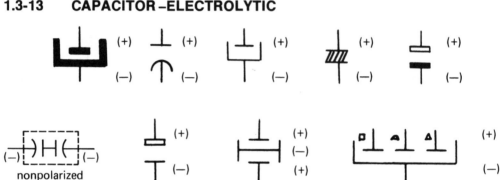

nonpolarized

1.3-14 CAPACITOR –VARIABLE

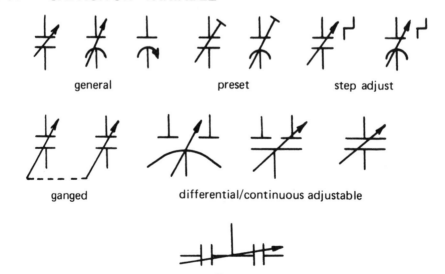

general   preset   step adjust

ganged   differential/continuous adjustable

split rotor

1.3-15 CELLS–PHOTOSENSITIVE

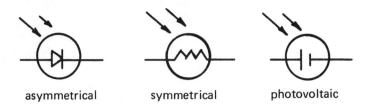

asymmetrical   symmetrical   photovoltaic

1.3-16 CIRCUIT BREAKER

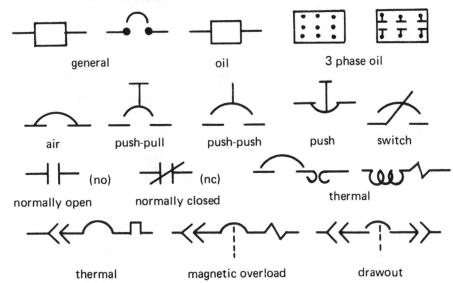

general   oil   3 phase oil

air   push-pull   push-push   push   switch

normally open (no)   normally closed (nc)   thermal

thermal   magnetic overload   drawout

1.3-17 COAXIAL CABLE

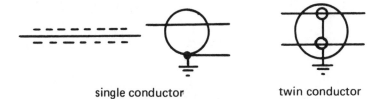

single conductor   twin conductor

1.3-18 CONDUCTOR

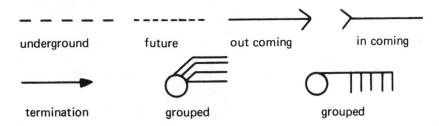

underground   future   out coming   in coming

termination   grouped   grouped

1.3-19   CONTACTS

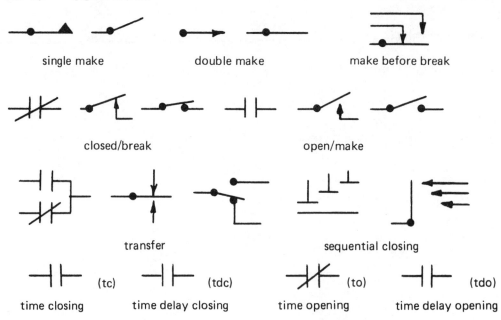

single make   double make   make before break

closed/break   open/make

transfer   sequential closing

—| |— (tc)   —| |— (tdc)   —|/— (to)   —| |— (tdo)
time closing   time delay closing   time opening   time delay opening

1.3-20   CONNECTOR

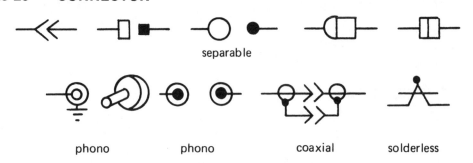

separable

phono   phono   coaxial   solderless

1.3-21   CONNECTOR –MALE PLUG

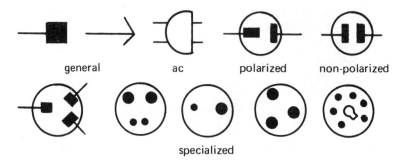

general   ac   polarized   non-polarized

specialized

1.3-22 CONNECTOR –FEMALE

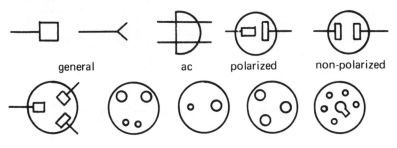

general   ac   polarized   non-polarized

specialized

1.3-23 COUPLERS –DIRECTIONAL

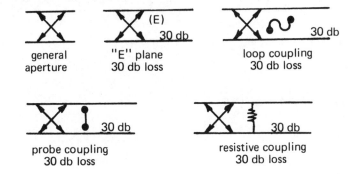

general   "E" plane   loop coupling
aperture   30 db loss   30 db loss

probe coupling   resistive coupling
30 db loss   30 db loss

1.3-24 COUPLING –HIGH FREQUENCY

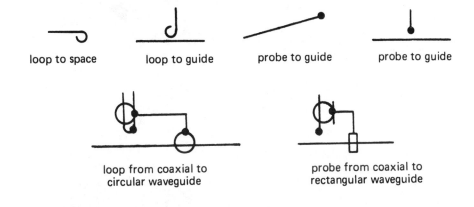

loop to space   loop to guide   probe to guide   probe to guide

loop from coaxial to   probe from coaxial to
circular waveguide   rectangular waveguide

1.3-25 CRYSTAL –DETECTOR

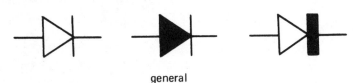

general

1.3-26   CRYSTAL

piezoelectric   general

1.3-27   DIODE (See Crystal Detector 1.3-25 and Rectifier-Halfwave 1.3-55)

1.3-28   FUSE

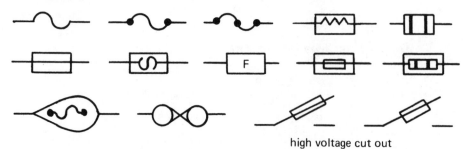

high voltage cut out

1.3-29   FILAMENT / HEATER

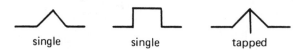

single   single   tapped

1.3-30   GROUND

earth   chassis   common connections

1.3-31   GENERATOR

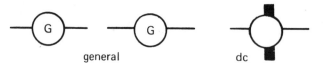

general   dc

1.3-32   HEADSET

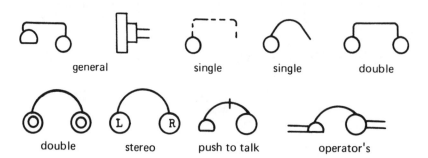

general   single   single   double

double   stereo   push to talk   operator's

1.3-33 INDUCTOR – AIR CORE

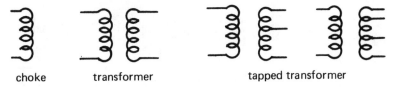

choke　　　transformer　　　　　tapped transformer

1.3-34 INDUCTOR – MAGNETIC / IRON CORE

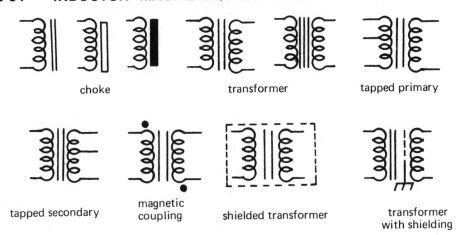

choke　　　　　　　　transformer　　　　　tapped primary

tapped secondary　　magnetic coupling　　shielded transformer　　transformer with shielding

1.3-35 INDUCTOR – ADJUSTABLE

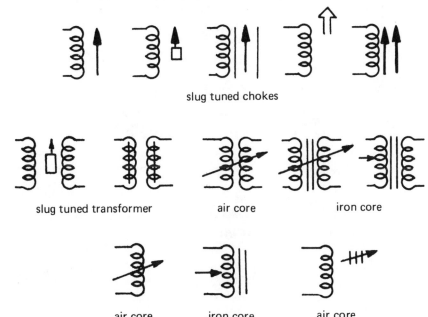

slug tuned chokes

slug tuned transformer　　air core　　iron core

air core　　iron core　　air core

1.3-36   INDUCTOR –TAPPED

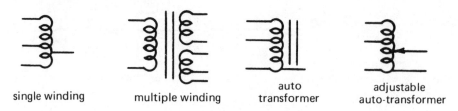

single winding   multiple winding   auto
                                               transformer   adjustable
                                                                   auto-transformer

1.3-37   INDUCTOR –POWDERED IRON CORE

choke   transformer

1.3-38   INDUCTOR –RESOLVER

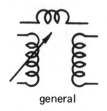

general

1.3-39   INDUCTOR –DYNAMOTOR

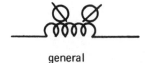

general

1.3-40   INDUCTOR –SATURABLE REACTOR

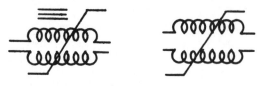

general

1.3-41   INDUCTOR –LINK COUPLING

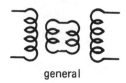

general

1.3-42   JACK

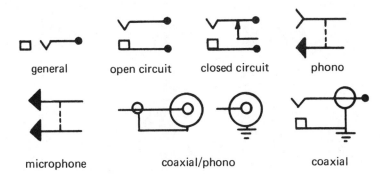

general   open circuit   closed circuit   phono

microphone   coaxial/phono   coaxial

1.3-43   KEY –TELEGRAPH

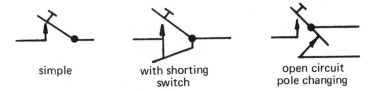

simple   with shorting   open circuit
                     switch   pole changing

1.3-44   LAMP –BULBS

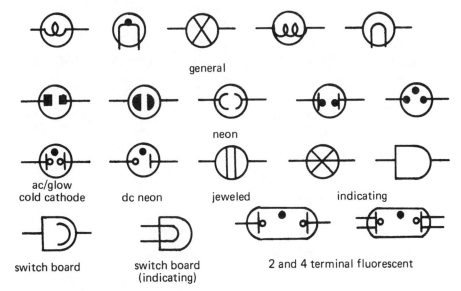

general

neon

ac/glow
cold cathode   dc neon   jeweled   indicating

switch board   switch board   2 and 4 terminal fluorescent
                  (indicating)

1.3-45   METER

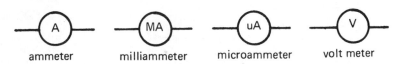

ammeter   milliammeter   microammeter   volt meter

1.3-45   METER, continued

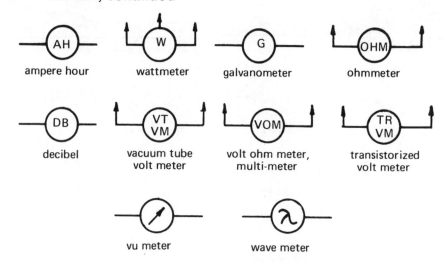

ampere hour   wattmeter   galvanometer   ohmmeter

decibel   vacuum tube
volt meter   volt ohm meter,
multi-meter   transistorized
volt meter

vu meter   wave meter

1.3-46   MICROPHONE

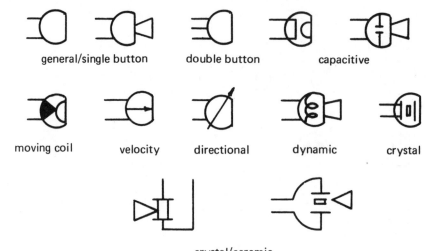

general/single button   double button   capacitive

moving coil   velocity   directional   dynamic   crystal

crystal/ceramic

1.3-47   MODE SUPPRESSION –HIGH FREQUENCY

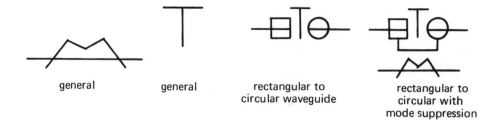

general   general   rectangular to
circular waveguide   rectangular to
circular with
mode suppression

1.3-48 MOTOR

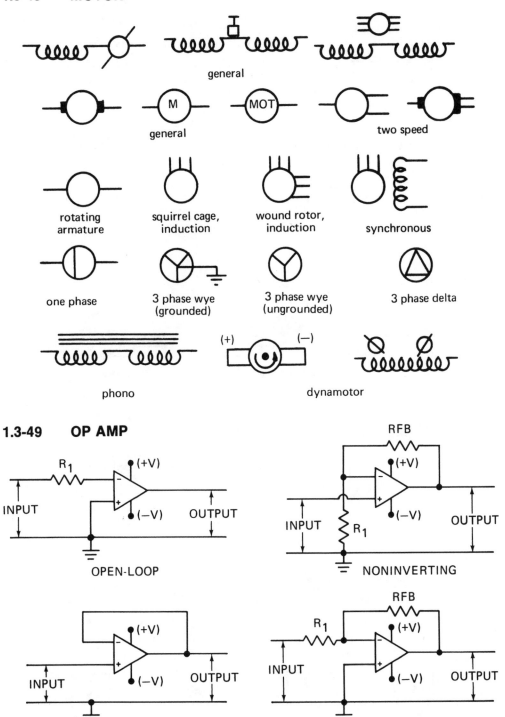

general

general

two speed

rotating armature

squirrel cage, induction

wound rotor, induction

synchronous

one phase

3 phase wye (grounded)

3 phase wye (ungrounded)

3 phase delta

phono

dynamotor

1.3-49 OP AMP

OPEN-LOOP

NONINVERTING

CLOSED LOOP

INVERTING (MOST POPULAR)

1.3-50   OSCILLATOR

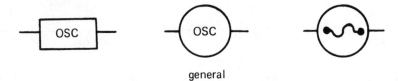

general

1.3-51   PHOTOELECTRIC EYE

general

1.3-52   PLUG–SIGNAL

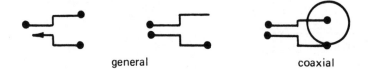

general   coaxial

1.3-53   PICKUP HEADS / CARTRIDGES

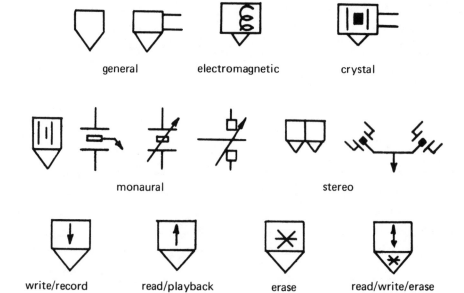

general   electromagnetic   crystal

monaural   stereo

write/record   read/playback   erase   read/write/erase

1.3-54   RECTIFIER –FULL WAVE

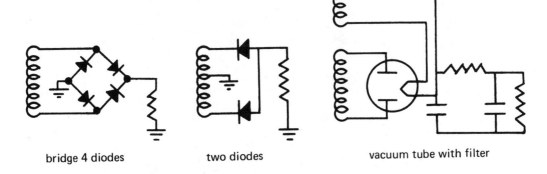

bridge 4 diodes   two diodes   vacuum tube with filter

1.3-55   RECTIFIER –HALF WAVE

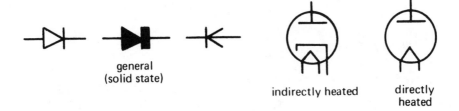

general
(solid state)

indirectly heated   directly
heated

1.3-56   RELAY

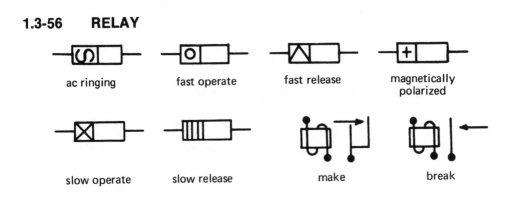

ac ringing   fast operate   fast release   magnetically
polarized

slow operate   slow release   make   break

1.3-57   RELAY –additional facts

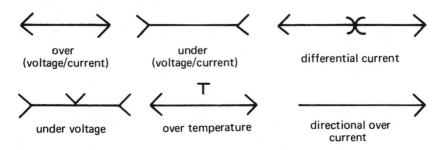

over
(voltage/current)   under
(voltage/current)   differential current

under voltage   over temperature   directional over
current

1.3-58   RESISTOR

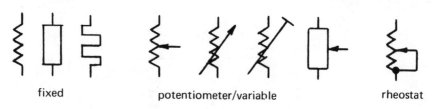

fixed   potentiometer/variable   rheostat

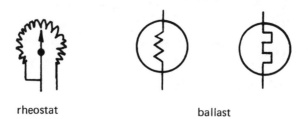

rheostat   ballast

1.3-59   RESISTOR –FUSIBLE

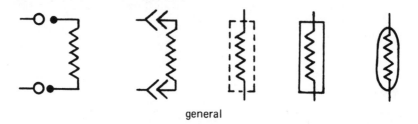

general

1.3-60   RESISTOR –TEMPERATURE COMPENSATED

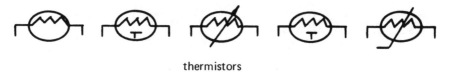

thermistors

1.3-61   RESISTOR –VOLTAGE DEPENDENT

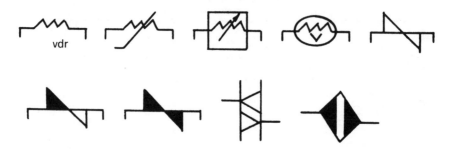

vdr

1.3-62 RESISTOR –LIGHT DEPENDENT

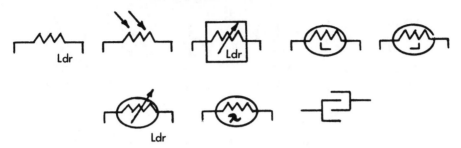

1.3-63 SPARK GAP

1.3-64 SPEAKER

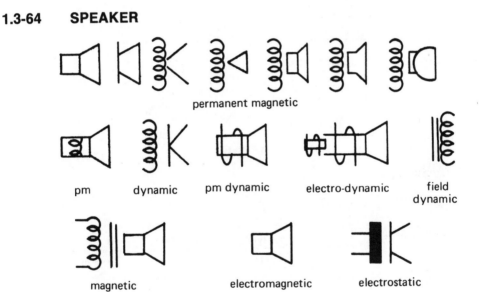

permanent magnetic

pm   dynamic   pm dynamic   electro-dynamic   field
                                                         dynamic

magnetic   electromagnetic   electrostatic

1.3-65 SWITCH –SINGLE POLE

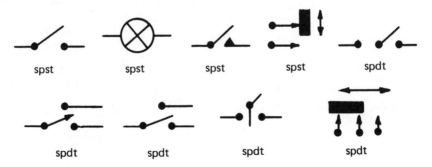

spst   spst   spst   spst   spdt

spdt   spdt   spdt   spdt

1.3-66   SWITCH –DOUBLE POLE

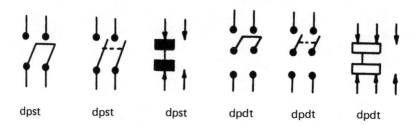

dpst   dpst   dpst   dpdt   dpdt   dpdt

1.3-67   SWITCH –ROTARY

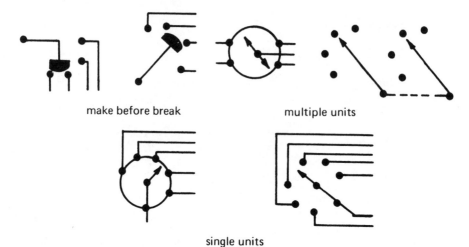

make before break   multiple units

single units

1.3-68   SWITCH –PUSH / PULL

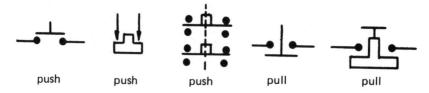

push   push   push   pull   pull

1.3-69   SWITCH –NONLOCKING

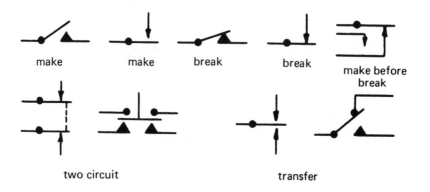

make   make   break   break   make before
                                                          break

two circuit   transfer

1.3-70 SWITCH –LOCKING

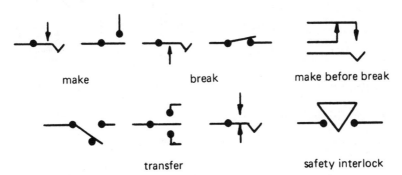

make   break   make before break

transfer   safety interlock

1.3-71 SWITCH –TIME DELAY

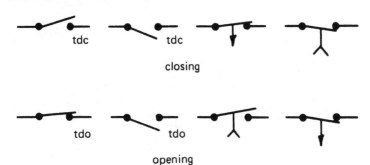

tdc   tdc

closing

tdo   tdo

opening

1.3-72 SWITCH –FLOW ACTIVATED

closing on flow increase   opening on flow increase

1.3-73 SWITCH –LEVEL ACTIVATED

closing with rising level   opening with rising level

1.3-74 SWITCH –PRESSURE ACTIVATED

closing with rising pressure   opening with rising pressure

1.3-75   SWITCH –TEMPERATURE ACTIVATED

closing with rising temperature   opening with rising temperature

1.3-76   SWITCH –WAFER

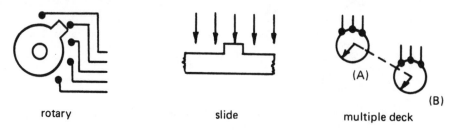

rotary   slide   multiple deck

1.3-77   SHIELDING

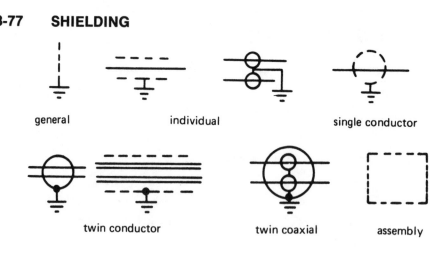

general   individual   single conductor

twin conductor   twin coaxial   assembly

1.3-78   SOURCE –VOLTAGE

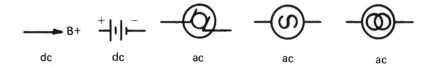

dc   dc   ac   ac   ac

1.3-79   SOURCE –CURRENT

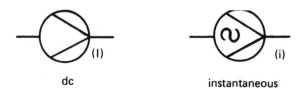

dc   instantaneous

1.3-80 SQUIB

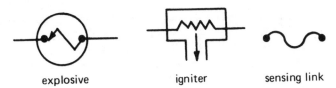

explosive   igniter   sensing link

1.3-81 SYNCHROS

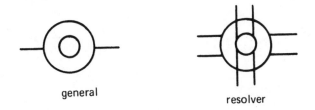

general

resolver

1.3-82 TERMINATION –LINE

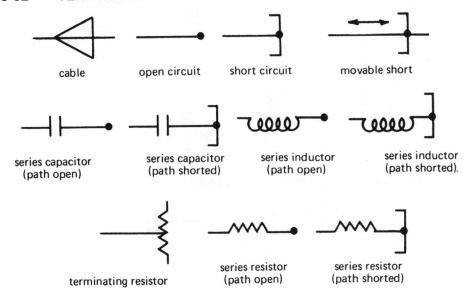

cable   open circuit   short circuit   movable short

series capacitor (path open)   series capacitor (path shorted)   series inductor (path open)   series inductor (path shorted).

terminating resistor   series resistor (path open)   series resistor (path shorted)

1.3-83 TERMINAL BOARD / STRIP

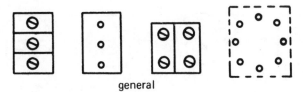

general

1.3-84   THERMOCOUPLE

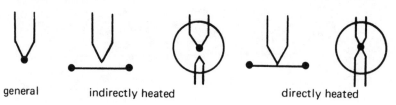

general   indirectly heated   directly heated

1.3-85   THERMO CUTOUT

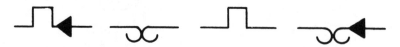

1.3-86   THERMO RELAY

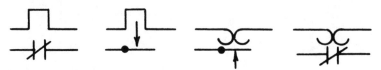

1.3-87   THERMOSTAT CONTACTS

break   break   make   make

1.3-88   THERMOSTAT –NONADJUSTABLE

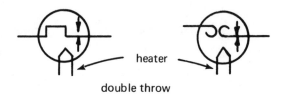

heater

double throw

1.3-89   THERMOSTAT –ADJUSTABLE

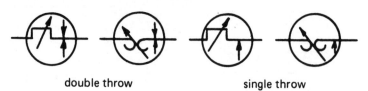

double throw   single throw

1.3-90   TRANSFORMER

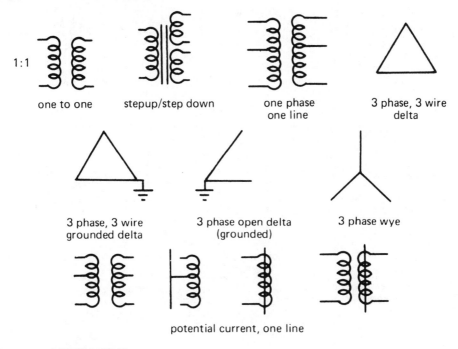

one to one   stepup/step down   one phase
one line   3 phase, 3 wire
delta

3 phase, 3 wire
grounded delta   3 phase open delta
(grounded)   3 phase wye

potential current, one line

1.3-91   VIBRATOR

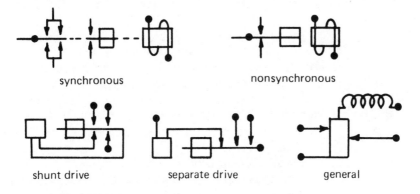

synchronous   nonsynchronous

shunt drive   separate drive   general

1.3-92   WAVEGUIDE

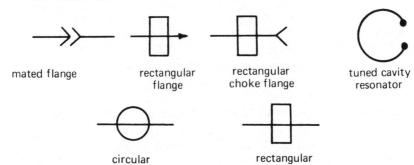

mated flange   rectangular
flange   rectangular
choke flange   tuned cavity
resonator

circular   rectangular

1.3-93   WAVEGUIDE–ROTARY JOINT

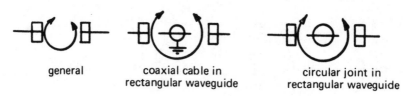

general   coaxial cable in   circular joint in
              rectangular waveguide   rectangular waveguide

1.3-94   WIRING

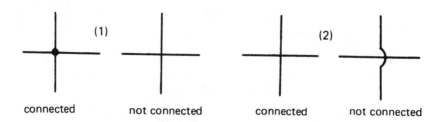

connected   not connected   connected   not connected

(1) connected and not connected (2) connected and not connected
*Schematic diagrams may use either #1 or #2, but not both.

1.4   COMPUTER TECHNOLOGY ABBREVIATION GLOSSARY

(A)   ACIA   Asynchronous Communication Interface Adapter
        ACM   Association for Computer Machinery
        ACU   Automatic Calling Unit
        ADAPSO   Association of Data Processing Service Organizations
        ADCCP   Advanced Data Communication Control Procedure
        ADLC   Advanced Data Link Controller
        AFIPS   American Federation of Information Processing Societies
        AIM   Avalanche Induced Migration
        ALU   Arithmetic Logic Unit
        ANSI   American National Standards Institute (formerly ASI)
        APPS   Automatic Parts Programming System
        APT   Automatically Programmed Tool
        AQL   Acceptable Quality Level
        ARQ   Automatic ReQuest for repeat (repetition)
        ARU   Audio Response Unit
        ASCII   American Standard Code for Information Interchange
        ASR   Automatic Send-Receive
        ATE   Automatic Testing Equipment
        ATG   Automatic Test Generation
        AVR   Automatic Voltage Regulator
        ATS   Automatic Test Systems / Sequence

(B)	BA	Bus Available
	BASIC	Beginner's All-Purpose Symbolic Instruction Code
	BBD	Bucket Brigade Device
	BCD	Binary Coded Decimal
	BDOS	Basic Disk Operating System
	BIOS	Basic Input/Output System
	BIT	Binary DigIT
	BOS	Basic Operating System
	BOT	Beginning Of Tape
	BPS	Bits Per Second
	BSAM	Basic Sequential Access Method
	BSC	Binary Synchronous Communication
	BV	Bus Vectored
(C)	CAD	Computer Aided Design
	CAI	Computer Aided Instruction
	CAM	Content Addressable Memory
	CAM	Computer Aided Manufacturing
	CCD	Charge Coupled Device
	CCE	Control Communication Executive
	CCP	Console Command Processor
	CE	Chip Enable
	CIM	Computer Input Microfilm
	CLK	CLocK
	CML	Current Mode Logic
	CMOS	Complementary Metal-Oxide-Semiconductor
	CNC	Computerized Numerical Control
	COBOL	COmmon Business Oriented Language
	COGO	COordinate GeOmetry
	COM	Computer Output Microfilm
	COMSAT	COMmunications SATellite corporation
	CPC	Computer Power Center
	CPE	Central Processing Element
	CP/M	Central Program for Microprocessors
	CPU	Central Processing Unit
	CRC	Cyclic Redundancy Check
	CROM	Control Read-Only Memory
	CRT	Cathode Ray Tube
	CSCR	Complementary Silicon Controlled Rectifier
	CSM	Combined Symbol Matching
	CTU	Control Terminal Unit
	CVSD	Continuous Variable Slope delta modulation Detector
(D)	DAA	Data Access Arrangement
	DAC	Digital to Analog Converter
	DAC	Data Acquisition and Control
	DAR	Data Access Register
	DAS	Data Acquisition System

	DATAMATION	Automatic data processing
	DBG	DeBuGging
	DCE	Data Communication Equipment
	DCS	Data Carrier System
	DCTL	Direct Coupled Transistor Logic
	DCU	Decade Counting Unit
	DCUTL	Direct Coupled Unipolar Transistor Logic
	DDCMP	Digital Data Communication Message Protocol
	DDR	Direct Data Register
	DIB	Data Input Bus
	DIP	Dual In-line Package
	DMA	Direct Memory Access
	DNC	Direct Numerical Control
	DOS	Disk Operating System
	DPMA	Data Processing Management Association
	DRAM	Dynamic Random Access Memory
	DSW	Device Status Word
	DTE	Data Terminal Equipment
	DTL	Diode-Transistor Logic
	DUV	Data Under Voice
(E)	EAM	Electrical Accounting Machine
	EAROM	Electrically Alterable Read Only Memory
	EBCDIC	Extended Binary Coded Decimal Interchange Code
	ECD	ElectroChromic Displays
	ECL	Emitter Coupled Logic
	EDP	Electronic Data Processing
	EEPROM	Electrically Erasable Programmable Read-Only Memory
	EEROM	Electrically Erasable Read-Only Memory
	EFTS	Electronic Funds Transfer System
	EOB	End Of Block
	EOF	End Of File
	EOM	End Of Message
	EOT	End Of Transmission
	EOT	End Of Tape
	EPROM	Electrically Programmable Read-Only Memory
(F)	FAST	Fixed Abrasive Slicing Technique
	FDM	Frequency Division Multiplexer
	FDOS	Floppy Disk Operating System
	FIFO	First In, First Out
	FORTRAN	FORmula TRANslation
	FOTS	Fiber Optic Transmission System
	FPLA	Field Programmable Logic Array
	FSC	Frequency Shift Coding
	FSK	Frequency Shift Keying
	FSM	Frequency Shift Modulation

(G)	GIGO	Garbage In, Garbage Out
	GPI	General Purpose Interface
	GPIA	General Purpose Interface Adapter
	GPR	General Purpose Register
(H)	HLL	High Level Logic
	HPL	High Performance Language
	HTL	High Threshold Logic
	HVL	High Voltage Logic
(I)	IC	Integrated Circuit
	IDC	Insulated Displacement Connector
	INTR	INTeRrupt
	I/O	Input-Output
	IOCS	Input-Output Control System
	IOP	Input-Output Processor
	IOT	Input-Output Transfer
	IPL	Initial Program Loader
	IPL	Information Processing Language
	IR	Instruction Register
	ISAM	Indexed Sequential Access Method
	ISL	Integrated Schottky Logic
	ISO	International Standardization Organization
	ITDM	Intelligent Time Division Multiplexing
	ITL	Integrated Injection Logic (I^2L)
	I^2L	Integrated Injection Logic
(J)	JCL	Job Control Language
(K)	KSAM	Keyed Sequential Access Method
	KSR	Keyboard Send, Receive
	KWIC	KeyWord In Context
(L)	LASER	Light Amplification by Stimulation of Emission of Radiation
	LCCC	Leadless Ceramic Chip Carriers
	LCD	Liquid Crystal Display
	LED	Light-Emitting Diode
	LIFO	Last In, First Out
	LISP	LISt Processing
	LSI	Large Scale Integration
(M)	MAR	Memory Address Register
	MBD	Magnetic Bubble Device
	MBM	Magnetic Bubble Memory
	MCP	Message Control Program
	MDR	Memory Data Register

1

	MIC	Microwave Integrated Circuits
	MICR	Magnetic Ink Character Recognition
	MIMD	Multiple Instruction, Multiple Data
	MIP	Multiple In-line Program
	MIS	Management Information System
	MIS	Metal Insulation Silicon
	MISD	Multiple Instruction Single Data
	MLB	MultiLayer Board
	MNOS	Metal Nitride Oxide Semiconductor
	MOD	MOving Domain memory
	MODEM	MOdulation / DEModulation
	MOS	Metal-Oxide-Semiconductor
	MPM	Multiprogramming control Program for Microprocessors
	MPS	MicroProcessor System
	MPS	MicroProcessor Series
	MPU	MicroProcessor Unit
	MQ	Multiplier-Quotient register
	MSB	Most Significant Bit
	MSD	Most Significant Digit
	MSI	Medium Scale Integration
	MTBF	Mean Time Between Failure
	MTTF	Mean Time To Failure
	MTTR	Mean Time To Repair
	MUX	MUltipleX
	MVS	Multiple Virtual Storage
(N)	NBV	NonBus Vectored
	NC	Numerical Control
	NDRO	NonDestructive ReadOut
	NMOS	N channel Metal-Oxide-Semiconductor
	NOOP	NO OPeration
	NRE	NonRecurring Engineering
	NRZ	NonReturn to Zero
(O)	OCR	Optical Character Recognition
(P)	PABX	Private Automatic Branch eXchange
	PAL	Programmable Array Logic
	PC	Program Counter
	PC	Programmable Controller
	PCB	Printed Circuit Board
	PCI	Programmable Communications Interface
	PCM	Pulse Code Modulation
	PCS	Program Control System
	PERT	Program Evaluation and Review Technique
	PGS	Program Generation System

	PIA	Peripheral Interface Adapter
	PIO	Processor Input, Output
	PISO	Parallel Input, Serial Output
	PIXEL	PIcture ELement
	PLA	Programmable Logic Array
	PLL	Phase-Locked Loop
	PRF	Pulse Repetition Frequency
	PM	Processor Module
	PMOS	"P" channel Metal-Oxide-Semiconductor
	POS	Point Of Sale
	PROM	Programmable Read-Only Memory
	PRT	Program Reference Table
	PSS	Porcelainized Steel Substrates
	PSU	Program Storage Unit
	PSW	Processor Status Word
(Q)	QAM	Quadrature Amplitude Modulation
	QSAM	Queue basic Sequential Access Method
	QTAM	Queued Telecommunication Access Method
(R)	RAEOM	Random Access Erase Only Memory
	RAM	Random Access Memory
	RB	Return to Bias
	RCS	Reloadable Control Store
	RCTL	Resistor-Capacitor-Transistor Logic
	RJE	Remote Job Entry
	RMM	Read Mostly Memory
	ROM	Read-Only Memory
	RPG	Report Program Generator
	RTBM	Real Time Bit Mapping
	RTC	Relative Time Clock
	RTE	Real Time Executive
	RTL	Resistor-Transistor Logic
	RTU	Remote Terminal Unit
	RTV	Room Temperature Vulcanizing
	RZ	Return to Zero
(S)	S	Slave / Standard
	SCRAM	StatiC Random Access Memory
	SDLC	Synchronous Data Link Control
	SDR	System Data Recorder file
	SF	Skip Flag
	SI	SuperImpose
	SIMD	Single Instruction Multiple Data
	SIPO	Serial In, Parallel Out
	SISD	Single Instruction Single Data
	SISO, SIO	Serial Input-Output

	SLICE	Subscriber Line Interface Circuit
	SOB	Short Of Block
	SOS	Silicon On Sapphire
	SPOOL	Simultaneous Peripheral Operations On Line
	SR	Switch Register
	SRV	Surface Recombination Velocity
	SSI	Small Scale Integration
	STD	Semiconductor on Thermoplastic on Dielectric
	SYSGEN	SYStem GENeration
	SYSLOG	SYStem LOG
(T)	TCAM	TeleCommunication Access Method
	TDM	Time Division Multiplexer
	TPA	Transient Program Area
	TRIB	Transfer Rate of Information Bits
	TSO	Time Sharing Option
	TTL	Transistor-Transistor Logic
(U)	UART	Universal Asynchronous Receiver/Transmitter
	UBC	Universal Block Channel
	ULA	Uncommitted Logic Arrays
	UPC	Universal Product Code
	UPS	Uninterruptible Power Supply
	USACII	U.S.A. standard Code for Information Interchange
	USART	Universal Synchronous/Asychronous Receiver/Transmitter
	USRT	Universal Synchronous Receiver/Transmitter
	UV	Ultra Violet
(V)	VAB	Voice Answer Back
	VDG	Video Display Generator
	VHS	Video Home System
	VHSIC	Very High Speed Integrated Circuit
	VLSI	Very Large Scale Integration
	VMOS	"V" groove Metal-Oxide-Semiconductor
	VRAM	Video Random Access Memory
	VRC	Vertical Redundancy Check
	VS	Virtual Storage
	VSP	Voice Synthesis Processor
(W)	WC	Word Counter
	WCS	Writable Control Store
	WP	Word Processing
	WPDP	Word Processing Data Processing
	WPM	Words Per Minute
	WS	Working Storage

1.5   DIGITAL CIRCUIT LOGIC SYMBOLS

1.5-1   AMPLIFIER

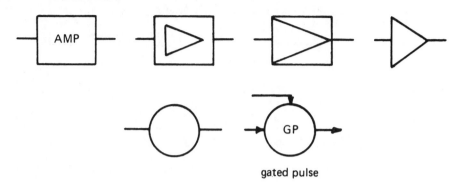

gated pulse

1.5-2   "AND" GATE

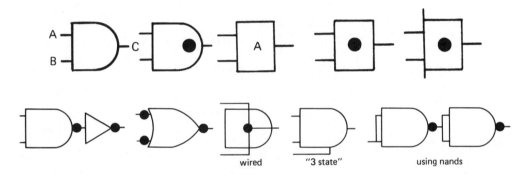

wired   "3 state"   using nands

"AND" GATE TRUTH TABLE

A	B	C	A	B	C	A	B	C
0	0	0	low	low	low	no	no	no
1	0	0	high	low	low	yes	no	no
0	1	0	low	high	low	no	yes	no
1	1	1	high	high	high	yes	yes	yes

THE NEEDS EVERYTHING GATE

1.5-3   "AND" GATE–MODIFIED

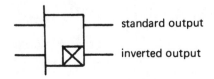

standard output

inverted output

1.5-4   "AND NOT"/INHIBITED GATE

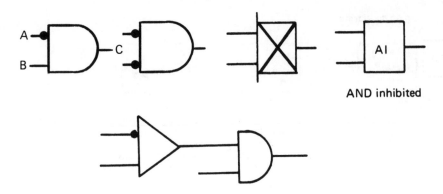

AND inhibited

"AND NOT" GATE TRUTH TABLE

A	B	C	A	B	C	A	B	C
0	0	0	low	low	low	no	no	no
1	0	0	high	low	low	yes	no	no
0	1	1	low	high	high	no	yes	yes
1	1	0	high	high	low	yes	yes	no

1.5-5   COMPLEMENTARY FLIP FLOP

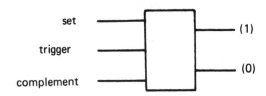

1.5-6   COMPLEMENT FLIP FLOP

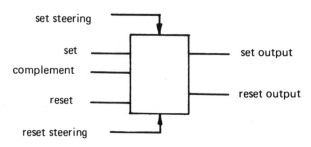

1.5-7 "EXCLUSIVE OR" GATE

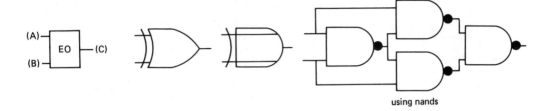

using nands

"EXCLUSIVE OR" GATE TRUTH TABLE

A	B	C	A	B	C	A	B	C
0	0	0	low	low	low	no	no	no
1	0	1	high	low	high	yes	no	yes
0	1	1	low	high	high	no	yes	yes
1	1	0	high	high	low	yes	yes	no

THE ANY BUT NOT ALL GATE

1.5-8 "EXCLUSIVE NOR" GATE

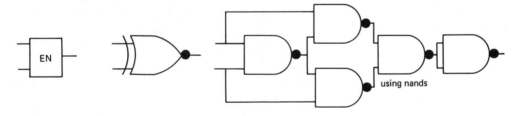

using nands

1.5-9 FULL ADDER

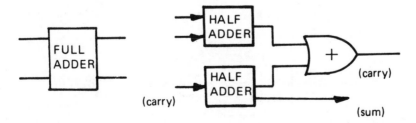

(carry)

(carry)

(sum)

1.5-10   HALF ADDER

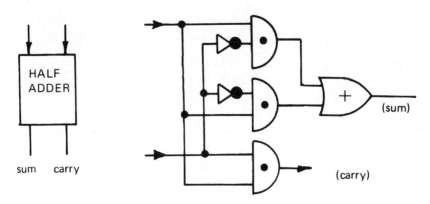

1.5-11   INVERTER

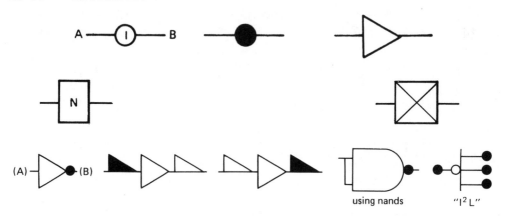

using nands   "I²L"

INVERTER TRUTH TABLE

A	B		A	B		A	B
0	1		low	high		yes	no
1	0		high	low		no	yes

1.5-12   LATCH FLIP FLOP

1.5-13   "NAND" GATE

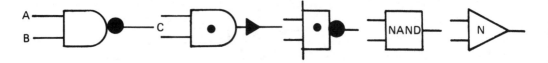

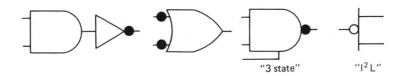

"NAND" GATE TRUTH TABLE

A	B	C	A	B	C	A	B	C
0	0	1	low	low	high	no	no	yes
1	0	1	high	low	high	yes	no	yes
0	1	1	low	high	high	no	yes	yes
1	1	0	high	high	low	yes	yes	no

1.5-14 "NOR" GATE

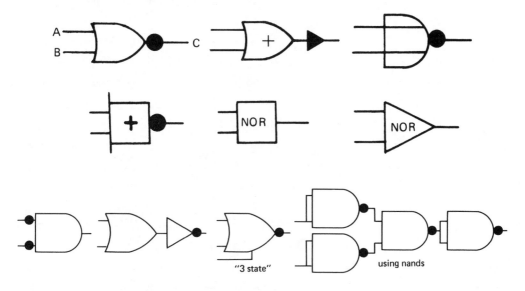

"NOR" GATE TRUTH TABLE

A	B	C	A	B	C	A	B	C
0	0	1	low	low	high	no	no	yes
1	0	0	high	low	low	yes	no	no
0	1	0	low	high	low	no	yes	no
1	1	0	high	high	low	yes	yes	no

1.5-15 "NOT" FUNCTION (See Inverters 1.5-11)

1.5-16   "OR" GATE

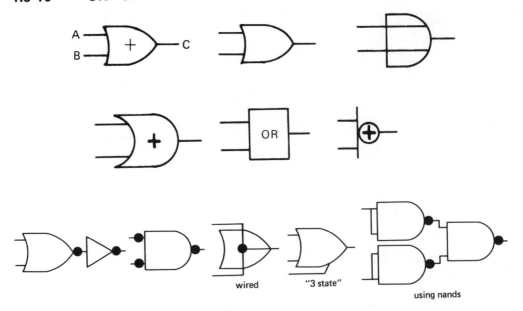

"OR" GATE TRUTH TABLE

A	B	C		A	B	C		A	B	C
0	0	0		low	low	low		no	no	no
1	0	1		high	low	high		yes	no	yes
0	1	1		low	high	high		no	yes	yes
1	1	1		high	high	high		yes	yes	yes

THE EITHER OR BOTH GATE

1.5-17   "OR NOT" FUNCTION

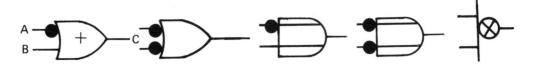

"OR NOT" TRUTH TABLE

A	B	C		A	B	C		A	B	C
0	0	1		low	low	high		no	no	yes
1	0	0		high	low	low		yes	no	no
0	1	1		low	high	high		no	yes	yes
1	1	1		high	high	high		yes	yes	yes

1.5-18 OSCILLATOR

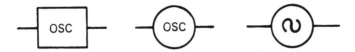

1.5-19 "RS" FLIP FLOP

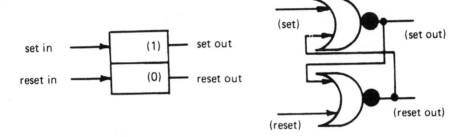

1.5-20 "RST" FLIP FLOP

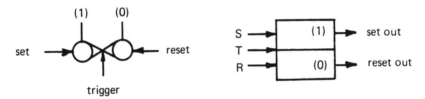

1.5-21 "T" FLIP FLOP

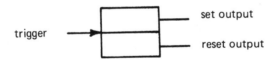

1.5-22 TIME DELAY

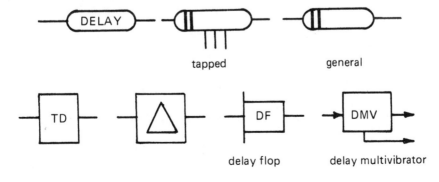

1.5-22   TIME DELAY, continued

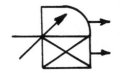 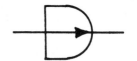

1.6   GREEK ALPHABET WITH SPECIALIZED MEANINGS

NAME	UPPERCASE	LOWERCASE	COMMON USE
Alpha	A	$\propto$, α	angles; absorption area, attenuation constant, coefficients, amplification factor, current gain
Beta	B	β, β	angles, flux density, coefficients, phase constant, current gain
Gamma	Γ	γ	conductivity, specific gravity, angles, propagation constant
Delta	Δ	δ, ∂	variation, density, angles, increment
Epsilon	E	ϵ	base for natural logarithms, dielectric constant, electrical intensity
Zeta	Z	ζ	impedance, coefficient, coordinates
Eta	H	η	hysteresis coefficient, efficiency, surface charge density, coordinates, intrinsic impedance
Theta	Θ	θ, Θ, ϑ	temperature; phase angle, time constant, reluctance
Iota	I	ι	current, vector unit
Kappa	K	κ	dielectric constant, susceptibility, coupling coefficient
Lamba	Λ	λ	wave length, attenuation constant
Mu	M	μ	micro, amplification factor, permeability
Nu	N	ν	reluctivity, frequency
Xi	Ξ	ξ	coordinates, output coefficient
Omicron	O	o	reference point/point in math

NAME	UPPERCASE	LOWERCASE	COMMON USE
Pi	Π	π	ratio of circumference to diameter = 3.1416
Rho	P	ρ	resistivity, coordinates, volume charge density
Sigma	Σ	σ, ς	sign of summation, electrical conductivity, leakage coefficient, conductivity, propagation constant
Tau	T	τ	time constant, time phase displacement, transmission factor
Upsilon	Y	υ	
Phi	Φ	ϕ, φ	magnetic flux, phase angles
Chi	X	χ	reactance, angles, electrical susceptibility
Psi	Ψ	ψ	dielectric flux, phase difference or angle, coordinates
Omega	Ω	ω	(uppercase-Ohms) (lowercase-angular velocity)

1.7 LETTER SYMBOL AND ABBREVIATION GLOSSARY

	MEANING	ABBREVIATION	SYMBOL
(A)	Adjustable	adj, ADJ	
	Admittance	————	y, Y
	Advanced low power Schottky	ALS	
	Advanced Schottky	AS	
	Alpha	————	α
	Alternating current	ac, AC	AC
	Alternating current—direct current	ac/dc AC/DC	
	Ambient	amb	
	American National Standards Institute	ANSI	
	American Radio Relay League	ARRL	
	American Society of Mechanical Engineers	ASME	
	American Standards Association	EIA (now USASI)	
	American wire gage	AWG	
	Ampere	a, A, amp, AMP	A
	Ampere hour	AMP HR	Ah
	Ampere turn	AT	A

	MEANING	ABBREVIATION	SYMBOL
	Amplification factor	Mu	μ
	Amplitude modulation	am, AM	AM
	Antenna	ant, ANT	
	Antilogarithm	antilog	
	Atmosphere	atm	
	ATTO (1×10^{-18})	a	
	Audio frequency	af, AF	
	Automatic frequency control	afc, AFC	
	Automatic gain control	agc, AGC	
	Automatic testing equipment	ATE	
	Automatic volume control	avc, AVC	
	Average	avg	
(B)	Bandpass frequency of resonant circuits	Af	
	Bayonet coupling	BNC	
	Beat frequency oscillator	bfo, BFO	
	Bel	B	
	Beta	———	β
	Binary coded decimal	BCD/bcd	
	Bits per second	BPS	
	British thermal unit	BTU	Btu
	Broadcast	bc, BC	
(C)	Calibrate	Cal	
	Calorie	CAL	cal
	Capacitance	———	c
	Capacitive reactance	———	X_c
	Capacitor/capacitance	cap	c, C
	Cathode ray oscilloscope	cro, CRO	
	Cathode ray tube	crt, CRT	
	Centi (1×10^{-2})	c	
	Centigram	cg	
	Centimeter (metre is preferred spelling)	———	cm
	Centimetre-gram-second	CGS	cgs
	Central processing unit	CPU	
	Characteristic output impedance	———	Z_0
	Charge	———	Q
	Circuit	ckt	
	Circular mil	c mil	
	Clockwise	cw, CW	
	Closed circuit television	CCTV	
	Collector	C	

MEANING	ABBREVIATION	SYMBOL
Common base	CB	
Common collector	CC	
Common emitter	CE	
Community antenna television	CATV	
Complementary metal-oxide-semiconductor	CMOS	
Computer aided design	CAD	
Computer aided manufacturing	CAM	
Conductance (old unit was mhos—new unit is siemens)	————	G (mhos)
	————	S (siemens)
Conductivity	————	σ
Constant	————	K
Continuous wave	cw	
Counterclockwise	CCW, ccw	
Cosecant	csc	
Cosine	cos	
Cotangent	cot	
Coulomb	————	C (not Q)
Counter-electromotive force	cemf, CEMF	
Coupling (coefficient of)	————	k
Coupling (resistor-capacitor)	————	R-C
Cubic centimetre (preferred spelling)	CC	cm^3
Cubic foot	CU FT	ft^3
Cubic foot per minute	CFM	ft^3/min
Cubic foot per second	CFS	ft^3/s
Cubic inch	CU IN	in^3
Cubic metre (preferred spelling)	CU M	m^3
Cubic millimetre	CU MM	mm^3
Current	————	I
Current (effective-rms value)	I eff	I
Current (instantaneous value)	————	i
Current (maximum value)	————	I max
Cycle (replaced with hertz)	C	c
Cycle per second	(old) cps	Hz (new)
(D) Decade counting unit	DCU	
Deci (1×10^{-1})	d	
Decibel	DB/dB	dB
Decibel against 1 mw standard	dBm	
Decibel against 1 watt standard	dBW	
Decibel against 1 volt standard	dBV	
Degrees (Celsius)	————	°C
Degrees (Fahrenheit)	————	°F
Degrees (Kelvins preferred, not degrees Kelvin)	————	K

MEANING	ABBREVIATION	SYMBOL
Deka ($1 \times 10 + ^1$)	da	
Density, flux in gauss	b	β
Diameter	d, dia, DIA	
Digital multimeter	DMM	
Digital voltmeter	DVM	
Diode transistor logic	DTL	
Direct coupled transistor logic	DCTL	
Direct current	dc, (DC preferred)	
Direct current working volts	dcwv, DCWV	
Direction finding	D/F	
Distance	———	d
Double pole, double throw	DPDT	
Double pole, single throw	DPST	
Dual in-line package	DIP	
(E) Electric displacement	———	D
Electrically alterable read-only memory	EAROM	
Electromotive force	emf, EMF	
Electronic Industries Association	EIA	
Electron volt	———	eV
Emitter coupled logic	ECL	
Energy-work	———	J
Equation	eq, EQ	
External	ext, EXT	
Extremely high frequency	EHF	
Extremely low frequency	ELF	
(F) Farad (unit of capacitance)	———	F
Federal Communications Commission	FCC	
Field effect transistor	FET	
Filament	Fil	
Flip chip	FC	
Foot	FT	ft
Foot per second	FPS	ft/s
Foot-poundal	ft-pdl	
Foot-pound force	FT LB F	ft . lb
Foot-second	ft-sec	
Force	———	N
Formula translation	FORTRAN	
Frequency	F, Freq	
Frequency (angular)	———	ω
Frequency modulation	fm, (FM preferred)	

	MEANING	ABBREVIATION	SYMBOL
(G)	Gain	————	A
	Gauss (unit of flux density)	————	β
	Giga $(1 \times 10^{+9})$	————	G
	Giga electron volt	————	GeV
	Gigahertz	————	GHz
	Gilbert (old unit for magnetomotive force)	gb, mmf	
	Gram	G	g
	Gravity	g	
	Greenwich mean time (civil time)	GMT, GCT	
	Ground	gnd, GND	
(H)	Hecto $(1 \times 10^{+2}$ normally avoided)	h	
	Henry (unit of inductance)	————	H
	Hertz (not per second)	————	Hz
	High frequency	hf, HF	
	Horsepower	HP	hp
	Hour	HR	h
(I)	Impact avalanche and transit time	IMPATT	
	Impedance	————	Z
	Inch	IN	in
	Inch per second	IPS	in/s
	Inductance (mutual)	————	M
	Inductance (self)	————	L
	Inductive reactance	————	X_L
	Infrared	IR	
	Infrared emitting diode	IRED	
	Inside diameter	ID	
	Institute of Electrical and Electronic Engineers	IEEE	
	Insulated gate field effect transistor	IGFET	
	Integrated circuit	IC	
	Integrated thyristor rectifier	ITR	
	Intensity-magnetic field	————	H
	Intermediate frequency	if, (IF preferred)	
	International Electrotechnical Commission	IEC	
	International Standards Organization	ISO	
	Interrupted continuous wave	icw	
(J)	Joint Electron Device Engineering Council	JEDEC	
	Junction diode	cr, CR	
	Junction field effect transistor	JFET	

MEANING	ABBREVIATION	SYMBOL
(K) Kilo $(1 \times 10^{+3})$	k	
Kiloampere	KA	
Kilogram	———	kg
Kilohertz	———	kHz
Kilohm	(slang usage-K)	k Ω
Kilometre (preferred spelling)	———	km
Kilovar	kvar	
Kilovolt	(slang usage-K volts)	kV
Kilovolt ampere	———	kVA
Kilowatt	———	kW
Kilowatt hour	———	kWh
(L) Lambert	L	
Large scale integrated circuit	LSI	
Least significant bit	LSB	
Least significant digit	LSD	
Length	———	l, L
Light-activated silicon controlled rectifier	LASCR	
Light-activated silicon controlled switch	LASCS	
Light-emitting diode	LED	
Limited space-charge accumulation	LSA	
Liquid crystal display	LCD	
Load resistor	———	R_L
Logarithm	Log	
Low frequency	LF	
(M) Magnetic flux density	———	β
Magnetic flux (Maxwell)	———	ϕ, Φ
Magnetic field strength	———	H
Magnetomotive force	mmf	
Mass	———	m, M
Maximum	MAX	
Maxwell	mx	
Medium scale integrated circuit	MSI	
Mega $(1 \times 10^{+6})$	m, M	M
Megahertz	———	MHz
Megavolt	MV	
Megohm	Meg (slang)	M Ω
Metal oxide semiconductor	MOS	
Metal oxide semiconductor field effect transistor	MOSFET	
Meter; metre preferred	———	m

MEANING	ABBREVIATION	SYMBOL
MHO	———	A/V, MHO
Micro (1×10^{-6})	———	μ
Microampere	———	μA
Microfarad	mfd, MFD, μfd	μF
Microhenry	———	μH
Micrometre (preferred spelling)	———	μm
Micromho (replaced by microsiemen μs)	———	μmho, S
Micromicrofarad (replaced by picofarad pF)	———	$\mu\mu$fd, mmfd, (pF preferred)
Microsecond	μS	
Microvolt	micro V, μV	
Microwatt	micro W, μW	
Milihenry	———	mH
Military	mil	
Milli (1×10^{-3})	———	m
Milliampere	———	mA
Millibar	———	m bar
Milligram	———	mg
Millimetre (preferred spelling)	———	mm
Millimho	———	m mho
Millions of cycles	(old) mega cps	(new) MHz
Millisecond	———	ms
Millivolt	———	mV
Milliwatt	———	mW
Minimum	MIN	
Minute	MIN	min
Modulated continuous wave	MCW	
Modulation, amplitude	am, AM	AM
Modulation factor	———	M
Modulation, frequency	fm, FM	FM
Modulation, percent of	———	M
Modulation, phase	pm, PM	PM
Modulation, pulse amplitude	pam, PAM	PAM
Modulation, pulse code	pcm, PCM	PCM
Modulation, pulse duration	pdm, PDM	PDM
Modulation, pulse position	ppm, PPM	PPM
Modulation, pulse width	pwm, PWM	PWM
Most significant bit	MSB	
Most significant digit	MSD	
Mutual conductance	———	gm, GM
Mutual inductance	———	M
(N) Nano (1×10^{-9})	———	n
Nanoampere	———	nA

MEANING	ABBREVIATION	SYMBOL
Nanofarad	———	nF
Nanohenry	———	nH
Nanometre (preferred spelling)	———	nm
Nanosecond	———	ns
Nanowatt	———	nW
National Electrical Manufacturers Association	NEMA	
National electrical code	NEC	
Negative	neg, NEG	B−
Neutralizing capacitor	C_n	
Newton	N	
No connection	NC	
Normally closed	NC	
Normally open	NO	
Number	no, #	

	MEANING	ABBREVIATION	SYMBOL
(O)	Oersted (obsolete unit of magnetic field intensity)	———	H
	Ohm (unit of resistance)	———	Ω
	Ohmmeter	———	Ωm (slang usage)
	Ohms per volt	———	Ω/V
	Operational amplifier	OP AMP	
	Oscillator	OSC	
	Oscilloscope	O-scope (slang)	
	Ounce	oz	
	Outside diameter	OD	

	MEANING	ABBREVIATION	SYMBOL
(P)	Parts per million	ppm	
	Peak	P, PK	
	Peak inverse voltage	PIV	
	Peak reverse voltage	PRV	
	Peak to peak	PP, PK-PK	
	Period	———	T
	Permeability (relative/absolute)	———	μ
	Permeance	———	P
	Phase-locked loop	PLL	
	Phase modulation	PM	
	PI	———	π
	Pico (1×10^{-12})	p	
	Picoampere	———	pA
	Picofarad	(old) mmf, MMF, $\mu\mu$f	pF (preferred)
	Picosecond	pS	
	Picowatt	pW	

MEANING	ABBREVIATION	SYMBOL
Positive	pos, POS	B+
Potentiometer	pot, POT	R
Pound	LB	lb
Pound per square foot	PSF	lb/ft^2
Pound per square inch	PSI	lb/in^2
Power	P, PWR	
Power (average)	Pav	
Power factor	PF	
Power (peak)	Ppk	
Pressure	pres, P	
Primary	PRI	
Printed circuit board	PCB	
Programmable read-only memory	PROM	
Programmable unijunction transistor	PUT	
Pulse amplitude modulation	PAM	PAM
Pulse code modulation	PCM	PCM
Pulse duration modulation	PDM	PDM
Pulse position modulation	PPM	PPM
Pulse recurrence frequency	PRF	
Pulse recurrence time	PRT	
Pulse repetition frequency	PRF	
Pulse width	PW	
Pulse width modulation	PWM	PWM

	MEANING	ABBREVIATION	SYMBOL
(Q)	Quality factor (X_L to R ratio)	———	Q
	Quantity of electricity (coil or capacitor merit)	———	Q
	Quiescent point	Q point	Q
	Quiet automatic volume control	QAVC	
(R)	Radian	———	rad
	Radio Electronics Television Manufacturers Association	RETMA (now EIA)	
	Radio-frequency	rf, RF	RF
	Radio-frequency interference	RFI, RF_I	
	Random access memory	RAM	
	Reactance	———	X
	Read-only memory	ROM	
	Receiver	rcvr	
	Rectifier	RECT	D, X, CR
	Reference	ref	
	Reluctance	rel	*R*
	Resistance	res	R
	Resistor-capacitor-transistor logic	RCTL	
	Resistance-capacitance coupling	RC	
	Resistivity	———	P

MEANING	ABBREVIATION	SYMBOL
Resistor-transistor logic	RTL	
Resonance frequency	————	F_r
Reverse recovery time	T_{RR}	
Revolutions per minute	RPM	r/min
Revolutions per second	RPS	r/s
Root mean square	rms, RMS	

(S)

MEANING	ABBREVIATION	SYMBOL
Schottky barrier diode	SBD	
Schottky barrier rectifier	SBR	
Schottky bidirectional switch	SBS	
Secant	sec	
Second (time)	SEC	s
Secondary	sec	
Semiconductor Industry Association	SIA	
Sensitivity	SENS	
Single cotton covered (wire covering)	SCC	
Single cotton enamel (wire covering)	SCE	
Single pole, double throw switch	SPDT	
Single pole, single throw switch	SPST	
Single sideband	SSB	
Single silk covered (wire covering)	SSC	
Silicon controlled rectifier	SCR	
Silicon unidirectional switch	SUS	
Sine	sin	
Small scale integration	SSI	
Small signal transistor	SST	
Square	SQ	
Square foot	SQ FT	ft^2
Square inch	SQ IN	in^2
Square metre (preferred spelling)	————	m^2
Standard	STD	
Standing wave ratio	SWR	
Super high frequency	SHF	
Susceptance	————	β
Switch	SW	
Synchronous	SYNC	

(T)

MEANING	ABBREVIATION	SYMBOL
Tangent	TAN	
Television	TV	
Temperature (absolute)	temp	T
Temperature coefficient	————	Tc
Temperature (degrees Centigrade)	————	°C
Temperature (degrees Fahrenheit)	————	°F
Tera $(1 \times 10^{+12})$	T	

MEANING	ABBREVIATION	SYMBOL
Terahertz	THz	
Thickness	———	t
Thermistor	R_t	t
Thousand of cycles/hertz per second	KC, KHz	
Time	———	t
Time constant	———	TC
Time of one cycle/hertz (dependent on frequency)	———	T
Transformer	xformer, XFMR	T
Transmit-receive	TR	
Transistor-transistor logic	TTL	
Transistorized voltmeter	TVM	
Trapped plasma avalanche transit time	TRAPATT	
Traveling wave tube	TWT	
Tuned radio frequency	TRF	
Turns (number)	———	N
(U) Ultrahigh frequency	uhf, UHF	
Ultraviolet	UV	
Unijunction transistor	UJT	
United States of America Standards Institute	USASI	
Universal time (Greenwich mean)	UT	
(V) Vacuum tube	V	
Vacuum tube voltmeter	VTVM	
Variable frequency oscillator	VFO	
Velocity of light (radiowaves)	———	C
Versus	VS, vs	
Very high frequency	vhf, VHF	
Very large scale integration	VLSI	
Very low frequency	vlf, VLF	
Voltage	Volt	V, E
Voltampere	———	VA
Voltage (average value)	V_{av}	E_{av}
Voltage controlled oscillator	VCO	
Voltage (effective/rms value)	Vrms, Eeff	E
Voltage (instantaneous value)	Vinst	e
Voltage (maximum value)	Vmax	Emax
Voltage regulator	———	VR
Voltage standing wave ratio	VSWR	
Volt-ohm-milliammeter	VOM	
Volume control	VC	
Volume unit	Vu	
Volume unit meter	Vu-m	

1

MEANING		ABBREVIATION	SYMBOL
(W)	Watt	W	W, P
	Watt hour	WH	Wh
	Wavelength	————	λ
	Weber	Wb	
	Working voltage, direct current	WVDC	

1.8   MATHEMATICAL SIGNS AND SYMBOLS

Everyone who has worked at a particular job for any duration of time develops and uses shortcuts or tricks of the trade. In mathematics, the same thing is true. One of the more popular tricks of the trade is to use symbols or abbreviations that reduce unnecessary writing. The following signs and symbols are those which are often used in our mathematical processes.

SYMBOLS	MEANING
1. $+$	1. plus; addition; positive; "OR" gate
2. $-$	2. minus; subtraction; negative
3. $\pm$	3. tolerance; plus or minus, positive or negative
4. $A \div B,\ A/B,\ \dfrac{A}{B},\ A:B$	4. division; A divided by B
5. $A \times B,\ A \cdot B,\ AB,\ (A)(B)$	5. multiplication; A times B
6. $(\ ),\ \{ \ \},\ [\ ]$	6. parentheses, braces and brackets for grouping
7. $=,\ ::$	7. equal to
8. $\cong,\ \approx$	8. approximately equal to
9. $\neq$	9. not equal to
10. $\equiv$	10. identical to
11. $<$	11. less than
12. $\nless$	12. not less than
13. $\leqq$	13. equal or less than
14. $>$	14. greater than
15. $\geqq$	15. equal or greater than
16. $\ngtr$	16. not greater than
17. $::,\ :$	17. proportional to (equals)
18. $:$	18. ratio
19. $\longrightarrow$	19. approaches as a limit
20. ∞	20. infinity
21. Δ	21. delta; increment of; change in

SYMBOLS	MEANING
22. $\sqrt{}\,,\sqrt{}$	22. square root
23. $\sqrt[n]{}$	23. Nth root
24. X^n	24. exponent of X; Nth power of X
25. $\text{Log},\ \text{Log}_{10}$	25. common logarithm
26. $\text{Ln},\ \text{Log}\,e$	26. hyperbolic, natural or napierian logarithm
27. $e,\ \epsilon$	27. epsilon; base of natural (hyperbolic) logarithm; 2.718
28. π	28. Pi; 3.1416
29. $\dfrac{1}{2\pi}$	29. 0.159
30. $\angle$	30. angle
31. $\llcorner$	31. right angle
32. $\perp$	32. perpendicular to
33. $\parallel$	33. parallel to; parallel
34. $\lvert N \rvert$	34. absolute value of N
35. $\overline{N}$	35. average value of N
36. $X^{-n},\ \dfrac{1}{X^n}$	36. reciprocal of Nth power of X
37. $N°$	37. N degrees
38. N'	38. N minutes; N feet
39. N''	39. N seconds; N inches
40. $\therefore$	40. therefore
41. $F(x)$	41. function of (X)
42. $C,\ K$	42. constant (when following an equal sign)
43. $\int$	43. integration (integral in calculus)
44. $_b\!\int^a$	44. integral between limits of a and b
45. α	45. varies directly as
46. $!$	46. factorial
47. Σ	47. summation
48. j	48. "j" operator, square root of minus one
49. ω	49. angular velocity $2\pi F$
50. Lim.	50. limit value of an expression
51. Sin	51. sine
52. Cos	52. cosine
53. Tan, tg, tang	53. tangent
54. Cot, ctg	54. cotangent
55. Sec	55. secant
56. Cosec	56. cosecant
57. Versin	57. versed sine
58. Covers	58. coversed sine
59. $\text{Sin}^{-1}\,A$, arc sin A	59. angle whose sine is A

1

1.9   SEMICONDUCTOR DEVICES

Perhaps someday, standards applied to semiconductor-related components will be as clear, concise, and reliable from manufacturer to manufacturer
as are color codes assigned to axial lead resistors. The agencies who, out of
necessity, have contributed to the standards manufacturers follow, and we rely
upon, have great difficulty with semiconductor standardizations being assigned
and adapted. Part of this problem is the rapid increase in the number of different
semiconductor devices, while another part is the difficulty in convincing manufacturers that their particular design is poor and that the agency type, size,
shape, style, or number is best.

This section of Chapter 1 will share with you those semiconductor facts
which seem to be commonplace in manufacturer practice although not necessarily "approved" as standards for that particular device.

1.9-1   PACKAGING STANDARDS

Prefixes such as "TO," standing for Transistor Outline, were meant to
define transistors having more than two leads; "DO" meaning Diode Outline,
defining diodes having only two terminals or leads; "MO" meaning, I think,
Metal Oxide for devices having five or more leads; and the "SP" prefix which
I believe stands for Special Purpose. These prefixes are commonly used to
describe semiconductor devices, but not exactly as planned by the standards
agencies. The "TO" prefix, for example, would describe only transistors having
more than two leads. This prefix would allow recognition by physical encapsula-
tion measurements and specifications. Numbers were to be added to the "TO"
prefix according to organizational standards, thereby making TO-1 the first
registered and, we hope, accepted size, etc., and additional numbers indicating
its registered "TO" number. Diode outline "DO" and other prefixes would
follow in the same manner.

Most manufacturers of semiconductor devices do use suggested lead
spacing tolerances, lead diameter tolerances, and in general the size-outline
with their assigned prefixes; but modifications are normally included. As an end
result, the "TO" prefix for transistors has application for germanium diodes,
triacs, diacs, silicon controlled rectifiers, light-emitting diodes, integrated circuits, plus more. We also find the "DO" prefix applied to light-emitting diodes,
diodes, rectifiers, and diacs. Prefix letters are substituted by style, case or
number-letter combinations plus subscripts, suffixes, and abbreviations. Some
of these identification prefix substitutes refer to press fits, stud mounts, and/or
heat radiators possibly used on or with semiconductor devices.

With all of these confusing facts, you can see that the problem exists
because one fact may not be true for another manufacturer's semiconductor
device. Some of the more popular prefixed shapes or packaging design characteristics are illustrated in Figure 1-9 A, B, C. The illustrations merely illustrate

common similar outlines often used, terminal/lead identification, and terminology encountered regardless of packaging styles manufactured. It must be remembered that each prefix, or case number has its own dimensions and is not implied in Figure 1-9 A, B, C.

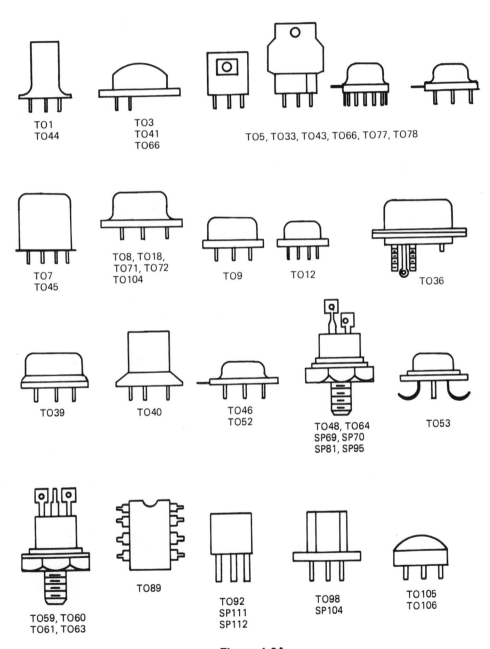

Figure 1-9A

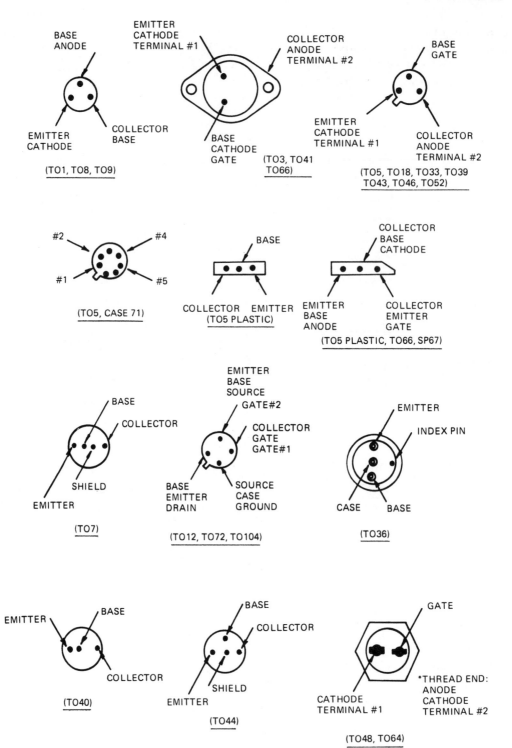

Figure 1-9B

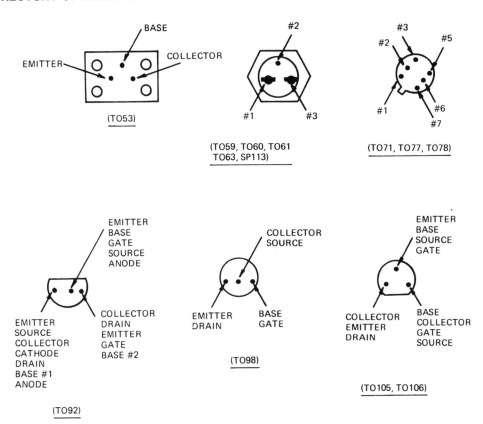

Figure 1-9B, continued

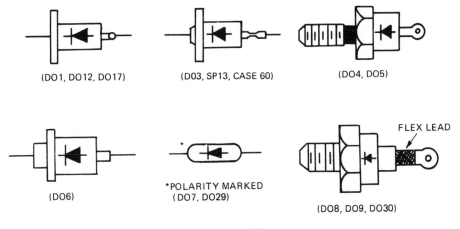

Figure 1-9C

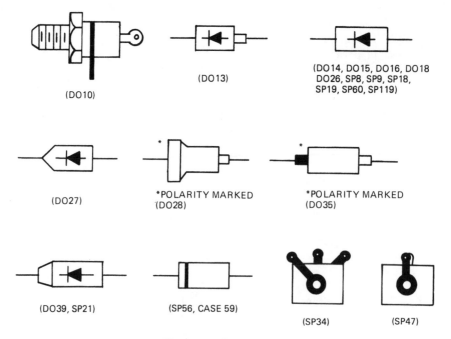

Figure 1-9C, continued

1.10   SOLID STATE SCHEMATIC SYMBOLS

1.10-1   REGION OHMIC CONNECTIONS

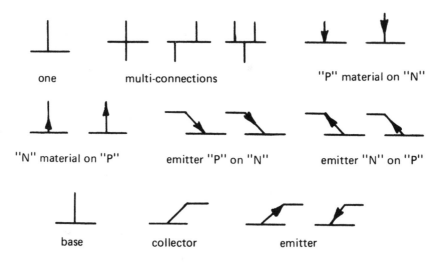

1.10-2   INTRINSIC REGION BETWEEN CONDUCTIVITY REGIONS

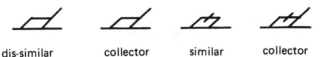

dis-similar   collector   similar   collector

1.10-3   NOTES FOR SEMICONDUCTORS

light dependent   temperature   tunneling   breakdown
                     dependent   device   device

1.10-4   ASYMMETRICAL SILICON BILATERAL SWITCH
(ASBS) (thyristor family)

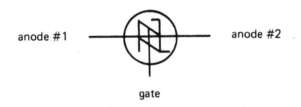

anode #1   anode #2

gate

(ASBS) (thyristor family)

1.10-5   ASYMMETRICAL SILICON CONTROLLED RECTIFIER
(ASCR) (thyristor family)

anode   cathode

gate

1.10-6   BACK DIODE (also see Zener Diodes 1.10-60)

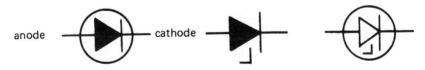

anode   cathode

1.10-7   BINISTER

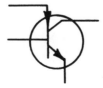

1.10-8   BIPOLAR VOLTAGE LIMITER

1.10-9   BREAKDOWN DIODE OR ZENER (also see Zener Diodes 1.10-60)

unidirectional   undirectional   bidirectional

1.10-10   CAPACITIVE DIODE (also see VARACTORS 1.10-59)
(varacter family)

anodes

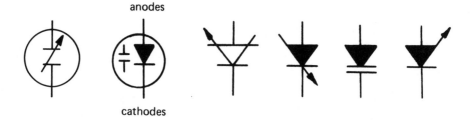

cathodes

1.10-11   COMPLEMENTARY SILICON CONTROLLED RECTIFIER

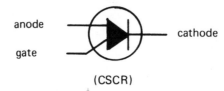

anode   cathode

gate

(CSCR)

1.10-12   COMPLEMENTARY UNIJUNCTION TRANSISTOR

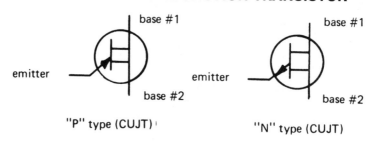

"P" type (CUJT)   "N" type (CUJT)

1.10-13   DARLINGTON AMPLIFIER

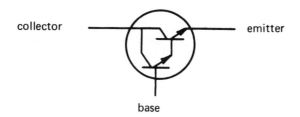

1.10-14   DIAC (BILATERAL TRIGGER)
(thyristor family)

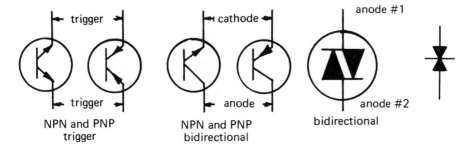

1.10-15   DIODE/RECTIFIER

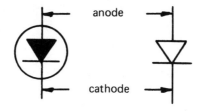

1.10-16   FIELD EFFECT DIODE

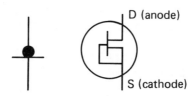

1.10-17   FIELD EFFECT TRANSISTOR (FET)—junction type

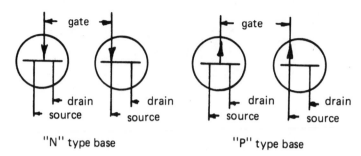

"N" type base   "P" type base

1.10-18   FIELD EFFECT TRANSISTOR – INSULATED GATE FIELD EFFECT (IGFET)

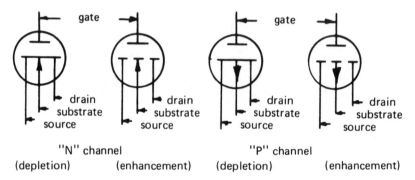

"N" channel   "P" channel
(depletion)   (enhancement)   (depletion)   (enhancement)

1.10-19   GATE TURN OFF SCR

(GTO) (thyristor family)

1.10-20   INFRARED EMITTING DIODE (see Light-Emitting Diodes 1.10-28)

1.10-21   INSULATED GATE FIELD EFFECT TRANSISTOR

(MOSFET family)

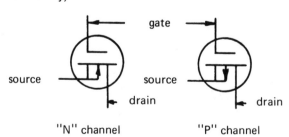

"N" channel   "P" channel

1.10-22   INTEGRATED CHOPPER TRANSISTOR

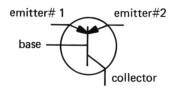

1.10-23   INTEGRATED VOLTAGE REGULATOR (IVA)

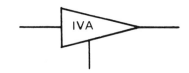

1.10-24   LIGHT-ACTIVATED PROGRAMMABLE UNIJUNCTION TRANSISTOR
(LAPUT) (thyristor family)

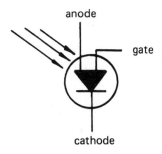

1.10-25   LIGHT-ACTIVATED SWITCH
(LAS) (thyristor family)

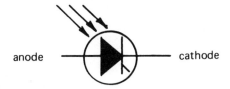

1.10-26   LIGHT-ACTIVATED SILICON CONTROLLED RECTIFIER
(LASCR) (thyristor family)

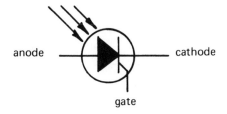

1.10-27   LIGHT-ACTIVATED SILICON CONTROLLED SWITCH
(LASCS) (thyristor family)

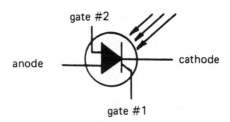

1.10-28   LIGHT-EMITTING DIODE (LED)

1.10-29   LIGHT SENSITIVE DARLINGTON AMPLIFIER

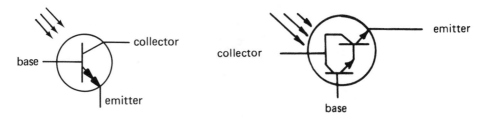

1.10-30   LIGHT SENSITIVE TRANSISTOR (see Photo Transistors 1.10-38)

**1.10-31   METAL-OXIDE-SEMICONDUCTOR FIELD EFFECT
TRANSISTOR**
(MOSFET) (thyristor family)

1.10-32   NPNP TRIODE SWITCH

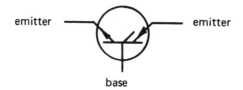

1.10-33   NPN TRANSISTOR

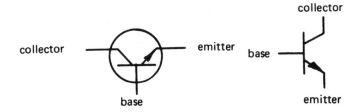

1.10-34   OPTOISOLATOR

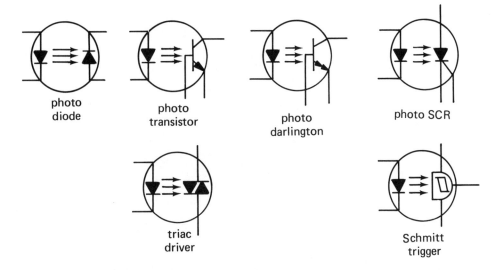

1.10-35   **PHOTO AMPLIFIER** (see Light Sensitive Darlington 1.10-29)

1.10-36   PHOTO DIODE

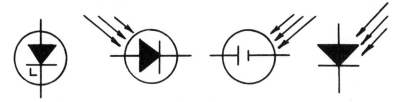

1.10-37   PHOTO FET (LIGHT SENSITIVE TRANSISTOR/PHOTO DETECTOR)

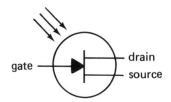

1.10-38   PHOTO TRANSISTOR

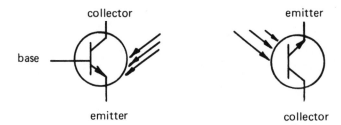

1.10-39   PIN DIODE

1.10-40   PIN TRIODE

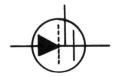

1.10-41   PNP TRANSISTOR

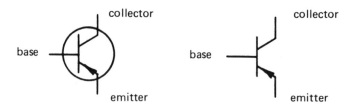

1.10-42   PNPN DIODE

1.10-43   PNPN TRIODE SWITCH

1.10-44   PROGRAMMABLE UNIJUNCTION TRANSISTOR
(PUT) (thyristor family)

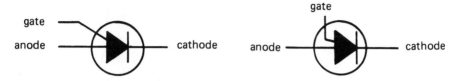

1.10-45   REVERSE CONDUCTING TRIODE
(RCT) (thyristor family)

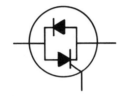

1.10-46   SCHOTTKY DIODE

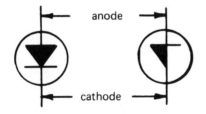

1.10-47   SILICON BILATERAL SWITCH
(SBS) (thyristor family)

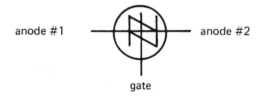

1.10-48   SILICON CONTROLLED RECTIFIER
(SCR) (thyristor family)

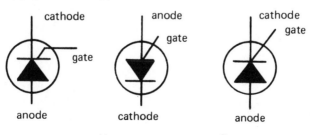

1.10-49   SILICON CONTROLLED SWITCH
(SCS) (thyristor family)

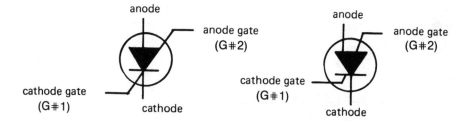

1.10-50   SILICON UNILATERAL SWITCH
(SUS) (thyristor family)

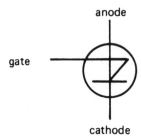

1.10-51   TEMPERATURE SENSITIVE DIODE

1.10-52   TETRODE TRANSISTOR

1.10-53   THYRECTOR

1.10-54 TRIAC (BILATERAL SCR) (thyristor family)

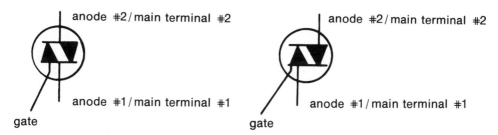

1.10-55 TRIGISTOR

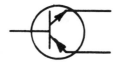

1.10-56 TRIODE (BIDIRECTIONAL)

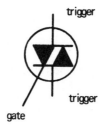

1.10-57 TUNNEL DIODE (ESKI DIODE)

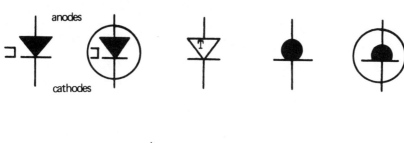

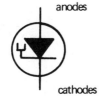

1.10-58   UNIJUNCTION TRANSISTOR (UJT)

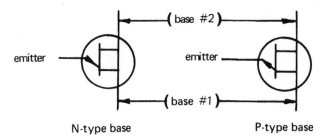

N-type base   P-type base

1.10-59   **VARACTOR** (also see Capacitive Diode 1.10-10)

1.10-60   ZENER DIODE (ALSO REFERRED TO AS FOLLOWS)

1. BACKWARD DIODE
2. BREAKDOWN DIODE
3. AVALANCHE DIODE
4. VOLTAGE REGULATOR
5. VOLTAGE REFERENCE

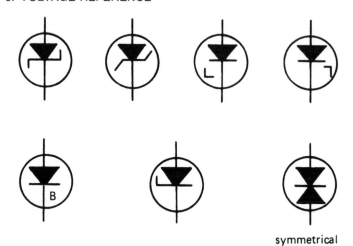

symmetrical

1.11 VACUUM TUBE SCHEMATIC SYMBOLS

1.11-1 BEAM FORMING PLATE ELECTRODES

1.11-2 BEAM POWER AMPLIFIER

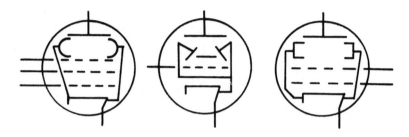

1.11-3 CATHODE ELECTRODE

1.11-4 CATHODE RAY INDICATOR

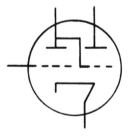

1.11-5 CATHODE RAY TUBE

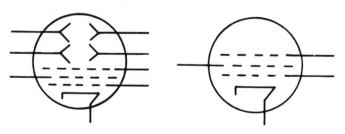

electrostatic deflection   magnetic deflection

1.11-6   COLD CATHODE ELECTRODE

1.11-7   COLD CATHODE GAS DIODE

1.11-8   DEFLECTING ELECTRODE

1.11-9   DIODE

directly heated   indirectly heated

1.11-10   DOUBLE CAVITY ENVELOPE

1.11-11   DUAL TRIODE

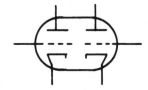

1.11-12   DUO-DIODE

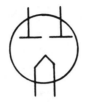

1.11-13   DUO-DIODE TRIODE

1.11-14   DYNODE ELECTRODE

1.11-15   EYE TUBE

1.11-16   EXCITER ELECTRODE

1.11-17   EXCITRON WITH GRID AND HOLDING ANODE

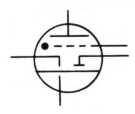

1.11-18   FILAMENT/HEATER ELECTRODE

1.11-19   GAS FILLED TUBE (SOFT TUBE)

1.11-20   GLASS ENVELOPE

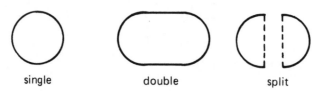

single   double   split

1.11-21   GRID ELECTRODE

1.11-22   IGNITER (MERCURY POOL TUBE)

1.11-23   IGNITRON WITH GRID

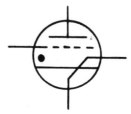

1.11-24   INTERNAL TUBE SHIELDING

1.11-25 LOOP COUPLING ELECTRODE

1.11-26 MAGNETRON

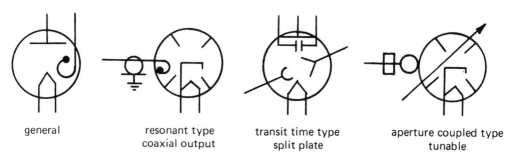

| general | resonant type coaxial output | transit time type split plate | aperture coupled type tunable |

1.11-27 MULTIPLIER PHOTO TUBE

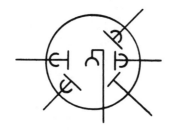

1.11-28 PENTAGRID CONVERTER

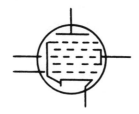

1.11-29 PENTODE

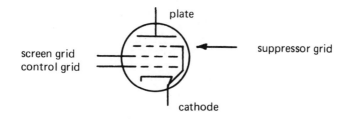

plate

screen grid
control grid

suppressor grid

cathode

1.11-30   PHOTO ELECTRIC CATHODE ELECTRODE

1.11-31   PHOTO TUBE

1.11-32   PLATE ELECTRODE   (ANODE)

1.11-33   POOL CATHODE ELECTRODE

1.11-34   SINGLE CAVITY ENVELOPE

1.11-35   SPLIT MAGNETRON

1.11-36 TETRODE

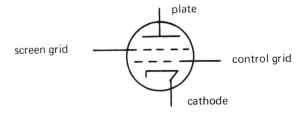

1.11-37 TRAVELING WAVE TUBE

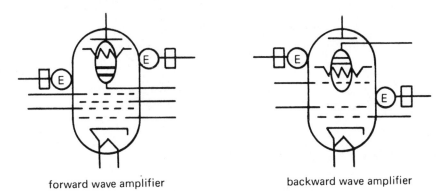

forward wave amplifier   backward wave amplifier

1.11-38 TRANSMIT-RECEIVE TUBE

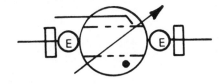

tunable aperture coupled

1.11-39 TRIODE

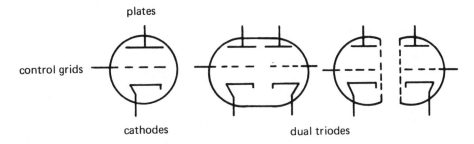

cathodes   dual triodes

1.11-40   VELOCITY MODULATED TUBE

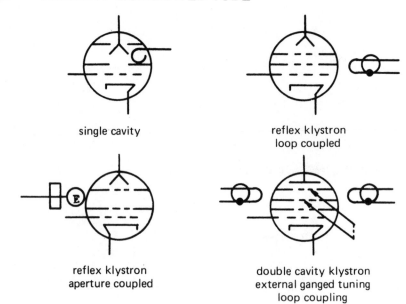

single cavity

reflex klystron
loop coupled

reflex klystron
aperture coupled

double cavity klystron
external ganged tuning
loop coupling

1.11-41   X-RAY TARGET ELECTRODE

1.11-42   X-RAY TUBE

filamentary cathode
with focusing grid

electrostatic
shielding

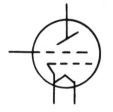

accelerating electrode
(control grid)

2 Essential Mathematical Data for Electronic Application

In order for you to work effectively in any facet of electronics, you are expected to use and understand mathematical concepts. Some of these concepts include arithmetic, algebra, geometry and trigonometry; along with these are complex numbers, vectors, logarithms, decibels, binary and octonary numbers, graphs, Boolean algebra, and advanced mathematics.

This chapter includes the type of data you will need to know for mastering electronics mathematics. Factual concepts will be written in almost a shorthand style, thereby avoiding a storybook approach and possibly some of those things that many of us call "nice to know" facts.

A general set of rules for mathematical calculation, that provides a correct order for operations, is listed here to aid in organizing your thoughts before any data are presented.

1. First add and subtract numbers, any numbers contained within brackets or parentheses that are to be divided, multiplied, raised to a power, or factored.

2. Multiply and divide numbers whose product or quotient is to be raised to a power or factored.

3. Determine the value for powers and roots.

4. Multiply and divide numbers within the terms.

5. Add and subtract the terms.

2.1 ARITHMETIC

2.1-1 ADDITION

Addition is the process used to find the total quantity of any like thing represented by two or more numbers. For the sake of terminology, the number

105

to be increased by addition of another number is called the *augend,* while the number to be added to the augend is called the *addend.* Obviously, the end result is the total, termed the *sum.*

Numbers can be added correctly only if they have related values. For example:

10 amperes (augend)		10 volts
+ 5 amperes (addend)	NOT	+ 5 amperes
15 amperes (sum)		15, but meaningless units

The magnitude of the units must be expressed in the same terms. You can add 10 amperes and 1000 milliamperes only if you convert one value into the other expressed value. This must be done although both are values expressing specific amounts of current.

10 amperes	Change to	10 amperes
+1000 milliamperes		+ 1 ampere
		11 amperes

Often, electronic calculations are written in much the same manner as is the writing on this line of print you are reading. The plus symbol indicates the addition process and is used to connect the terms. For example:

$$1,000 \text{ mA} + 10,000 \text{ mA} = 11,000 \text{ mA}$$
1st term plus 2nd term equals sum

2.1-2   SUBTRACTION

The operation involved in determining the difference between two like-numbered units is called subtraction. The minus symbol separates the terms when written on one line sequence. If you had $X_L = 45$ ohms and $X_C = 30$ ohms, the reactance value would be:

45 ohms − 30 ohms = 15 ohms	or	45 ohms
(X_L) minus (X_C) equals (Z)		−30 ohms
		15 ohms

The number 45 is called the *minuend,* the value of 30 is called the *subtrahend,* and the number of 15 is termed the *remainder.* As in the addition process, make sure all numbers represent the same unit of electronic measurement: that is, keep kilowatts with kilowatts, and microfarads with microfarads. Convert if necessary.

2.1-3   MULTIPLICATION

Multiplication is indicated whenever a times sign ($\times$) is inserted between numbers, or when a dot ($\cdot$) is seen, or when parentheses ( ) or brackets [ ] are used, or when letter or letter-number combinations are written as AB, or 4A, etc. The number to be multiplied is called the *multiplicand,* the number by which the mutliplicand is multiplied is the *multiplier* and the answer or result is termed the *product.*

If three resistors in a series circuit had the same resistance of 10 ohms, the total resistance could be obtained by adding the 10 ohm value (concrete value) together three times to achieve the answer. We could, however, multiply the concrete value of 10 ohms by a nonmeasurable unit value of 3 to obtain the same answer having the same related units of ohms as the concrete number.

Electronics utilizes the facts which when multiplied together, even though their units of measure aren't the same, result in success. For example, volts times amperage equals watts, amperage times resistance equals voltage. Each has its own unit of measurement, but the *product* is in the desired unit.

2.1-4   DIVISION

The indicated operation for division might be seen written: (ten divided by 5), or $\dfrac{10}{5}$, or $10 \div 5$, or $10/5$, $5\overline{)10}$ or $5\overline{)10}$. All of these mean the same. The number to be divided (10) is the *dividend,* the *divisor* (5) is the number being divided into the dividend, and the answer is called the *quotient.*

Numbers having the same or different values of measurable units can be divided and still yield the desired quotient. For example, the total resistance of a series circuit is 1000 ohms and each of the ten resistors has the same resistance: what then is the value of each resistor? Solution: divide the 1000 units of total resistance by the non-measurable unit 10, indicating the number of resistors. The answer 100 is still in the related unit of ohms. The same units might be illustrated via amplifier output voltage gain where output volts divided by input volts equals a number having no units. A different unit illustration is solving for resistance when voltage and current values are known.

Resistance in ohms equals voltage in volts divided by current in amperes. The answer is in the unit of ohms.

2.1-5   FRACTIONS

All fractions have some number divided by another number. The number written above the horizontal line (divide symbol) or to the left of a diagonal line (divide symbol) is called the *numerator* and the number under the horizontal line or to the right of the diagonal line is called the *denominator.*

Since fractions actually denote division, all of the rules for division apply. In reality, the numerator is the *dividend* and the denominator is the *divisor*.

Fractions are called *simple* if the numerator and denominator are whole numbers called *integers*. A *complex* fraction is one which has either a numerator or denominator in fraction form. *Proper* fractions are those which have smaller numerators than denominators. *Improper* fractions are those whose numerators are equal to or greater than their denominators. The term *mixed number* refers to a number plus a fraction combination.

There may be many times when working with fractions, that you will need to alter the numerator and denominator of a fraction without changing its value. The reasons for doing this are:

1. To simplify by reducing to its lowest terms
2. To find a common denominator for addition or subtraction operations
3. To change improper fractions to mixed numbers for the sake of recognition
4. To change mixed numbers to improper fractions for multiplication or division operations.

Alteration without change of value is possible if the numerator and denominator are multiplied or divided by the same number.

Hence:

$$\frac{1}{5} \times \frac{1}{1} = \frac{1}{5}$$

OR

$$\frac{1}{5} \times \frac{2}{2} = \frac{2}{10} \qquad \text{AND} \qquad \frac{2}{10} = \frac{1}{5}$$

OR

$$\frac{1}{5} \times \frac{8}{8} = \frac{8}{40} \qquad \text{AND} \qquad \frac{8}{40} = \frac{1}{5}$$

All of these equal one another.

In changing improper fractions to mixed numbers, perform the division process as indicated. For example:

$$\frac{19}{3} = \begin{array}{r} 6 \\ 3\overline{)19} \\ \underline{18} \\ 1 \end{array} = 6\tfrac{1}{3}$$

In changing mixed numbers to improper fractions follow this guide. For example: $8\,{}^{10}/_{16}$

1. Change the whole number 8 into an equivalent number.

$$8 \times \frac{16}{16} = \frac{128}{16}$$

2. Add the fraction to the whole number fractional equivalent.

$$\frac{128}{16} + \frac{10}{16} = \frac{138}{16}$$

Note: Mixed numbers must be changed to improper fractions before division or multiplication processes.

2.1-5A Addition and Subtraction of Fractions

There are two basic rules to follow when adding fractions.

Rule 1: When fractions are added, their denominators must be the same. If they are different, you must convert to a common denominator. For example:

$$\frac{3}{8} + \frac{3}{4} + \frac{1}{2} = \frac{3}{8} + \frac{6}{8} + \frac{4}{8}$$

Rule 2: After obtaining a common denominator, add the numerators but keep the same common denominator. The solution, using the previous example, is:

$$\frac{3}{8} + \frac{6}{8} + \frac{4}{8} = \frac{13}{8} \qquad \text{or } 1\frac{5}{8}$$

There are also two basic rules to follow when subtracting fractions.

Rule 1: The same as for adding: if the denominators are different, you must convert to a common denominator. For example:

$$\frac{10}{8} - \frac{1}{4} - \frac{1}{2} = \frac{10}{8} - \frac{2}{8} - \frac{4}{8}$$

Rule 2: After obtaining the common denominator, subtract the numerators, but keep the denominator. The answer is:

$$\frac{10}{8} - \frac{2}{8} - \frac{4}{8} = \frac{10 - 2 - 4}{8} = \frac{10 - 6}{8} = \frac{4}{8} \text{ OR } \frac{1}{2}$$

2.1-5B Multiplication and Division of Fractions

When multiplying a whole number (integer) by a fraction, or vice versa, multiply the numerator of the fraction by the whole number and write this product over the denominator. In other words, divide the denominator into the new numerator. For example:

$$\frac{3}{16} \times 3 = \frac{9}{16}$$

To multiply one fraction by another fraction, first multiply the numerators together, then multiply the denominators together. If they aren't the same, divide the new denominator into the new numerator. To illustrate this:

$$\frac{5}{3} \times \frac{2}{4} = \frac{10}{12} \text{ OR } \frac{5}{6}$$

When dividing a fraction by a whole number, consider the whole number as a fraction since one is its denominator, then invert the divisor and multiply. For example:

$$\frac{3}{8} \div 4 = \frac{3}{8} \div \frac{4}{1} = \frac{3}{8} \times \frac{1}{4} = \frac{3}{32}$$

To divide a whole number by a fraction the same basic concept holds true because:

$$10 \div \frac{4}{5} = \frac{10}{1} \times \frac{5}{4} = \frac{50}{4}$$

or a fraction by a fraction:

$$\frac{9}{16} \div \frac{1}{8} = \frac{9}{16} \times \frac{8}{1} = \frac{72}{16}$$

Note: When dividing mixed numbers, first change the mixed numbers to improper fractions, then proceed as previously indicated.

2.1-6   POWERS AND ROOTS

Mathematics used in electronics can often seem confusing, but in reality, if you understand the signs and symbols, the only real problem is cranking out the answers. *Powers* of numbers are denoted by an *exponent* written above and to the right of the number. This is a simplified way of writing that a number is multiplied by itself a number of times. An example would be solving for power when the current is 5 amps and the resistance is 10 ohms. Rather than writing $P = 5 \times 5 \times 10$, it is written $P = (5)^2 \times 10$, which means the same thing $(P = I^2R)$.

Finding *roots* of a number is simply the reverse of finding the power. The radical sign and the exponent are the two notations used to designate the root of a number. If a radical sign ($\sqrt{\ }$) does not have a number called an *index* with it, the square root operation is indicated. If, however, an index number is assigned with the radical sign, then that root operation is indicated. For example: The square root of 81 is written $\sqrt{81}$, the cube root of 27 is $\sqrt[3]{27}$, the fifth root of 243 is $\sqrt[5]{243}$, etc. Exponent notation is almost as simple because square roots are illustrated by the exponent ½, cube roots by the exponent ⅓, fifth roots by the exponent $\frac{1}{5}$, etc.

To illustrate this method, the previous examples will be written as $81^{\frac{1}{2}}$ (square root of 81), $27^{\frac{1}{3}}$ (cube root of 27) and $243^{\frac{1}{5}}$ for the fifth root of 243.

2.1-6A   Square Root Calculations

Many occasions arise in electronics calculations when square roots must be found and your handy square root table is elsewhere. These general rules will revive your memory for finding your square root.

> *Rule 1.*   Divide the number into two digit groups, beginning from the decimal point.
>
> *Rule 2.*   Find the largest number whose value when squared is equal to or less than the digits in the first number group.
>
> *Rule 3.*   Write this number above the first group.
>
> *Rule 4.*   Write the square of that number under the first group, and subtract.
>
> *Rule 5.*   Draw a division line above the remainder found after subtracting, then write the digits found in the second group of numbers to the right of the remainder. The resulting number is called the dividend.

This next step involves a multiple guess type of approach because a trial divisor will be discovered.

> *Rule 6.*   Multiply the first digit of the root (first number written in rule 3) by two and write this product to the left of the dividend. This number, when multiplied by 10, is the trial divisor.
>
> *Rule 7.*   Determine how many times the trial divisor can be divided into the dividend. Remember, it must be equal to or less than the dividend. Write this number above the second group of numbers.
>
> *Rule 8.*   Add this new number, called the second digit of the root, to the trial divisor, then multiply the complete divisor by the second digit of the root and write this product under the dividend.
>
> *Note:* If the product is greater than the dividend, the complete trial divisor and second digit of the root must be decreased by one and rules 7 and 8 must be repeated.
>
> *Rule 9.*   Subtract the product from the dividend, and write the third group of numbers to the right of the remainder to complete a new dividend. Draw a division line above this dividend.

Rule 10. Multiply the first two digits of the root by two, and write this product to the left of the dividend.

Rule 11. Find out how many times the new divisor, when multiplied by ten, can be divided into the new dividend, then write this number above the third group of numbers.

Rule 12. Add this number to the trial divisor, then multiply the complete trial divisor by the third digit root number recorded above the third group of numbers, and then write this product under the dividend.

The next step is to repeat rules 9-12 as often as you wish, depending upon how many significant figures you wish. If you add zeroes, add them in groups of two, thereby minimizing the confusion.

For example, we will show the square root for the number 243.

Rule #1	$\sqrt{2\ 43.}$		
		Rules #9 and 10	$30 \begin{array}{\|l} \overline{1\ 25} \\ 18\ 00 \end{array}$
example rewritten: *Rules #2 and 3*	$\sqrt{\overset{1}{2\ 43.}}$		
Rule #4 *Rule #5*	$\begin{array}{\|l} \overline{1} \\ \overline{1\ 43} \end{array}$	example rewritten:	$\sqrt{\overset{1\ \ 5.\ 5\ \ \ \ 8}{2\ 43.\ 00\ 00}}$
example rewritten:	$\sqrt{\overset{1}{2\ 43.}}$		$25 \begin{array}{\|l} \overset{1}{1\ 43} \end{array}$
Rule #6	$20 \begin{array}{\|l} \overset{1}{1\ 43} \end{array}$		$305 \begin{array}{\|l} \overline{1\ 25} \\ 18\ 00 \end{array}$
example rewritten:	$\sqrt{\overset{1\ \ 5}{2\ 43.00}}$		$3108 \begin{array}{\|l} \overline{15\ 25} \\ 2\ 75\ 00 \end{array}$
Rules #7 and 8	$25 \begin{array}{\|l} \overset{1}{1\ 43} \end{array}$	*Rules #11 and 12*	$\begin{array}{\|l} \overline{2\ 48\ 64} \\ 26\ 36 \end{array}$

2.1-6B   Addition and Subtraction of Powers and Roots

Most of us have discovered that there is our own way of doing something, the wrong way, and the right way. The right way when adding or subtracting powers and roots will provide you with the correct answer if you follow these rules and don't make any calculation errors.

Rule 1. Find the power or root value before adding or subtracting.

For example: To add 2^4 to $\sqrt{9}$ and subtract 10, first determine the power and root values as shown:

$$\sqrt{9} +\ 2^4 - 10 =$$
$$3 + 16\ - 10 =$$
$$19\ - 10 = 9$$

2.1-6C   Multiplication and Division of Powers and Roots

Multiplication or division processes can be performed before finding root or power equivalents for a number if all of the numbers having the power or root designations are of equal value. *The exponents are added during multiplication processes as indicated.*

Multiplication example for powers
$$10 \times 10^2 \times 10^3 = 10^{1+2+3} = 10^6$$

Multiplication example for roots
$$\sqrt{3} \times \sqrt{3} = 3^{1/2} \times 3^{1/2} = 3^{2/2} = 3$$

Multiplication example for power and roots
$$3^2 \times \sqrt{3} = 3^{4/2} \times 3^{1/2} = 3^{4/2\ +\ 1/2} = 3^{5/2}$$

What $3\frac{5}{2}$ really means is $\sqrt{3^5}$ or the square root of the number three, multiplied by itself five times. This could be solved using two general methods. The first method is to multiply $3 \times 3 \times \sqrt{3}$ and obtain 9×1.73 or 15.57 as the answer. Another method would be to multiply three by itself five times, obtaining the number 243, and then take the square root of 243. The final answer would be 15.58.

Note: If a number expressed as a power or root is raised to another power or factored into another root, the exponents are multiplied. The number three squared raised to the third power is written $(3^2)^3$ and is equal to 3^6. The square root of the number first cubed is written $(5^3)^{1/2}$. If you follow the above suggestion, $5^{3/2}$ would be its equivalent.

All of the previous information involving multiplying powers of roots had the same number as its base. If the numbers having power or root designations are unequal, you must determine the power and root of the number before multiplying. To illustrate this procedure we will multiply five squared by four cubed. First determine what five squared equals, then what four cubed equals, and then multiply.

$$5^2 \times 4^3 = 25 \times 64 = 1600$$

Dividing like numbers having exponents is as simple as multiplying if you know the rule when performing the division process. The rule for dividing like numbers with exponents is: subtract the exponent of the divisor from the exponent of the dividend. The following examples illustrate this.

$$3^5 \div 3^3 = 3^{5-3} = 3^2 \quad \text{OR} \quad \frac{3^5}{3^3} = \frac{3 \times 3 \times 3 \times 3 \times 3}{3 \times 3 \times 3} = 3 \times 3$$

2.1-7   RATIOS

A *ratio* is a simple means of comparing two quantities which are measured in the same unit. The gain of an amplifier circuit is always expressed as:

$$\text{gain} = \frac{\text{output}}{\text{input}}$$

If the input signal is 0.3 volts, and the output signal is 18 volts, the gain ratio would be:

$$\text{gain} = \frac{18v}{0.3v} = \frac{60}{1} = 60 \quad \text{OR} \quad \text{gain} = 18:0.3 = 60:1$$

For what it's worth, when written in ratio form (60:1), the number 60 is called the *antecedent* and the number 1 is called the *consequent*. The antecedent is the same as dividend and the consequent is the same as denominator or divisor. Regardless of what you call them, both terms of the ratio may be multiplied or divided by the same number without changing the value of the ratio.

2.1-8   PROPORTIONS

A proportion is actually an equality of ratios. For example, a series circuit forms a voltage divider, and if 100 volts are applied to the input, and 10 volts appeared across the output, then the proportions could be written in any of the following ways:

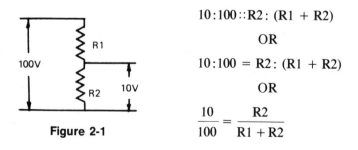

Figure 2-1

$$10:100::R2:(R1 + R2)$$

OR

$$10:100 = R2:(R1 + R2)$$

OR

$$\frac{10}{100} = \frac{R2}{R1 + R2}$$

The first term (10) and the fourth term (R1 + R2) are called *extremes*. The second term (100) and third term (R2) are called *means*.

In order to find the value of one unknown term, and to prove a proportion is correct, any one of the following rules or methods may be used. For simplicity, the previous example will be used. The value for resistor R1 will be 18 ohms, and resistor R2 will be 2 ohms.

Rule 1: The product of the means equals the product of the extremes.

$$10:100 = R2 : (R1 + R2)$$

$$10:100 = 2 : 20$$

$$\text{product of means } 100 \times 2 = 200$$

$$\text{product of extremes } 10 \times 20 = 200$$

Rule 2: The product of the means divided by either of the two extremes equals the other extreme.

$$10:100 = 2 : 20$$

$$\text{product of means } 100 \times 2 = 200$$

$$\frac{200}{10} = 20 \quad \text{OR} \quad \frac{200}{20} = 10$$

Rule 3: The product of the extremes divided by either of the two means equals the other mean.

$$10:100 = 2:20$$

$$\text{product of extremes } 10 \times 20 = 200$$

$$\frac{200}{100} = 2 \quad \text{OR} \quad \frac{200}{2} = 100$$

2.1-9   INVERSE PROPORTIONS

Two numbers are inversely proportional when one number will increase in value while the other is decreased in value.

Ohm's Law is a good illustration of inverse proportions in action because Ohm's Law states that the current (I) through a resistor (R) is equal to the voltage (E) dropped across the resistor divided by the resistor's resistance. Needless to say, if the voltage is constant and the resistance is doubled, the current is halved; or if the voltage remains the same and the resistance is halved, the current is doubled. The current flow through the resistor is inversely proportional to the resistance.

2.1-10   PERCENTAGES

Percentages in electronics are used to express proportions, efficiencies, changes, and tolerances of various components and circuits. The percentage notation, represented by the symbol %, means by the hundred and is used to compare quantities. The percentage range is from zero to 100%.

To find a quantity expressed as a percentage of a number, convert the percent to a decimal or common fractional value and multiply the number by this value. For example:

$$60\% \text{ off list price of } 5.85 \text{ is: } 5.85 \times 60\% = 5.85 \times 0.6 = 3.57$$

An application of finding the percentage of one quantity with respect to another quantity would be expressing efficiency. If an amplifier has an input wattage of 110 and has an output wattage rating of 50, its percentage of efficiency is easily found by dividing the output by the input, moving the decimal point two places to the right, and then adding the percent symbol. For example:

$$\text{Efficiency} = \frac{\text{output power}}{\text{input power}}$$

$$\text{Efficiency} = \frac{50}{110} \times 100\% = 0.4545 \times 100\% = 45.45\%$$

2.1-10A   Converting Decimals to Percent

The percent notation is considered to represent two decimal places since 1% is equal to 0.01 in decimal form. Any decimal can be converted to a percent by moving the decimal two places to the right and by adding the percent symbol. For example, 0.159 equals 15.9%.

2.1-10B   Converting Common Fractions to Percent

When converting a common fraction to a percent, you must first change the fraction to a decimal by dividing the numerator by the denominator, and then convert the decimal to a percent. The following example illustrates this process:

$$\frac{1}{8} = 0.125 \times 100\% = 12.5\%$$

2.1-10C   Converting Percent to Decimals

Omit the percent symbol and move the decimal point two places to the left to change a percent to a decimal. The following equation shows this conversion:

$$63.6\% = 0.636$$

2.1-10D   Converting Percent to Common Fractions

A number written as a percent is converted to a common fraction by omitting the percent symbol, writing the number which had the percent symbol as a numerator and 100 as the denominator. This forms the fraction. Reduce it into its lowest terms as shown, then convert to fractional equivalents.

$$37.5\% = \frac{37.5}{100} = 0.375 = \frac{3}{8}$$

2.1-11   SCIENTIFIC NOTATION

A thorough knowledge of the powers of ten and their use will greatly assist you in solving problems. Often it is necessary to make calculations involving certain electronic values, and both large and small numbers are used. Use of the powers of ten will enable you to work problems having very small decimal values or very large decimal whole numbers with minimum difficulty.

Since we manipulate large and small numbers using powers of ten, they are listed here through the twelfth power. Only twelve are illustrated because seldom is there need to go beyond this exponent in electronics.

POWERS OF TEN

$10^0 = 1$	$10^0 = 1$
$10^1 = 10$ deka (D) (da)	$10^{-1} = 0.1$ deci (d)
$10^2 = 100$ hecto (h)*	$10^{-2} = 0.01$ centi (c)
$10^3 = 1000$ kilo (k)	$10^{-3} = 0.001$ milli (m)
$10^4 = 10,000$ myra (My)	$10^{-4} = 0.0001$
$10^5 = 100,000$	$10^{-5} = 0.000,01$
$10^6 = 1,000,000$ mega (M)	$10^{-6} = 0.000,001$ micro (μ)
$10^7 = 10,000,000$	$10^{-7} = 0.000,000,1$
$10^8 = 100,000,000$	$10^{-8} = 0.000,000,01$
$10^9 = 1,000,000,000$ giga (G)	$10^{-9} = 0.000,000,001$ nano (n)
$10^{10} = 10,000,000,000$	$10^{-10} = 0.000,000,000,1$
$10^{11} = 100,000,000,000$	$10^{-11} = 0.000,000,000,01$
$10^{12} = 1,000,000,000,000$ tera (T)	$10^{-12} = 0.000,000,000,001$ pico (p)

* hecto – normally avoided

Any decimal fraction may be readily expressed by the scientific notation method (the number ten times a negative power of ten) while multiples of ten expressed as ten to the proper positive power of ten represent large decimal values.

For convenience in calculations, the numbers to the left of the decimal point are limited to a one-digit number (a number between one and ten), and the remainder of the significant figures are placed to the right of the decimal point.

The power of ten multiplier is adjusted accordingly. For example, various fractions and whole numbers containing the digits 3142 may be expressed as follows:

$$0.0003142 = 3.142 \times 10^{-4}$$
$$0.003142 = 3.142 \times 10^{-3}$$
$$0.03142 = 3.142 \times 10^{-2}$$
$$0.3142 = 3.142 \times 10^{-1}$$
$$3.142 = 3.142 \times 10^{0}$$
$$31.42 = 3.142 \times 10^{1}$$
$$314.2 = 3.142 \times 10^{2}$$
$$3142.0 = 3.142 \times 10^{3}$$
$$31420.0 = 3.142 \times 10^{4}$$

Changing numbers to powers of ten

$$0.000193 = 1.93 \times 10^{-4}$$
$$0.0196 = 1.96 \times 10^{-2}$$
$$177,560 = 1.7756 \times 10^{5}$$
$$1,535 = 1.535 \times 10^{3}$$
$$159,000 = 1.59 \times 10^{5}$$

Changing powers of ten to decimals

$$5.1 \times 10^{6} = 5,100,000.$$
$$3.5 \times 10^{3} = 3,500$$
$$5.8 \times 10^{2} = 580$$
$$1.60 \times 10^{-4} = 0.000,160$$
$$6.28 \times 10^{-2} = 0.0628$$

2.1-11A   Multiplying Powers of Ten

In multiplication, exponents having the same base (which is the present case) are added. Multiplication then is expressed as:

$$10^{a} \times 10^{b} = 10^{a+b}$$

For example, multiply 0.0027 by 135.8.

Solution: (A) Convert both numbers to powers of ten.

$$0.0027 = 2.7 \times 10^{-3}$$
$$135.8 = 1.358 \times 10^{2}$$

(B) Multiply the numbers and add the exponents.

$$3.6666 \times 10^{-1}$$

Note: Rules for multiplication of exponents must be employed.

2.1-11B   Dividing Powers of Ten

Division of numbers having exponents to the same base (10 in our case) is accomplished by subtracting the divisor exponent from the dividend exponent. Division is expressed as follows:

$$\frac{10^a}{10^b} = 10^{a-b}$$

For example, divide 0.036666 by 0.00882.

Solution: (A) Convert both numbers to powers of ten.

$$\frac{0.036666 = 3.6666 \times 10^{-2}}{0.00882 = 8.82 \times 10^{-3}}$$

(B) Divide the numbers and subtract the exponents.

0.4157×10^1

(C) Convert to a standard answer.

4.157

Note: Rules for dividing exponents must be employed.

2.1-11C   Raising Powers Using Powers of Ten

When raising a number expressed as a power of ten to an additional power, the exponent of the base is multiplied by the exponent denoting the power. This is expressed as:

$$(10^a)^b = 10^{ab}$$

For example, square the number 0.001.

Solution: Express the number as a power of ten.

Since: $0.001 = 1 \times 10^{-3}$
Then $(1 \times 10^{-3})^2 = 1 \times 10^{-6} = 0.000001$

2.1-11D   Extracting Roots Using Powers of Ten

When extracting roots of a number expressed as a power of ten, the exponent of the base is divided by the exponent indicating the root. This is expressed as:

$$\sqrt[b]{10^a} = 10^{a/b}$$

For example, extract the square root of 10,000.

Solution: Write the number as a power of ten, then proceed.

$$10,000 = 1 \times 10^4$$

$$\sqrt{10^4} = 10^{4/2} = 10^2 = 100$$

2.2   ALGEBRA

Algebra is a more useful tool, when analyzing and solving technical problems, than is arithmetic. The main reason for its usefulness is that algebra has a unique combination of arithmetic, mathematics, and alphabetical letters that are substituted for numbers. The common practice of using the first letters in the alphabet to represent the known quantities, and the last of the letters in the alphabet to represent the unknown quantities, has been modified somewhat for electronic calculations. Modification is necessary to avoid further confusion, since specific electronic quantities are easily represented by using the beginning letter or the common electronic symbol. Some of these specific quantities are represented in this way: Power P, Impedance Z, Voltage E, Current I, Resistance R, etc.

These letters or symbols are called *literal numbers* or *general numbers*. Sometimes, expressions may require individual recognition, especially if several quantities use the same letter or symbol. *Subscripts* are used to indicate any differences and help provide identity for each quantity. These subscripts are actually small numbers or letters that are written somewhat below and to the right of the letter or symbol.

An algebraic *expression* is another way of saying *formula,* or since it indicates *equality* of quantities, an *equation*. Algebraic expressions are solved by substituting numerical values for the unknown symbols, and are reduced to their simplest form when performing the indicated operations. Addition, subtraction, multiplication, division, and square roots used in algebra are handled in the same manner as they were in arithmetic. Hints, laws, and rules for each operation will be covered in later algebraic sections.

2.2-1   COEFFICIENTS AND TERMS

A number or letter written before a quantity (indicating multiplication) is called a *coefficient. Terms* are those numbers or groups of letters and numbers that are separated by a plus or minus sign. Algebraic expressions have their own identity based upon the number of terms an equation has. The *monomial* expression has only one term ($P = IE$) while the rest of the algebraic expressions are grouped under the general heading of *polynomial*. This simply means that the equation has more than one term. A *binomial* is a polynomial having two terms ($RT = R_1 + R_2$) and a polynomial having three terms is called a *trinomial* ($RT = R_1 + R_2 + R_3$).

All coefficients used in algebraic expressions consist of a sign being either positive or negative (written or understood) and a particular *magnitude*. The magnitude is called an *absolute value*. This number is or can be enclosed between two parallel vertical lines. For example, the absolute value of a 150-volt source regardless of its polarity is written $|150|$. The absolute value of -150 volts is the same as for 150 volts, since the same amount of electrical force is indicated.

2.2-2 ADDITION

The following rules apply to algebraic addition processes:

1. When the numbers have like signs (both positive, or both negative) find the sum of the absolute values and then prefix the total with the common sign.

$$+8 +4 = +12 \quad \text{OR} \quad -8 +(-4) = -12$$

2. If the numbers have unlike signs, determine the difference between the absolute values and then prefix the remainder with the sign of the larger absolute value.

$$+8 +(-4) = +4 \quad \text{OR} \quad -8 +4 = -4$$

Note: If more than two terms are added, find the sum of the first two terms, then add this sum to the third term, then add this second sum to the fourth term, etc.

2.2-3 SUBTRACTION

The rule for algebraic subtraction involves multiplying the subtrahend by a minus one to change the subtrahend's sign. The problem is then that of addition since the algebraic sum is then found.

$$\begin{array}{c} +8 \\ -(+4) \\ \hline +4 \end{array} = \begin{array}{c} +8 \\ -4 \\ \hline +4 \end{array} \quad \text{OR} \quad \begin{array}{c} -8 \\ -(-4) \\ \hline -4 \end{array} = \begin{array}{c} -8 \\ +4 \\ \hline -4 \end{array}$$

Note: If several terms are to be subtracted, change all the necessary signs required for subtractions, and then find the algebraic sum of the terms.

2.2-4 MULTIPLICATION

Algebraic multiplication is governed by the following rules:

1. The product of two numbers having like signs (either both positive or both negative) is positive.

$$+8 \times (+4) = +32 \quad \text{OR} \quad -8 \times (-4) = +32$$

2. When multiplying two numbers having unlike signs, the product is negative.

$$-8 \times (+4) = -32 \quad \text{OR} \quad +8 \times (-4) = -32$$

Note: To find the product of more than two numbers, multiply the first two numbers, then use that product to multiply by the third number, multiply that product by the fourth number, etc.

2.2-5   DIVISION

The following rules apply to algebraic division operations:

1. Two numbers, divided by numbers having like signs, have a positive quotient.

$$\frac{+8}{+4} = +2 \quad \text{OR} \quad \frac{-8}{-4} = +2$$

2. The quotient of two numbers having unlike signs will be negative.

$$\frac{+8}{-4} = -2 \quad \text{OR} \quad \frac{-8}{+4} = -2$$

2.2-6   POWERS / EXPONENTS

A positive answer is always obtained when a positive number is squared (multiplied by itself) or when a negative number is multiplied by itself an even number of times. For example:

1. $E \times E = E^2$
2. $(-3)^2 = (-3)(-3) = +9$
3. $E \times E \times E = E^3$
4. $(-2)^4 = (-2)(-2)(-2)(-2) = +16$

A negative answer is obtained when negative numbers are raised to odd powers as indicated:

$$(-2)^3 = (-2)(-2)(-2) = (-2)(+4) = -8$$
$$-E^3 = (-E)(-E)(-E)$$

Numbers raised to powers can be handled in the following two ways:

By Dividing

$$\frac{3^2}{3^4} = \frac{3 \times 3}{3 \times 3 \times 3 \times 3} = \frac{1}{3^2}$$

or

By Subtracting exponents

$$\frac{3^2}{3^4} = 3^{2-4} = 3^{-2}$$

Any number having a negative power can be changed without altering its meaning, in the manner following, by taking the reciprocal.

$$3^{-2} = \frac{1}{3^2}$$

2.2-7 ROOTS

A root is indicated by a radical sign and index number (unless a square root is understood), or by a fractional exponent which is the reciprocal of the index number. The general form for a root of a quantity may be written as $_x\sqrt{A}$ or $A^{1/x}$. The letter A represents the quantity to be equally factored and is called the *radicand* when the radical sign is used and the *base* when the fractional exponent is used. The letter X represents the number of factors to be found. The rules for handling algebraic roots are as follows.

1. Odd roots of positive numbers are positive and odd roots of negative numbers are negative.

$$\sqrt[3]{27} = 3 \qquad OR \qquad \sqrt[3]{-27} = -3$$

2. Even roots of a positive number can be either positive or negative and are often indicated by the double positive-negative ($\pm$) sign.

$$\sqrt{9} = \pm 3$$

3. The root of a fraction is equal to the root of the numerator divided by the root of the denominator.

$$\sqrt{\frac{E^2}{R}} = \frac{\sqrt{E^2}}{\sqrt{R}} = \frac{E}{\sqrt{R}}$$

4. When finding the product of roots that have the same radicand, first write the roots in their fractional exponent form, and then write the product as a common base adding the exponents.

$$\sqrt{P} \times \sqrt[4]{P} = P^{1/2} \times P^{1/4} = P^{1/2 + 1/4} = P^{3/4}$$

5. To find quotients of roots having the same radicand, write the roots in their fractional exponent form, and then write the quotient as the common base to the exponent of the numerator minus the exponent of the denominator.

$$\frac{\sqrt{P}}{\sqrt[5]{P}} = P^{1/2} \times P^{-1/5} = P^{1/2 - 1/5} = P^{5/10 - 2/10} = P^{3/10}$$

6. *Rationalizing a denominator* is an operation including a fraction that has a square root quantity in its denominator. These fractions are changed into an integer when multiplying the numerator and denominator by the square root quantity.

$$\frac{1}{\sqrt{2}} = \frac{1}{\sqrt{2}} \times \frac{\sqrt{2}}{\sqrt{2}} = \frac{\sqrt{2}}{\sqrt{2} \times \sqrt{2}} = \frac{\sqrt{2}}{2}$$

7. A square root in a two-term denominator of a fraction can be changed to an integer by multiplying both the numerator and denominator by the conjugate of the denominator. A conjugate is simply the sum of two terms and the difference of the same two terms. For example:

$$\frac{1}{4 + \sqrt{P}} = \frac{4 - \sqrt{P}}{(4 + \sqrt{P})(4 - \sqrt{P})} = \frac{4 - \sqrt{P}}{16 - \sqrt{P^2}} = \frac{4 - \sqrt{P}}{16 - P}$$

2.2-7A   Basic Algebraic Root Relationships

The following equations illustrate root identities that may prove their worth when solving problems.

$$1. \ \sqrt[x]{AB} = \sqrt[x]{A} \ \sqrt[x]{B}$$

$$2. \ \sqrt{\frac{A}{B}} = \frac{\sqrt[x]{A}}{\sqrt[x]{B}}$$

$$3. \ \sqrt[x]{A} \ \sqrt[y]{A} = A^{\frac{1}{x} + \frac{1}{y}}$$

$$4. \ \frac{\sqrt[x]{A}}{\sqrt[y]{A}} = A^{\frac{1}{x} - \frac{1}{y}}$$

$$5. \ \frac{1}{\sqrt{A}} = \frac{\sqrt{A}}{A}$$

$$6. \ [\sqrt[x]{A}]^{\frac{1}{y}} = \sqrt[xy]{A}$$

2.2-8   HOW TO HANDLE TWO-TERM MATHEMATICAL PROCESSES

Binomials are algebraic expressions consisting of two terms. These particular algebraic expressions are subject to multiplication, division, addition, subtraction, raising to powers and taking roots. The following data will illustrate the basics necessary when accomplishing mathematical operations.

2.2-8A   Square of Binomial Sums

The algebraic expression $A + B$, having two terms, called a binomial, can be squared by multiplying or by applying a simple rule.

Multiplying:
$$\begin{array}{r} A + B \\ A + B \\ \hline A^2 + AB \\ + AB + B^2 \\ \hline A^2 + 2AB + B^2 \end{array}$$

Rule: Square the first term, add twice the product of the two terms, then add the square of the second term:

$$(A + B)^2 = A^2 + 2AB + B^2$$

2.2-8B   Square of a Binomial Difference

The algebraic binomial expression $E - IR$ can be squared either by multiplying or by using a simple rule.

Multiplying:
$$\begin{array}{r} E - IR \\ E - IR \\ \hline E^2 - EIR \\ - EIR + IR^2 \\ \hline E^2 - 2EIR + IR^2 \end{array}$$

Rule: Square the first term, subtract twice the product of the two terms, then add the square of the second term.

$$(E - IR)^2 = E^2 - 2EIR + IR^2$$

2.2-8C   Product of Binomial Sums and Differences

These two ways of solving algebraic expressions prove to be useful when handling complex numbers involving the "j" operator used in electronic calculations. To illustrate this, $R + jX$ and $R - jX$ will be examined.

Multiplication:
$$\begin{array}{r} R + jX \\ R - jX \\ \hline R^2 + RjX \\ - RjX - jX^2 \\ \hline R^2 \qquad - jX^2 \end{array}$$

Rule: Square the first term, then subtract the square of the second term.

$$(R + jX)(R - jX) = R^2 - jX^2$$

2.2-8D   Binomial Products Having One Common Term

In the following illustrations, the basic binomials will be $A + B$, $A + C$ for the multiplication of binomial sums; $A - B$, $A - C$ for the binomial differences, and $A + B$, $A - C$ for the binomial sum and differences.

Binomial sum
(multiplication)

$$
\begin{array}{r}
A + B \\
A + C \\
\hline
A^2 + AB \\
+ AC + BC \\
\hline
A^2 + AB + AC + BC
\end{array}
$$

Binomial differences
(multiplication)

$$
\begin{array}{r}
A - B \\
A - C \\
\hline
A^2 - AB \\
- AC + BC \\
\hline
A^2 - AB - AC + BC
\end{array}
$$

Binomial sum and differences
(multiplication)

$$
\begin{array}{r}
A + B \\
A - C \\
\hline
A^2 + AB \\
- AC - BC \\
\hline
A^2 + AB - AC - BC
\end{array}
$$

2.2-9   ALGEBRAIC FRACTIONS

Arithmetic operations involving addition, subtraction, division, and multiplication of fractions are similar basic operations when working with algebraic fractions. The only real difference is that algebraic fractions may involve positive numbers, negative numbers, literal quantities, and unknown quantities. To aid in algebraic fraction calculations, the following is given.

When working with fractions, three sign positions of the fraction must be examined for its implied mathematical sign. These three sign positions are: (1) directly preceding the whole fraction, (2) directly before the numerator, and (3) directly before the denominator.

Rule 1: Mathematical signs of any two of the three positions may be changed without altering the fraction's value.

$$
+ \frac{+A}{+B} = + \frac{-A}{-B} = - \frac{(-A)}{+B} = - \frac{+A}{(-B)}
$$

Note: Polynomials can be changed also in fraction form by changing each sign for each term (MULTIPLYING BY A MINUS ONE).

$$
Ax^2 - Bx + C = - (-Ax^2 + Bx - C)
$$

2.2-9A   Addition or Subtraction

When adding or subtracting fractions, a common denominator must first be found. We will demonstrate only the addition process, since the algebraic operation is the same. We will calculate the total current flowing through two resistors connected in parallel.

The formula is: $I_T = \dfrac{E_{R1}}{R_1} + \dfrac{E_{R2}}{R_2}$

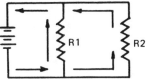

Figure 2-2

Total current equals the voltage dropped across R_1 divided by the resistance of R_1 plus the voltage dropped across resistor 2 divided by the resistance of R_2.

Finding the common denominator:

$$I_T = \frac{E_{R1}}{R_1} + \frac{E_{R2}}{R_2} = \frac{E_{R1}}{R_1 R_2} + \frac{E_{R2}}{R_1 R_2}$$

Rewrite the equation by writing the algebraic sum of the numerators over the common denominator.

$$I_T = \frac{E_{R1} + E_{R2}}{R_1 R_2}$$

Since E is common to both terms in the numerator, it is factored out and thereby simplifies and solves the equation:

$$I_T = \frac{E\,(R_1 + R_2)}{R_1 R_2}$$

2.2-9B   Multiplication

Algebraic and arithmetic fractions are multiplied by similar methods, in that multiplication of the numerators obtains the new numerator while multiplying the denominators provides the new denominator. As in solving arithmetic fraction problems, equal factors in both the numerator and denominator should be cancelled to simplify the operation. For example:

$$\frac{A}{B} \cdot \frac{C}{A} = \frac{AC}{BA} = \frac{C}{B}$$

2.2-9C   Division

The same rules used in arithmetic when dividing fractions are used in algebraic fraction division. To divide by a fraction, simply invert the divisor and multiply:

$$\frac{\dfrac{A}{B}}{\dfrac{C}{D}} = \frac{A}{B} \cdot \frac{D}{C} = \frac{AD}{BC}$$

2.2-10   SOLVING ALGEBRAIC EQUATIONS

Algebraic equations are easily solved when all of the rules involving algebra are employed as needed in the ways illustrated in this section.

The general mathematical operations outlined under arithmetic in this chapter also have their place in solving algebraic equations as you may have already determined. All of this application of rules helps one to solve the equation for its unknown. Often, in algebra, as in arithmetic, the equation must be reduced or changed into a simpler form. When this is done in algebra, the process is called *factoring*.

2.2-10A   Factoring

A *factor* is a common letter or number which appears in an equation. A *common factor* is that letter or number which appears in two or more terms in the same equation. The product of all factors that are common to a group of terms is called "*the highest common factor.*" An example of a common factor would be found in an equation used to find the source voltage (Es) for a series circuit having two resistors:

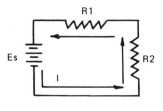

Figure 2-3

$$Es = I_{R1} + I_{R2}$$

The terms on the right of the equal sign can be factored since the current (I) is the same through both resistors and therefore is common to both resistors $Es = I_{R1} + I_{R2}$. The equation after factoring the common term would resemble:

$$Es = I\ (R_1 + R_2)$$

2.2-10B   Solving Quadratic Equations by Factoring

Whenever factoring the common factor from each term in an expression, arrange the resulting terms in an ascending or descending order to aid in determining whether it still can be factored. By doing this, you might discover a quadratic equation since every quadratic equation takes on the $AX^2 + BX + C = 0$ form. The letter X represents the unknown, and the letters A and B represent any positive or negative numerical value, including zero. In order to factor an equation, common factors must be determined. This simply means what times what equals the equation and what is common within the terms. To illustrate this, the following equations show what expressions times what expressions are equal. (Refer to Section 2.2-8 for additional details.)

$$(1)\ A^2 + 2AB + B^2 = (A + B)^2$$
$$(2)\ A^2 - 2AB + B^2 = (A - B)^2$$
$$(3)\ A^2 - B^2 = (A + B)(A - B)$$

To factor the equation $X^2 + 9X + 14$, you must find the factors of 14 representing the C term in $A\,X^2 + B\,X + C$, paying particular attention to the values which, when added together, equal the numerical value of B in the $A\,X^2 + B\,X + C$ form.

The factors of 14 are:	*The sums of the factors are:*
$14 = 14 \times 1$	$14 + 1 = 15$
$14 = 2 \times 7$	$2 + 7 = 9$

2

Since the sum of the two factors 2 and 7, when added together equals the B term, these are the factors of the equation. The following equation may be written.

$$(X + 2)(X + 7) = X^2 + 9X + 14$$

To satisfy an equation, the unknown or unknowns must be determined. In solving quadratic equations, we arrange the equation so that it equals zero. When solving a quadratic equation having one unknown, arrange the equation so that one expression or member is the product of the two factors, and the other member is zero. Set each of the factors equal to zero and solve for the unknown or unknowns. To illustrate this, the previous example will be used.

1. Write the equation so the right-hand member equals zero.

$$X^2 + 9X + 14 = 0$$

2. Factor the left-hand member still equaling zero.

$$(X + 2)(X + 7) = 0$$

3. Solve each of the factors for the value of X when each factor is said to equal zero.

$$X + 2 = 0 \qquad\qquad X + 7 = 0$$
$$\text{AND}$$
$$X = -2 \qquad\qquad X = -7$$

This results in the roots of the equation, and when substituted for the unknown, will satisfy the original equation.

$$X^2 + 9X + 14 = 0 \qquad\qquad X^2 + 9X + 14 = 0$$
$$(-2)^2 + 9(-2) + 14 = 0 \qquad (-7)^2 + 9(-7) + 14 = 0$$
$$4 - 18 + 14 = 0 \qquad\qquad 49 - 63 + 14 = 0$$
$$-18 + 18 = 0 \qquad\qquad -63 + 63 = 0$$
$$0 = 0 \qquad\qquad\qquad 0 = 0$$

Since the equation is satisfied, you have found the correct roots.

2.2-10C   Solving Quadratic Equations by Completing the Square

Sometimes a quadratic equation cannot readily be solved by factoring. However, another method called completing the square may solve it by making the unknown terms part of a square. The following equation illustrates this completing the square method.

The equation is: $12P^2 = 29P - 14$

Step 1. Divide both sides of the equation by the coefficient of the unknown term that is squared. *Do not simplify by actually dividing.*

$$\frac{(12P^2)}{12} = \frac{29P}{12} - \frac{14}{12}$$

Step 2. Group the unknown terms together on the left side of the equal sign and place the constant term on the right. Simplify only the term that is squared.

$$P^2 - \frac{29P}{12} = -\frac{14}{12}$$

Step 3. Select a value equal to one-half the coefficient used for the second term, square this value, and add it to both sides of the equation. In our example we keep the numerator (29) and double the denominator (12) before squaring and adding.

$$P^2 - \frac{29P}{12} + \left(\frac{29}{24}\right)^2 = \left(\frac{29}{24}\right)^2 - \frac{14}{12}$$

Step 4. Find the factors of the quadratic expression written on the left of the equal sign.

$$\left(\frac{P-29}{24}\right)\left(\frac{P-29}{24}\right) = \left(\frac{29}{24}\right)^2 - \frac{14}{12}$$

Step 5. Find the common denominator for the terms on the right side of the equal sign.

$$\left(\frac{P-29}{24}\right)\left(\frac{P-29}{24}\right) = \left(\frac{29}{24}\right)^2 - \frac{24(2)}{24(2)}\frac{14}{12}$$

$$\left(\frac{P-29}{24}\right)\left(\frac{P-29}{24}\right) = \left(\frac{29}{24}\right)^2 - \frac{672}{(24)^2}$$

$$\left(\frac{P-29}{24}\right)\left(\frac{P-29}{24}\right) = \frac{841\text{-}672}{(24)^2}$$

Step 6. Take the square root of each term in the equation.

$$\sqrt{\left(\frac{P-29}{24}\right)\left(\frac{P-29}{24}\right)} = \sqrt{\frac{841\text{-}672}{(24)^2}}$$

$$\frac{P-29}{24} = \sqrt{\frac{841\text{-}672}{(24)}}$$

$$\frac{P-29}{24} = \pm\frac{13}{24}$$

Step 7. Solve for the two unknowns by transposing and performing the indicated mathematical operations.

$$P = \frac{29}{24} + \frac{13}{24} = +\frac{42}{24} = \frac{7}{4} \quad answer\ \#1$$

$$P = \frac{29}{24} - \frac{13}{24} = +\frac{16}{24} = \frac{2}{3} \quad answer\ \#2$$

2.2-10D   Solving Quadratic Equations by a Quadratic Formula

A third popular method used to solve quadratic equations is one that employs the quadratic formula, which solves for the unknown without too much effort. The formula is:

$$X = -B \pm \sqrt{\frac{B^2 - 4AC}{2A}}$$

Since quadratic equations resemble the familiar $AX^2 + BX + C$ form, application of this formula is quite simple after the equation is rearranged, because the values for A, B, and C are substituted into it. To illustrate this, we will solve the following equation:

$$E = \frac{1}{E + 1} + 3$$

First, we must arrange the equation in the quadratic form $AX^2 + BX + C = 0$.

From: $E = \dfrac{1}{E + 1} + 3$

$E - 3 = \dfrac{1}{E + 1}$

$(E - 3)(E + 1) = 1$

$E^2 - 2E - 3 = 1$

Into: $E^2 - 2E - 4 = 0$ (*quadratic form* $AX^2 + BX + C = 0$)

Second, we write the quadratic formula and then substitute the coefficients for A, B, and C.

Formula $\quad X = \dfrac{-B \pm \sqrt{B^2 - 4AC}}{2A}$

Substitution $X = \dfrac{-(-2) \pm \sqrt{(-2)^2 - 4(1)(-4)}}{2(1)}$

Solution $\quad X = \dfrac{2 \pm \sqrt{4 + 16}}{2} = \dfrac{2 \pm \sqrt{20}}{2} = \dfrac{2 \pm \sqrt{(4)(5)}}{2}$

$X = \dfrac{2 \pm 2\sqrt{5}}{2} \quad$ OR $\quad X = 1 \pm \sqrt{5}$

2.2-10E   Solving Higher Order Equations Having Quadratic Form

Higher order equations of the $3R^4 - R^2 - 25 = 0$ variety can be solved using the quadratic formula if the original equation is simplified. If we substituted another unknown, say (W), for R^2, then R equals $\sqrt{W}$ and the following would be true.

instead of: $3R^4 - R^2 - 25 = 0$
we have: $3W^2 - W - 25 = 0 \quad$ (*AX^2 + BX + C form*)

If we write the quadratic formula and substitute the values we solve for the new unknown and then for the original unknown:

$$X = \frac{-B \pm \sqrt{B^2 - 4AC}}{2A} \qquad \text{OR } W = \frac{-1 \pm \sqrt{(-1)^2 - 4(3)(-25)}}{2(3)}$$

$$W = \frac{-1 \pm \sqrt{1 + 300}}{6}$$

$$\text{THEN: } W = \frac{-1 + 17.35}{6} = \frac{16.35}{6} = 2.73$$

$$\text{AND: } W = \frac{-1 - 17.35}{6} = \frac{-18.35}{6} = -3.06$$

Since earlier we said $R = \sqrt{W}$, then the value for the unknown letter R is:

$$R = \sqrt{2.73} \quad \text{AND} \quad R = \sqrt{-3.06}$$

2.2-11   SIMULTANEOUS EQUATION SOLUTIONS

Often in electronics, two or more equations must be used when describing circuitry operation. Since an equation having only one unknown cannot be written and still adequately describe the particular phenomenon, simultaneous equations are used. Two or more equations satisfied by the same values of the unknown will be illustrated in three separate ways. The first will be using addition and subtraction methods, the second is solved by substitution, and the third method is that of comparison.

2.2-11A   Solving Simultaneous Equations by Addition or Subtraction

Simultaneous equations may be added or subtracted, thereby eliminating all but one unknown when following the following procedures. The equations used will describe the voltages in a two-source network. The unknown will be the two separate currents flowing in their circuit. The circuit we will describe, using two equations, will be:

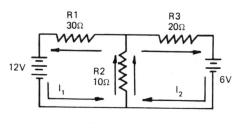

Figure 2-4

Step 1: Write the equations for the voltages around the two closed loops created when the currents flow through the resistors. Keep the variable quantities on the left and the constant terms on the right of the equal sign.

The first equation	The second equation
$ER_1 + ER_2 = 12V$	$ER_2 + ER_3 = 6V$
or: $30I_1 + 10I_1 + 10I_2 = 12$	$10I_1 + 10I_2 + 20I_2 = 6$
simplified: $40I_1 + 10I_2 = 12$	$10I_1 + 30I_2 = 6$

Step 2: Arrange the two equations as if adding or subtracting the two.

$$40I_1 + 10I_2 = 12 \text{ (first equation)}$$
$$\underline{10I_1 + 30I_2 = 6} \text{ (second equation)}$$

Step 3: Multiply either equation by a number which will allow one of the like terms to cancel when the equations are subtracted. In our case we will multiply the second equation by 4 and will subtract from the other. Rearrange, if necessary, to keep the unknown positive.

$$40I_1 + 120I_2 = 24 \text{ (second equation)}$$
$$\underline{-(40I_1 + 10I_2 = 12)} \text{ (first equation)}$$
$$+ 110I_2 = 12$$

Step 4: Solve for the unknown.

$$110I_2 = 12$$
$$I_2 = \frac{12}{110} = 0.109 \text{ amperes}$$

Step 5: Plug this unknown into one of the original equations to solve for the other current.

$$(\textit{First equation}) \ 40I_1 + 10I_2 = 12$$
$$40I_1 + 10(0.109) = 12$$
$$40I_1 + 1.09 = 12$$
$$40I_1 = 10.91$$
$$I_1 = \frac{10.91}{40} = 0.2727 \text{ amperes}$$

Step 6: Check the solutions by substituting the two current values into one or both of the original equations.

$$(\textit{Second equation}) \qquad 10I_1 + 30I_2 = 6$$
$$10(0.2727) + 30(0.109) = 6$$
$$2.727 + 3.270 = 6$$
$$5.997 \approx 6$$

Naturally, in this case we did not carry out our calculations far enough to equal the 6 volts, but for practice, it is close enough.

2.2-11B   Solving Simultaneous Equations by Substitution

Two simultaneous equations having the same unknown quantity or quantities may be solved by substituting the value of one unknown in one

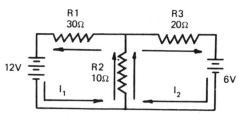

Figure 2-5

equation for the same unknown in the other equation. The previous example for a two-source network will be used in solving for the currents.

Step 1: Write the equations describing the voltages around the closed loops shown in Figure 2-5. (Refer to 2.2-11A, Step 1.)

First equation

$$40I_1 + 10I_2 = 12$$

Second equation

$$10I_1 + 30I_2 = 6$$

Step 2: Solve one equation for one unknown in terms of the other unknown.

$$\text{First equation } 40I_1 + 10I_2 = 12$$

$$40I_1 = 12 - 10I_2$$

$$I_1 = \frac{12 - 10I_2}{40} = \frac{6 - 5I_2}{20}$$

Step 3: Substitute this value of the unknown for the same unknown in the second equation and solve for one unknown.

$$\text{Second equation } 10I_1 + 30I_2 = 6$$

$$10\left(\frac{6 - 5I_2}{20}\right) + 30I_2 = 6$$

$$60 - 50I_2 + 600I_2 = 120$$

$$60 + 550I_2 = 120$$

$$550I_2 = 60$$

$$I_2 = 0.109 \text{ amperes (one answer)}$$

Step 4: Substitute the value for the unknown just solved for into either one of the two original equations, and solve for the other unknown.

Second equation $10I_1 + 30I_2 = 6$
$$10I_1 + 30(0.109) = 6$$
$$10I_1 + 3.270 = 6$$
$$10I_1 = 2.73$$
$$I_1 = 0.273 \text{ amperes (answer)}$$

Step 5: Check the answers by substituting the two unknown values into one or both of the original equations.

Second equation check $10I_1 + 30I_2 = 6$
$$10(0.273) + 30(0.109) = 6$$
$$2.73 + 3.27 = 6$$
$$6 = 6$$

2.2-11C   Simultaneous Equation Solutions by Comparison

An unknown can be eliminated in a simultaneous equation when both equations are solved for the same unknown quantity. Since these unknowns must satisfy both equations, they are said to be equal. It is on this basis that we will solve the same equations used in the two previous examples, showing how to solve them by comparison methods.

Step 1: Write the equations for the circuitry illustrated in Figure 2-5.

First equation	*Second equation*
$40I_1 + 10I_2 = 12$	$10I_1 + 30I_2 = 6$

Step 2: Pick one common unknown in both equations and solve for it in terms of the other unknown.

First equation	*Second equation*
$40I_1 + 10I_2 = 12$	$10I_1 + 30I_2 = 6$
$40I_1 = 12 - 10I_2$	$10I_1 = 6 - 30I_2$
$I_1 = \dfrac{12 - 10I_2}{40}$	$I_1 = \dfrac{6 - 30I_2}{10}$
$I_1 = \dfrac{6 - 5I_2}{20}$	$I_1 = \dfrac{3 - 15I_2}{5}$

Step 3: Since both unknowns are equal to each other, we can solve for the other unknown in the following manner.

First equation I_1 = Second equation I_1

$$\frac{6 - 5I_2}{20} = \frac{3 - 15I_2}{5}$$

$$30 - 25I_2 = 60 - 300I_2$$

$$30 - 25I_2 + 300I_2 = 60$$

$$275I_2 = 30$$

$$I_2 = \frac{30}{275}$$

$$I_2 = 0.109 \text{ ampere (first answer)}$$

Step 4: Substitute this quantity for the same unknown in either of the original equations, and then solve for the other unknown quantity.

First equation $40I_1 + 10I_2 = 12$
$40I_1 + 10(0.109) = 12$
$40I_1 = 12 - 1.09$

$$I_1 = \frac{10.91}{40}$$

$$I_1 = 0.273 \text{ amperes}$$

Step 5: To verify the solutions, solve either or both equations using the values just calculated.

Equation two $10(I_1) + 30(I_2) = 6$
$10(0.273) + 30(0.109) = 6$
$2.73 + 3.27 = 6$
$6 = 6$ check

Simultaneous equations having three or more unknowns in three or more equations can be solved using the general methods outlined in 2.2-11A through 2.2-11C.

A common step sequence for solving three unknown quantities in three equations is as follows:

Step 1: Use only two of the three equations to form an equation having only two known quantities.

Step 2: Use the equation written for Step 1 and one of the original equations to form a second equation having only two unknown quantities. The second equation should have the same unknowns as the first equation having two unknown quantities.

Step 3: Take the two simplified equations with two unknown quantities and solve for one unknown in terms of the other unknown.

Step 4: Substitute the results obtained in Step 3 for the unknown quantities in any of the original equations solving for the third unknown.

Step 5: Check your answers by substituting your values into one or all of the three original equations.

2.3   PLANE GEOMETRY

This portion of Chapter 2 will provide you with a condensed view of geometry, dealing with the rules, terminology, postulates and facts needed to solve electronic problems with mathematical wisdom.

2.3-1   POSTULATES

Sometimes things may be accepted without proof. In geometry, principles just accepted are called postulates and serve to develop rules for arithmetic and algebraic relationships. The following postulates are those most often relied upon for all mathematical processes.

1. The shortest distance between two points is a straight line.
2. Only one straight line can be drawn between any two points.
3. Two straight lines will not intersect at more than one point.
4. You may extend a straight line to any distance.
5. A geometric figure can be moved from one position to another without altering its basic form or magnitude.
6. All 90 degree angles (right angles) are equal.
7. All straight lines have a straight angle of 180 degrees.
8. In a flat surface (plane), only one perpendicular to a line can be drawn from a point placed on either side of the plane.
9. Angles having the same supplement are equal.
10. Angles having the same complement are equal.
11. Vertical angles are equal.
12. A line segment can be bisected at only one point.
13. All angles can be bisected by only one line.
14. All the sides of a square are equal.
15. All radii of the same circle are equal.
16. All diameters of the same circle are equal.
17. A straight line can intersect a circle at only two points.
18. If the two points where a straight line intersects a circle coincide, the line is tangent to the circle.

19. A circle intersects another circle only at two points.

20. The diameter of a circle bisects the circle.

21. There are 360 degrees in a square and in a circle.

2.3-2   ANGLES

Angles are generally divided into five separate groups, as illustrated in Figure 2-6. The first is called the *right angle* since a line drawn perpendicular to another line forms a 90 degree angle. The second group is called the *acute angle* because the angle formed is less than 90 degrees. The third group, called the *obtuse angle*, has an angle that is greater than 90 degrees, but less than 180 degrees. The fourth group is the *straight line*. Its angle is formed when the sides extend in opposite directions from the *vertex* or point where the lines meet. The fifth group, called the *reflex angle*, has more than 180 degrees, but less than 360 degrees for its angle.

Since two straight lines that meet at a point can and do form angles, the sides and the angle formed can be used for angle identification. Angles formed by two straight lines are normally represented by the letter symbol "O," the Greek letter theta (Θ), the geometry angle symbol ($\angle$) plus the letter O or Θ, or by writing the assigned letters representing the line terminates preceded by the angle symbol ($\angle$ AOC). These concepts are shown in Figure 2-6 for the five angle groups.

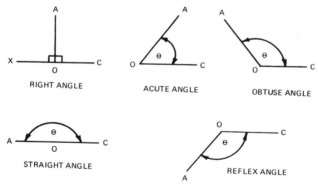

Figure 2-6

Since all of the angles illustrated in Figure 2-6 share a common vertex and common sides, the angles are called *adjacent angles*. The right angle example shows angles "XOA" and "AOC" having a small square at the point where line "AO" is drawn. These squares represent an angle of 90 degrees or that the line is perpendicular to line "XC."

The application of geometry involves three basic angle relationships termed *complementary angles, supplementary angles,* and *vertical angles.*

Complementary angles are formed whenever two angles added together equal a right angle of 90 degrees. Angle AOC shown in Figure 2-7 equals 90 degrees, and angles AOB plus BOC when combined also equal the required 90 degrees. Hence, the complementary angles are AOB and BOC.

The supplementary angles in Figure 2-7 are formed when the two angles added together equal a straight angle having 180 degrees. Angle DOF equals 180 degrees and angles "DOE" plus "EOF" when added together also equal 180 degrees. The supplementary angles are "DOE" and "EOF."

Vertical angles consist of two lines that intersect in the same manner as illustrated in Figure 2-7. The opposite angles formed are called vertical angles and are recognized as being "IOH," "GOJ," and angles "IOG" and "HOJ."

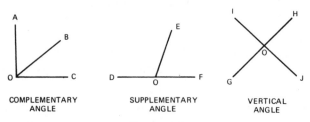

| COMPLEMENTARY | SUPPLEMENTARY | VERTICAL |
| ANGLE | ANGLE | ANGLE |

Figure 2-7

2.3-3   TRIANGLES

The terms and definitions for all triangles are listed here in brief form, but will serve your needs in geometry, trigonometry, and other related maths for electronic applications.

1. The portion of a plane surrounded by three straight lines is called a *triangle*.

2. The straight lines forming the triangle are called its *sides*.

3. The sum of the triangle sides is its *perimeter*.

4. The angle within the triangle formed by any two sides is its *interior angle*.

5. The angle formed by any side and the extension of another side is an *exterior angle*.

6. One side of a triangle is most often drawn as a horizontal line with the remaining two sides drawn above it.

7. The bottom side is called the *base;* however, any side of the triangle can be designated as the base.

8. The angle opposite the base is termed the *vertex angle* and serves as the vertex of the triangle.

9. The perpendicular distance from the vertex of the triangle to its base is called the *altitude*.

10. If a triangle is a right triangle, the side opposite the right angle (the longest side) is termed the *hypotenuse*.

The five general types of triangles illustrated in Figure 2-8 are briefly described in the following way. The *acute triangle* has its interior angles somewhat less than a right angle which has 90 degrees. The *right triangle* has one right angle and two acute angles. The *obtuse triangle* has one obtuse angle (greater than 90 degrees) and two acute angles. The *isosceles triangle* can be identified easily because it has two equal sides and two equal angles. The last triangle, an *equilateral triangle* or equiangular triangle, has three equal sides and three equal angles.

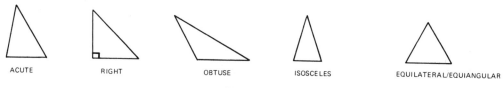

ACUTE   RIGHT   OBTUSE   ISOSCELES   EQUILATERAL/EQUIANGULAR

Figure 2-8

2.3-4   CIRCLES

The simple circle that you and I recognize is geometrically described in the following similar manner: a plane figure bounded by a single curved line, every point of which is equally distant from the point at the center of the figure. Now that you have the idea of what a circle really is, we will provide the terminology in a simpler form. Figure 2-9 illustrates the following facts.

1. The curved line forming the circle is called the *circumference*.
2. A straight line drawn between the center of the circle and any point on its circumference is termed the *radius*.
3. A *chord* is a straight line (called a straight line segment) that joins any two points of the circle's circumference.
4. A chord that happens to pass through the center of the circle is called the *diameter*.
5. The diameter is actually twice the length of the circle's radius.
6. A straight line that touches a circle, but does not cross its circumference, is a *tangent* of the circle.
7. The point at which the tangent touches the circumference of the circle is called the *point of tangency*.
8. A straight line that cuts a circumference in two points but not at a circle's center is a *secant* of that circle.
9. A *central angle* within a circle is an angle that has its vertex at the center of the circle and whose sides are the radii of the circle.
10. An *inscribed angle* within a circle is an angle whose vertex is in the circumference of the circle and whose sides are chords.
11. Circles having a common center are called *concentric circles*.

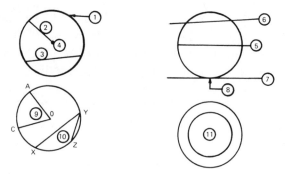

Figure 2-9

1. Circumference	7. Tangent
2. Radius	8. Point of tangency
3. Chord	9. Central angle (AOC)
4. Center	10. Inscribed angle (XYZ)
5. Diameter	11. Concentric circles
6. Secant	

2.4   TRIGONOMETRY

This portion of Chapter 2 deals with the specialized mathematics called trigonometry. Trigonometry applies the rules and laws of arithmetic for its numbers, the rules and laws of algebra in its equations, the rules and laws of geometry, and the rules and laws of relationships of triangle angles and their sides during application. Since most of the important rules, facts, and laws serving as the foundation for this specialized math have been uncovered earlier in this chapter, the following rules, facts, and guidelines will be introduced in a concise manner with a minimum of previous data review.

2.4-1   TRIGONOMETRIC RELATIONS

A high percentage of electronic calculations involving alternating current must be expressed mathematically using right triangle facts and angle designations to accurately describe the electronic phenomenon. Relationships used to describe these phenomena are based upon the acute angle (the angle equal to or less than 90 degrees) and the sides of a right triangle. There are six functions of the right triangle for angles employed in trigonometry. The names for the six functions and their abbreviations are:

1. Sine (sin)	4. Cotangent (cot)
2. Cosine (cos)	5. Secant (sec)
3. Tangent (tan)	6. Cosecant (csc)

The functions of the right triangle provide a usable number, after some calculation, which corresponds to an angle measurement in degrees. The illustration in Figure 2-10 will serve as an aid, providing meaning to the function name and angle references.

The longer side marked with the smaller letter "c" illustrated in Figure 2-10 represents the *hypotenuse*. The hypotenuse, as you remember, is always the longest side of any right triangle. The terms "opposite" or "adjacent" sides used in describing the trigonometric functions have movable meanings depending upon which of the three angles in the triangle you are talking about. For example, the sine function for angle "A" has as its opposite side the letter "a" while the sine function for angle "B" has the letter "b" representing its opposite side, and in like manner the sine function for angle "C" would have the letter "c" indicating its opposite side.

$$\text{Sine} = \frac{\text{Opposite side}}{\text{Hypotenuse}}$$

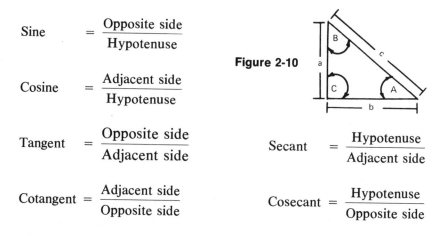

Figure 2-10

$$\text{Cosine} = \frac{\text{Adjacent side}}{\text{Hypotenuse}}$$

$$\text{Tangent} = \frac{\text{Opposite side}}{\text{Adjacent side}}$$

$$\text{Secant} = \frac{\text{Hypotenuse}}{\text{Adjacent side}}$$

$$\text{Cotangent} = \frac{\text{Adjacent side}}{\text{Opposite side}}$$

$$\text{Cosecant} = \frac{\text{Hypotenuse}}{\text{Opposite side}}$$

2.4-2   TRIGONOMETRIC APPLICATION

Application of any one function would not be possible unless someone, someplace, at sometime developed its relationships. Rather than sharing with you the tedious calculations essential to generate such truths, the following formulas can be applied directly to trigonometry-related problems if you know the values for the indicated side and angle for your problem. Use Figure 2-10 as a reference to aid in recognizing the side or angle.

It should be pointed out that this information is *only* valid when applied to right triangle problems and that if you know any two measurements (angle and side, or two sides), all of the other data pertinent to that right triangle problem can be solved. To illustrate the usefulness of the listed formulas, we will show how to solve for the three unknowns when side "a" and side "b" are given.

The electronic problem involves a 400 ohm resistor which is connected in series with an inductor having an inductive reactance of 300 ohms. Naturally, the question would be what is the total impedance of this circuit, but we won't

Values you know (sides and angles)	Formulas to use in solving for the unknown		
1. side a, side b	$c = \sqrt{a^2 + b^2}$	$\text{Tan } A = \dfrac{a}{b}$	$\angle B = 90° - \angle A$
2. side a, hypotenuse c	$b = \sqrt{c^2 - a^2}$	$\text{Sin } A = \dfrac{a}{c}$	$\angle B = 90° - \angle A$
3. side b, hypotenuse c	$a = \sqrt{c^2 - b^2}$	$\text{Sin } B = \dfrac{b}{c}$	$\angle A = 90° - \angle B$
4. hypotenuse c, angle B	$b = c \text{ Sin } B$	$a = c \text{ Cos } B$	$\angle A = 90° - \angle B$
5. hypotenuse c, angle A	$b = c \text{ Cos } A$	$a = c \text{ Sin } A$	$\angle B = 90° - \angle A$
6. side b, angle B	$c = \dfrac{b}{\text{Sin } B}$	$a = b \text{ Cot } B$	$\angle A = 90° - \angle B$
7. side b, angle A	$c = \dfrac{b}{\text{Cos } A}$	$a = b \text{ Tan } A$	$\angle B = 90° - \angle A$
8. side a, angle B	$c = \dfrac{a}{\text{Cos } B}$	$b = a \text{ Tan } B$	$\angle A = 90° - \angle B$
9. side a, angle A	$c = \dfrac{a}{\text{Sin } A}$	$b = a \text{ Cot } A$	$\angle B = 90° - \angle A$

stop there because we can figure out what the other two angles would be also, as you will soon see.

    The best way to begin any reactive AC problem is first to draw the circuit, second, to draw the right triangle equivalent for the circuit, and then to solve the problem using appropriate rules and laws of mathematics. The circuit and impedance triangle, shown in Figure 2-11, illustrates the value of resistance and inductive reactance for the right triangle sides. The right triangle used for Figure 2-10 is also shown in Figure 2-11, to illustrate similarities of previously defined materials.

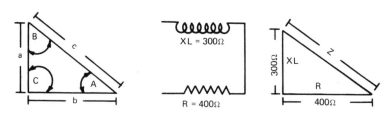

Figure 2-11

Since side "a" represents 300 ohms, side "b" represents 400 ohms, and side "c" the total impedance, direct application can be made as this mathematical process indicates.

Since $c = \sqrt{a^2 + b^2}$ then:

$$Z = \sqrt{(X_L)^2 + (R)^2}$$

$$Z = \sqrt{(300)^2 + (400)^2}$$

$$Z = \sqrt{90,000 + 160,000}$$

$$Z = \sqrt{250,000}$$

$$Z = 500 \text{ ohms}$$

The total impedance for the series circuit is 500 ohms. The data for the problem was plugged into the formulas in row #1 of the previous data chart since we knew the value for both sides of the triangle. Angle "A" or angle "B" could be determined in a similar manner once the data for your particular problem is substituted into the appropriate formula. For example, we shall show how to apply the data found in Figure 2-11 when solving for angles "A" and "B."

Since Tan "A" $= \dfrac{a}{b}$ (refer to row #1, 3rd column of formulas)

Then: Tan "A" $= \dfrac{300}{400}$ (refer to Figure 2-11)

Tan "A" $= 0.75$

This number, when looked up in a Natural Trigonometric Functions Table, will provide us with the exact angle value or its approximate angle for the tangent function equaling 0.75. If you were to find this number in the Natural Trigonometric Function Chart, only an approximate angle between 36 degrees, 50 minutes and 37 degrees could be found. The more exact answer often demanded for electronic calculation must be determined by interpolation, a process that will be illustrated after we demonstrate how to solve for the "B" angle.

Angle "B" can be found by applying the facts of the problem to the formula listed in row #1, 4th column or by taking the tangent function of it. Either method should result in the same angle value as indicated next.

$\angle$ "B" $= 90°$ minus $\angle$ A	(OR)	Tan "B" $= \dfrac{b}{a}$
$\angle$ "B" $= 90°$ minus about $37°$		Tan "B" $= \dfrac{400}{300}$
$\angle$ "B" $=$ approximately $53°$		Tan "B" $= 1.333$

Angle "B" equals an angle of somewhere between 36 degrees, 50 minutes and 37 degrees. Since this is the same approximate value obtained for angle "A," the mathematical process called interpolation need only be done once because it will provide us with the same answer for both angles as you shall see.

It should be pointed out that trigonometric tables needed for trigonometric values and interpolation often list angles ranging from 0 to 45 degrees on the left column reading them from top to bottom. Angles ranging from 45 to 90 degrees are listed in the right column and are read from bottom to top. The Natural Trigonometric Functions Table for the numbers we are interested in resembles the following table data.

0 to 45 DEGREES	SIN	COS	TAN	COT	SEC	CSC	
36 - 00'	0.5878	0.8090	0.7265	1.376	1.236	1.701	54 - 00'
36 - 50'	0.5995	0.8004	0.7490	1.335	1.249	1.668	53 - 10'
37 - 00'	0.6018	0.7986	0.7536	1.327	1.252	1.662	53 - 00'
	COS	SIN	COT	TAN	CSC	SEC	45 to 90 DEGREES

The corresponding angles for the number 0.75 representing the Tan "A" function and the number 1.333 representing the Tan "B" function is determined in this way. Tangent "A" equaling 0.75 will be interpolated first.

1. Find the two closest numbers for the tangent function and their angles. Since the two closest numbers 0.7490 and 0.7536 are listed under the tangent function listed at the top of the chart, the angles are those shown on the left of the table.

2. Record this data in the following way.

$$36° \ 50' \quad = 0.7490$$

$$\text{Tan "A"} = 0.7500$$

$$37° \ 00' \quad = 0.7536$$

3. Then, if 36° 50' is less than the unknown angle, and 37° 00' is larger than the unknown, the solution can be found by knowing that 37 degrees also equals 36 degrees, 59 minutes, 60 seconds or 36° 59' 60". We will change this to another equivalent of 36° 58' 120" for greater accuracy.

$$\frac{37° \ 00' - \text{Tan "A"}}{37° \ 00' - 36° \ 50'} = \frac{0.7536 - 0.7500}{0.7536 - 0.7490}$$

$$\frac{36° \ 59' \ 60" - \text{Tan "A"}}{36° \ 60' - 36° \ 50'} = \frac{0.0036}{0.0046}$$

$$\frac{36° \ 59' \ 60'' - \text{Tan "A"}}{10'} = 0.78$$

$$\text{Tan "A"} = 36° \ 58' \ 120'' - (10)(0.78)$$

$$\text{Tan "A"} = 36° \ 58' \ 120'' - 7' \ 80''$$

$$\text{Tan "A"} = 36° \ 51' \ 40''$$

Angle "A" illustrated in Figure 2-11 is 36 degrees, 51 minutes, 40 seconds, which is somewhat closer than our estimate of somewhere between 36 degrees, 50 minutes and 37 degrees. Angle "B" can be evaluated in the same general manner as angle "A" or for simplicity, since we know angle "C" is 90 degrees and angle "A" is 36° 51' 40" then:

$$\text{Angle "B"} = 90° - \text{angle "A"}$$

$$\angle \text{"B"} = 89° \ 59' \ 60'' - 36° \ 51' \ 40''$$

$$\angle B = 53° \ 08' \ 20''$$

The right triangle problem, illustrated in Figure 2-11, can be checked for angle accuracy since in any triangle the sum of its angles will equal 180 degrees. If you add the three angles, "A," "B," and "C" together, the result is 179° 59' 60" or the equivalent of 180 degrees.

2.4-3 QUADRANT SIGNS AND FUNCTION RELATIONS

The circle, illustrated in Figure 2-12, will serve as a basis for quadrant division and trigonometric function angle relationships. The circle is divided in half twice by two axes. The axis drawn north and south is called the "Y" axis while the axis drawn east and west is called the "X" axis. These two axes divide the circle into four equal quadrants consisting of 90 degrees each. Quadrant I has angles ranging from 0 to 90 degrees, quadrant II has angles from 90 to 180 degrees, quadrant III from 180 to 270 degrees, and quadrant IV from 270 to 360 degrees.

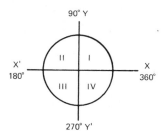

Figure 2-12

The signs for the X and Y magnitudes would be positive in the first quadrant. The signs for the second quadrant would be mixed; Y is positive and X' is negative. Both Y' and X' in the third quadrant would be negative. The fourth quadrant magnitudes for X and Y' would be mixed; Y' is negative while X is positive. Rather than remembering the above facts and relating them to different functions and trying to recall the range of numbers corresponding to the angles for each quadrant, the following chart provides instant recall with less mental fatigue. Figure 2-12 should be referred to for quadrant and angle limits.

Trigonometric Function	Quadrant I 0 to 90°	Quadrant II 90 to 180°	Quadrant III 180 to 270°	Quadrant IV 270 to 360°
Sine	Positive 0 to 1	Positive 1 to 0	Negative 0 to −1	Negative −1 to 0
Cosine	Positive 1 to 0	Negative 0 to −1	Negative −1 to 0	Positive 0 to 1
Tangent	Positive 0 to ∞	Negative ∞ to 0	Positive 0 to ∞	Negative ∞ to 0
Cotangent	Positive ∞ to 0	Negative 0 to ∞	Positive ∞ to 0	Negative 0 to ∞
Secant	Positive 1 to ∞	Negative ∞ to −1	Negative −1 to ∞	Positive ∞ to −1
Cosecant	Positive ∞ to 1	Positive 1 to ∞	Negative ∞ to −1	Negative −1 to ∞

Since trigonometric function tables use only those angles found within quadrant I, we must relate angles greater than 90 degrees to quadrant one facts in order to use Trigonometric Tables. With application of the data enclosed in the previous chart, we shall record what each function means in three quadrants. The first quadrant is omitted because all of its functions are positive and can be found directly in the Trigonometric Function Tables.

The trigonometric functions for an angle (ϕ) in the second quadrant are the same functions as for an angle represented by $180° - \phi$. This will allow us to use the functions listed in the Trigonometric Tables. Follow the functions listed in the previous chart, paying attention to the sign given for each function. The second quadrant functions are:

$$\text{Sin } \phi = \text{Sin } (180° - \phi) \qquad \text{Cot} = -\text{Cot } (180° - \phi)$$
$$\text{Cos } \phi = -\text{Cos } (180° - \phi) \qquad \text{Sec} = -\text{Sec } (180° - \phi)$$
$$\text{Tan } \phi = -\text{Tan } (180° - \phi) \qquad \text{Csc} = \text{Csc } (180° - \phi)$$

The functions for the angle ϕ in the third quadrant are as follows. Note the sign similarity from the chart previously used.

$$\text{Sin } \phi = -\text{Sin } (\phi - 180°) \qquad \text{Cot } \phi = \text{Cot } (\phi - 180°)$$

$$\text{Cos } \phi = -\text{Cos } (\phi - 180°) \qquad \text{Sec } \phi = -\text{Sec } (\phi - 180°)$$

$$\text{Tan } \phi = \text{Tan } (\phi - 180°) \qquad \text{Csc } \phi = -\text{Csc } (\phi - 180°)$$

If you have been following the chart, you should be able to write the functions for the angle ϕ found in the fourth quadrant. They are as follows:

$$\text{Sin } \phi = -\text{Sin } (360° - \phi) \qquad \text{Cot } \phi = -\text{Cot } (360° - \phi)$$

$$\text{Cos } \phi = \text{Cos } (360° - \phi) \qquad \text{Sec } \phi = \text{Sec } (360° - \phi)$$

$$\text{Tan } \phi = -\text{Tan } (360° - \phi) \qquad \text{Csc } \phi = -\text{Csc } (360° - \phi)$$

2.4-4   FUNCTIONS OF ANGLES GREATER THAN 360 DEGREES

The secret of solving problems involving angles greater than 360 degrees is based on the fact that the trigonometric functions are the same once an equivalent angle relationship is obtained. In order to understand this concept, we will show how to find the cosine function for an angle of 950 degrees.

To begin, we divide the 950 degree angle by 360 degrees so that a relationship to an angle less than 360 degrees may be obtained.

Divide 950° by 360°:

$$
\begin{array}{r}
2 \\
360\overline{\smash{\big)}\,950} \\
720 \\
\hline
230
\end{array}
$$

The remainder of 230 degrees is the secret number since it will provide us with the same trigonometric function for 950 degrees. After observing which quadrant the remainder of 230 degrees is in, the cosine function equation can be written and solved. Since it is in the third quadrant, the sign for the function is negative and is written as follows:

$$\text{Cos } 230° = -\text{Cos } (230° - 180°)$$

$$\text{Cos } 230° = -\text{Cos } 50°$$

$$\text{Cos } 230° = -0.6428$$

2.4-5   COMBINED ANGLE FUNCTION FORMULAS

You will, from time to time, be required to solve electronic problems having trigonometric functions of more than one angle. These angles might be added, subtracted, divided, or multiplied. Since direct mathematical processes cannot be applied, another method put in formula form will aid you when the conditions arise. The following formulas are listed according to the mathematical process needed for adding or subtracting angles, etc.

2.4-5A   Sum of Two Angles

1. $\text{Sin}\ (A + B) = \text{Sin A Cos B} + \text{Cos A Sin B}$

2. $\text{Cos}\ (A + B) = \text{Cos A Cos B} - \text{Sin A Sin B}$

3. $\text{Tan}\ (A + B) = \dfrac{\text{Tan A} + \text{Tan B}}{1 - \text{Tan A Tan B}}$

4. $\text{Cot}\ (A + B) = \dfrac{\text{Cot A Cot B} - 1}{\text{Cot B} + \text{Cot A}}$

2.4-5B   Difference of Two Angles

1. $\text{Sin}\ (A - B) = \text{Sin A Cos B} - \text{Cos A Sin B}$

2. $\text{Cos}\ (A - B) = \text{Cos A Cos B} + \text{Sin A Sin B}$

3. $\text{Tan}\ (A - B) = \dfrac{\text{Tan A} - \text{Tan B}}{1 + \text{Tan A Tan B}}$

4. $\text{Cot}\ (A - B) = \dfrac{\text{Cot A Cot B} + 1}{\text{Cot B} - \text{Cot A}}$

2.4-5C   Twice the Angle

The following formulas were generated by letting A equal B, and instead of writing the function (sine, cosine, etc.) and then (A + A), its equivalent is written:

1. $\text{Sin}\ (A + A) = \text{Sin 2A}$
$\text{Sin 2A} = 2\ \text{Sin A Cos A}$

2. $\text{Cos}\ (A + A) = \text{Cos 2A}$
$\text{Cos 2A} = \text{Cos}^2 A - \text{Sin}^2 A$
$\text{Cos 2A} = 1 - 2\ \text{Sin}^2 A$
$\text{Cos 2A} = 2\ \text{Cos}^2 A - 1$

3. $\text{Tan}\ (A + A) = \text{Tan 2A}$
$\text{Tan 2A} = \dfrac{2\ \text{Tan A}}{1 - \text{Tan}^2 A}$

$\text{Tan 2A} = \dfrac{2}{\text{Cot A} - \text{Tan A}}$

4. $\text{Cot}\ (A + A) = \text{Cot 2A}$
$\text{Cot 2A} = \dfrac{\text{Cot}^2 A - 1}{2\ \text{Cot A}}$

$\text{Cot 2A} = \dfrac{\text{Cot A} - \text{Tan A}}{2}$

2.4-6   TRIGONOMETRIC IDENTITIES AND FORMULAS

1. $\text{Sin } A = \sqrt{1 - \text{Cos}^2 A}$

2. $\text{Sin } A = \dfrac{\text{Tan } A}{\sqrt{1 + \text{Tan}^2 A}}$

3. $\text{Sin } A = \dfrac{1}{\sqrt{1 + \text{Cot}^2 A}}$

4. $\text{Sin } A = 2 \text{ Sin } \tfrac{1}{2}A \text{ Cos } \tfrac{1}{2}A$

5. $\text{Sin } A = \dfrac{2 \text{ Tan } \tfrac{1}{2}A}{1 + \text{Tan}^2 \tfrac{1}{2}A}$

6. $\text{Sin }^2 A - \text{Sin }^2 B = \text{Cos }^2 B - \text{Cos}^2 A$
7. $\text{Sin }^2 A - \text{Sin }^2 B = \text{Sin } (A + B) \text{ Sin } (A - B)$
8. $\text{Sin } A \text{ Sin } B = \tfrac{1}{2} \text{Cos } (A - B) - \tfrac{1}{2} \text{Cos } (A + B)$
9. $\text{Sin } A \text{ Cos } B = \tfrac{1}{2} \text{Sin } (A + B) + \tfrac{1}{2} \text{Sin } (A - B)$
10. $2 \text{ Sin }^2 A = 1 - \text{Cos } 2A$
11. $\text{Cos } A = \sqrt{1 - \text{Sin }^2 A}$

12. $\text{Cos } A = \dfrac{1}{\sqrt{1 + \text{Tan }^2 A}}$

13. $\text{Cos } A = \dfrac{\text{Cot } A}{\sqrt{1 + \text{Cot }^2 A}}$

14. $\text{Cos } A = \dfrac{1 - \text{Tan}^2 \tfrac{1}{2}A}{1 + \text{Tan}^2 \tfrac{1}{2}A}$

15. $\text{Cos } A \text{ Cos } B = \tfrac{1}{2} \text{Cos } (A - B) + \tfrac{1}{2} \text{Cos } (A + B)$
16. $\text{Cos }^2 A - \text{Sin }^2 B = \text{Cos }^2 B - \text{Sin }^2 A$
17. $\text{Cos }^2 A - \text{Sin }^2 B = \text{Cos } (A + B) \text{ Cos } (A - B)$
18. $2 \text{ Cos }^2 A = 1 + \text{Cos }^2 A$

19. $\text{Tan } A = \dfrac{\text{Sin } A}{\text{Cos } A}$

20. $\text{Tan } A = \dfrac{1}{\text{Cot } A}$

21. $\text{Tan } A + \text{Tan } B = \dfrac{\text{Sin } (A + B)}{\text{Cos } A \text{ Cos } B}$

22. $\text{Tan } A - \text{Tan } B = \dfrac{\text{Sin } (A - B)}{\text{Cos } A \text{ Cos } B}$

23. $\text{Tan A Tan B} = \dfrac{\text{Tan A} + \text{Tan B}}{\text{Cot A} + \text{Cot B}}$

24. $\text{Cot A} = \dfrac{\text{Cos A}}{\text{Sin A}}$

25. $\text{Cot A} = \dfrac{1}{\text{Tan A}}$

26. $\text{Cot A} + \text{Cot B} = \dfrac{\text{Sin (A + B)}}{\text{Sin A Sin B}}$

27. $\text{Cot A} - \text{Cot B} = \dfrac{\text{Sin (A} - \text{B)}}{\text{Sin A Sin B}}$

28. $\text{Cot A Cot B} = \dfrac{\text{Cot A} + \text{Cot B}}{\text{Tan A} + \text{Tan B}}$

2.5   COMPLEX NUMBERS AND VECTORS

Real and imaginary numbers, when combined, form complex numbers. These complex numbers are used extensively when performing AC calculations for series, parallel, and series-parallel circuits containing RL, RC, and RLC components. This portion of Chapter 2 will provide you with the working knowledge essential for performing mathematical operations of addition, subtraction, division, and multiplication of complex numbers. This material also applies its concepts to vectorial analysis of electronic phenomenon.

2.5-1   "j" FACTOR / OPERATOR

Frequently in mathematics the "j" factor or "j" operator is encountered. The "j" factor is *imaginary*. Since there is no *real* number which when squared equals -1, the $\sqrt{-1}$ is used. In mathematics $\sqrt{-1}$ is usually represented as "i" but in electronics this would cause confusion with current so we use "j" which equals $\sqrt{-1}$ also.

Generally, positive and negative *real* numbers have graphical representation on the horizontal (x) axis while the vertical (y) axis has imaginary numbers represented, as shown in Figure 2-13. Often the X' is indicated with a minus

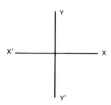

Figure 2-13

(−) sign and the X with a positive (+) sign. In like manner the Y and Y′ become the + j and the − j representing the imaginary values. By using this process, both real and imaginary values can be represented on the same graph, as illustrated in Figure 2-14.

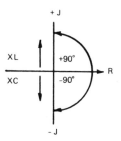

Figure 2-14

When graphically plotted, resistance is treated as a *real* number since there is no phase change. Reactances on the other hand are plotted as if they were imaginary. This method helps us to remember the phase relationship of reactances, and simplifies vectorial manipulation.

2.5-2   VECTORS

A vector is used to describe a quantity that has both mass and direction. The direction of the vector is indicated by an arrow, while an angle, normally called *theta* (Θ), provides its direction when compared to the real number axis. The mass, magnitude, or absolute value of the vector is its length. There are three general ways, methods, or forms used to provide the vectorial solutions. The three forms expressed by formulas will be outlined first; then, helpful examples will follow.

The main advantage the *polar form* provides us with is an easier way to write vectorial relationships. An example of a written polar form vector is:

$$A\angle\Theta \quad \text{where:} \quad \text{A is the magnitude}$$
$$\Theta \text{ is the direction angle}$$

The *rectangular form* is commonly used when addition or subtraction is necessary, but is not generally used when division, multiplication, roots, or power processes are required. An example of the rectangular form is:

$$A + jB \text{ or } A - jB \quad \text{where:} \quad \text{A is the real number magnitude}$$
$$\pm j \text{ is the "j" operator}$$
$$\text{B is the imaginary numbers' magnitude}$$

The *trigonometric or circular form* is easily recognized because of the trigonometric functions included within its vector descriptions. An example of the trigonometric form is:

A $(\cos \Theta + j \sin \Theta)$ where: A is the magnitude

OR Θ is the direction angle

A $(\cos \Theta - j \sin \Theta)$ $\pm$ j is the "j" operator

2.5-3   POLAR FORM VECTOR REPRESENTATION

Polar vector notation requires four basic parts which define the vector. These are: (a) *magnitude*, (2) *angle symbol*, (3) *sign of the angle*, and (4) *number of degrees*. In order to show the relationships of the four parts of a polar form described vector, we will draw a vector for an airplane flying at a speed of 500 miles per hour in a northeastern direction. Figure 2-15 illustrates this particular vector.

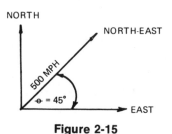

Figure 2-15

If you are vectorially alert, you will note that the magnitude is 500, the angle symbol is Θ, the sign of the angle is positive, and the number of degrees is 45. All of the four basic parts are defined, and therefore this vector can be written in polar form. The complete polar notation is written as 500 $\angle+$ 45 and is read by saying 500 at positive 45 degrees.

2.5-3A   Polar Form Multiplication and Division Processes

Since polar notation is a mathematical term, it can be treated as such during computation. If, for example, you have two vectors in polar form, you can multiply the two or you can divide one by the other by following these simple rules.

Multiplication Rule

$(30 \angle 20°) \, (10 \angle 20°) = 300 \angle 40°$

1. Multiply the magnitudes (30) (10) = 300
2. Add the angles 20° + 20° = 40°

Division Rule

$$\frac{30 \angle 30°}{10 \angle 20°} = 3 \angle 10°$$

1. divide the magnitudes $\dfrac{30}{10} = 3$

2. subtract (algebraically) the angle of the divisor from the angle of the dividend:

$$30° - 20° = 10°$$

You can add or subtract vectors in polar form *if the angles are exactly the same*. In application, the magnitude of each vector is added or subtracted and the original angle is used. Thus, if vector $10 \angle +33°$ is added to $10 \angle +33°$ the result is $20 \angle +33°$ or if $20 \angle +45°$ is subtracted from $50 \angle +45°$ the result would be $30 \angle +45°$. When vectors do not have the same exact angle, such as $6 \angle +33° + 10 \angle +45°$ or $20 \angle -90°$ minus $30 \angle +90°$ the mathematical processes of addition and subtraction cannot be accomplished in the above manner. You can, however, add or subtract vectors whose angles differ if you convert to the rectangular form of notation.

2.5-4   RECTANGULAR FORM VECTOR REPRESENTATION

Vectors stated in rectangular coordinates can be readily added or subtracted since their vertical components (''j'' operator) always lie on the same line, while the real numbers are always on the horizontal line. The first vector example used to illustrate the polar notation will be used here also. Refer to Figure 2-16.

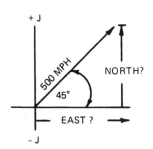

Figure 2-16

In order to describe a vector for an airplane flying at 500 mph at a 45° angle, the rectangular form becomes a trigonometric problem because we are analyzing the rate at which the airplane is traveling both north and east. To illustrate the mathematical process for the rectangular form, we will solve only for the quantity marked north.

Since the side of Θ equals 45° which also equals $\dfrac{\text{opposite}}{\text{hypotenuse}}$

Then: $\sin 45° = \dfrac{\text{north (N)}}{500}$

$$0.707 = \frac{N}{500}$$

$$N = 500 \ (0.707)$$

$$N = 353.5$$

In rectangular notation we have a magnitude of 500 at a given north or "j" operator direction. The rectangular form $500 + j\,353.5$ accurately describes this data.

2.5-4A   Rectangular Form Addition and Subtraction Process

To add or subtract vectors stated in rectangular notation, addition and subtraction are accomplished merely through algebraic manipulation. For example:

$$
\begin{array}{rll}
 & 6 + j4 & \\
(+) & \underline{8 - j6} & \\
 & 14 - j2 &
\end{array}
\qquad \text{OR} \qquad
\begin{array}{rl}
 & 10 + j10 \\
(-) & \underline{14 - j8} \\
 & -4 + j18
\end{array}
$$

2.5-4B   Rectangular Form Multiplication Process

Vectors stated in rectangular notation may be directly multiplied if we treat each vector as a binomial. For example, we will multiply a vector of $5 + j4$ by $10 - j4$.

$$
\begin{array}{l}
5 + j4 \\
\underline{10 - j4} \\
50 + j40 \\
\underline{\ \ \ - j20 - j^2 16} \\
50 + j20 - j^2 16 \ \text{(multiplication completed)}
\end{array}
$$

Since $j^2 = -1$ then:

$$50 + j20 - (-1)\,(16)$$

$$50 + j20 + 16 = 66 + j20 \ \text{(simplified answer)}$$

2.5-4C   Rectangular Form Division Process

Vectors stated in rectangular notation may also be divided. In our example, vector $6 + j5$ will be divided by vector $4 + j2$. Both the denominator and the numerator must be multiplied by the conjugate of the denominator. The conjugate is determined simply by changing the one sign between the terms in the denominator. All of this is accomplished as follows:

$$\frac{6 + j5 \ (4 - j2)}{4 + j2 \ (4 - j2)} = \frac{24 + j8 - j^2 10}{16 - j^2 4} = \frac{24 + j8 - (-1)(10)}{16 - (-1)(4)} = \frac{34 + j8}{20}$$

$1.7 + j0.4$ is the simplified answer.

2.5-5   TRIGONOMETRIC/CIRCULAR FORM

We will reemploy the vector illustrated for the airplane whose speed was 500 mph in a northeast direction to tie together what has been discussed. Polar form, as you will recall, was simply the vector magnitude and the angle (500 $\angle +45°$), and the rectangular form used trigonometry to solve for either the north or east unknown quantity. When using the trigonometric or circular method, both of the unknown quantities (north and east) are found after one mathematical calculation. In application, the magnitude of the vector is multiplied by the cosine function of the angle and sine function of the angle and is written as: magnitude (Cos $\Theta \pm j$ Sin Θ). All of this is pulled together in Figure 2-17 since 500 (Cos 45° + j Sin 45°) equals 500 (0.707 + j 0.707). The resulting answer tells us both the eastern and northern unit of measurement. All of this is told in the trigonometric notation 353.5 + j353.5.

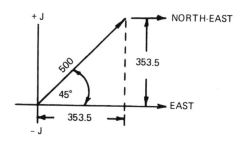

Figure 2-17

The same problem could have also been solved graphically if drawn to scale; then the desired answer could be measured. Graphic solutions, however, do not give as much accuracy because of human drawing errors or measuring accuracy. For this reason, vector problems are normally solved using trigonometry.

2.5-6   VECTOR ADDITION

Vectors may be directly added or subtracted. To illustrate the addition process, suppose that we had two different magnitudes at different angles. Vector "A" is 3 at 40° and vector "B" is 2 at 20°, as illustrated in Figure 2-18.

Figure 2-18

One good way of providing a rough check for the answer is first to draw vector "A" and then to draw vector "B" starting at the end of vector "A." This is called a *line vector drawing* and is shown in Figure 2-19. The answer (hypotenuse) is the dotted line extending from point x to point y. If each vector were drawn to scale, the hypotenuse probably would measure roughly about 4.8 to 4.9. A protractor used to measure the new angle would show that an angle of about 30 degrees existed. The resultant vector, according to our line vector drawing, should be about 4.8 or 4.9 at 30 degrees. We shall, for accuracy's sake, solve this vector addition problem using the following methods.

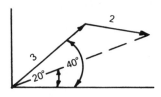

Figure 2-19

For greater accuracy, the same problem can be solved using trigonometry after first changing both vectors 3 ∠ 40° and 2 ∠ 20° to the rectangular form. To change from the polar form to the rectangular form, simply draw the vector as shown in Figures 2-20A and 2-20B. After doing this, the solutions are as follows:

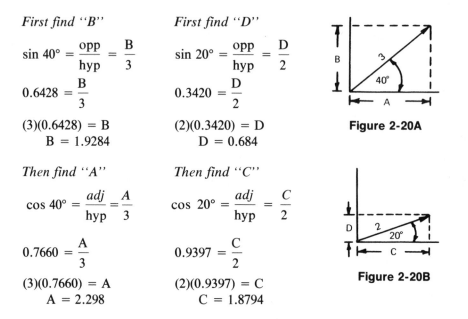

First find "B"

$$\sin 40° = \frac{opp}{hyp} = \frac{B}{3}$$

$$0.6428 = \frac{B}{3}$$

$$(3)(0.6428) = B$$
$$B = 1.9284$$

Then find "A"

$$\cos 40° = \frac{adj}{hyp} = \frac{A}{3}$$

$$0.7660 = \frac{A}{3}$$

$$(3)(0.7660) = A$$
$$A = 2.298$$

First find "D"

$$\sin 20° = \frac{opp}{hyp} = \frac{D}{2}$$

$$0.3420 = \frac{D}{2}$$

$$(2)(0.3420) = D$$
$$D = 0.684$$

Then find "C"

$$\cos 20° = \frac{adj}{hyp} = \frac{C}{2}$$

$$0.9397 = \frac{C}{2}$$

$$(2)(0.9397) = C$$
$$C = 1.8794$$

Figure 2-20A

Figure 2-20B

If we now take this data and add the rectangular forms representing both vectors as shown below, we can continue by applying these values to an equivalent triangle, thereby completing the problem.

Rectangular form addition:

$$2.2980 + j\ 1.9284 \quad \text{for vector } 3 \angle 40°$$
$$\underline{1.8794 + j\ 0.6840} \quad \text{for vector } 2 \angle 20°$$
$$4.1774 + j\ 2.6124 \quad \text{vectors sum in rectangular form}$$

Since we have determined the values for the individual vector problems, we can redraw the triangles as illustrated in Figures 2-21A and 2-21B.

Solving for angle Y

$$\text{Tan } y = \frac{\text{opp}}{\text{adj}} = \frac{2.6124}{4.1774}$$

$$\text{Tan } y = 0.6253$$

$$y = 32.0°$$

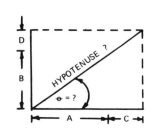

Figure 2-21A

Solving for X

$$\text{Sin } y = \frac{\text{opp}}{\text{hyp}} = \frac{2.6124}{x}$$

$$0.5299 = \frac{2.6124}{x}$$

$$x = \frac{2.6124}{0.5299}$$

$$x = 4.93$$

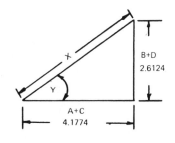

Figure 2-21B

The resulting vector is 4.93 $\angle$ + 32° which is somewhat more accurate than the previous 4.8 or 4.9 at 30° obtained in the line vector method previously used.

2.5-7   CAPACITIVE REACTANCE VECTORS

The formula for capacitive reactance is:

$$X_C = \frac{1}{2\ \pi\ fC}$$

X_C = capacitive reactance (ohms)
π = 3.14
f = frequency in hertz
C = capacitance in farads

Since current flow is strong and then reduces while the capacitor is building up a charge, the effect of capacitive reactance (X_C) is delayed. Because of this delay, the vectorial illustrations shown in Figure 2-22 are drawn 90° clockwise with respect to pure resistance.

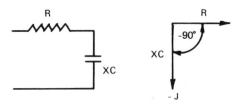

Figure 2-22

2.5-8   INDUCTIVE REACTANCE VECTORS

The formula for inductive reactance is:

$$X_L = 2 \pi fL$$

X_L = inductive reactance (ohms)
π = 3.14
f = frequency in hertz
L = inductance in henries

Inductive reactance (X_L) is high initially, so current is slow in building up; hence, X_L leads R, and its vectorial representation is drawn 90° before pure resistance, as indicated in Figure 2-23.

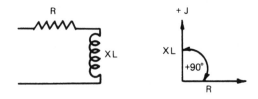

Figure 2-23

2.5-9   IMPEDANCE VECTORS

Impedance is a vectorial combination of reactance and resistance; the total opposition to current flow in an AC circuit. In addition to the impedance (Z) magnitude, its phase angle (Θ) must be considered. Figures 2-24A and 2-24B illustrate the X_L and X_C impedance vectors.

Impedance calculations can be accomplished graphically, trigonometrically, or algebraically. Trigonometrically is best if both the size of impedance and the value of Θ are desired. Algebraically, using the Pythagorean Theorem, will give the ohmic value for impedance, but not the phase angle Θ.

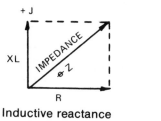

Inductive reactance | Capacitive reactance

Figure 2-24A | **Figure 2-24B**

2.5-10   RESONANCE VECTORS

When both forms of reactance are present, the circuit can become resonant. For any RLC circuit this condition occurs at only one specific frequency.
The resonance formula is:

$$Fr = \frac{1}{2\pi\sqrt{LC}}$$ where: Fr is the resonant frequency
                                            L is in henries
                                            C is in farads
                                            $\pi = 3.14$

At this specific frequency (resonance), X_C and X_L cancel completely.
The circuit, however, does contain both inductance and capacitance, and acts
as if it were only resistive, as indicated in Figure 2-25.

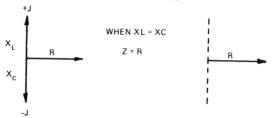

Figure 2-25

X_L and X_C as vectors are 180° apart and cancel each other. This happens
at resonance. However, when the circuit is not at the resonance frequency, the
circuit may act either capacitive or inductive depending upon which value of
reactance is greater. When one reactive component is larger than the other,
impedance (Z) is computed by subtracting the two reactive values. This is
illustrated by Figure 2-26.

WHEN $X_L \neq X_C$

$$Z = \sqrt{R^2 + (X_L - X_C)^2}$$

Figure 2-26

2.6   LOGARITHMS

Logarithms, once understood, provide shortcuts for lengthy electronic mathematical operations. Calculations involving exponents, powers, and roots can be accomplished more easily using logarithms than using arithmetical processes.

A logarithm of any given number by definition is an exponent that indicates the power the given base must be raised to equal the given number.

There are two logarithm systems commonly used in electronic calculations. The first is called the *common* or *Briggsian* system of logarithms. The number 10 is used as the base for the common logarithm system. The second logarithm system is called the *natural* or *Napierian* system. The Greek letter epsilon (ϵ), which approximately equals 2.718, is used for the base for the natural logarithm system.

It might be noted that any positive number, with the exception of unity, is or can be used for a base in a logarithm system. The particular system used for calculations is indicated in the equation by the subscript that follows the abbreviation. For example, the equation $X = \text{Log } 10N$ has the number ten for its base; the equation $X = \text{Log } 2N$ has the number two for its base; the equation $X = \text{Log } \epsilon N$ uses the Greek letter Epsilon as its base; and the equation $X = \text{Log } bN$ uses the letter "b" for its base. If for some reason the base is not indicated, as in the equation $X = \text{Log } N$, the base of ten is understood, but if the equation is written in this manner, $X = \text{ln } N$, then the base is understood to be the Greek letter epsilon.

2.6-1   COMMON OR BRIGGSIAN LOGARITHMS

Logarithms consist of two basic parts; a whole number termed the *characteristic* and a decimal number called the *mantissa*. The mantissa is normally the only part recorded in logarithm tables and often even the decimal points are omitted. The characteristics are determined by inspection of the number as you will soon discover when applying the following rules and facts.

2.6-1A   Positive Characteristics

The characteristic of a logarithm for any number greater than the whole number one is always positive. The value of the characteristic is equal to one digit less than the number of digits required to write the whole number. For example, the characteristics for the following logarithmic equations are as follows:

Number		Characteristic
Log 1	=	0
Log 10	=	1
Log 100	=	2

Number		Characteristic
Log 1,000	=	3
Log 10,000	=	4
Log 100,000	=	5
Log 1,000,000	=	6

Since the logarithm for 1 is 0 and the logarithm for 10 is 1, it should be evident that the logarithm for numbers between 1 and 10 will be somewhere between 0 and 1. In the same manner, a number between 10 and 100 would have a logarithm between 1 and 2.

2.6-1B   Negative Characteristics

The characteristic for any number less than the whole number one is always negative. The value of the characteristic is equal to one digit more than the number of zeros counted between the decimal point and the first significant digit which is not a zero. This is illustrated in the following logarithmic equations.

Number		Characteristic
Log 0.1	=	-1
Log 0.01	=	-2
Log 0.001	=	-3
Log 0.0001	=	-4
Log 0.00001	=	-5
Log 0.000001	=	-6

For convenience, negative logarithms are usually transformed into an equivalent positive characteristic form. Characteristics of logarithms for any number less than one are simply written as differences between a new number representing the characteristic and the numbers of zeros between the decimal point and first significant digit. A negative number written after the mantissa will, after subtracting it from the new characteristic number, equal the negative logarithm. In order to understand this process, follow this listed data carefully.

Number	Characteristic		Transformed logarithm
Log 0.1	-1	=	$9.0000-10$
Log 0.01	-2	=	$8.0000-10$
Log 0.001	-3	=	$7.0000-10$
Log 0.000 0001	-7	=	$3.0000-10$
Log 0.000 000 000 000 001	-15	=	$5.0000-20$

Whenever nine or less zeros exist between the decimal point and first significant digit, a -10 is written after the mantissa. In like manner, whenever there are 10 to 19 zeros between the two references, a -20 is written.

2.6-1C   Logarithm Mantissas

Logarithmic tables give in the body of the tables the mantissa of logarithms for numbers ranging from 1 to somewhere in the hundreds or perhaps even thousands depending upon which tables you have. The number of places listed in these tables also may vary from four-place, five-place, or higher, depending upon the size of the table.

When locating a mantissa for a number, the decimal point in the number can be disregarded because the mantissa is the same regardless of the decimal point position in the original number. This is demonstrated as follows:

$$\text{Log } 500.00 = 2.6990$$
$$\text{Log } 50.00 = 1.6990$$
$$\text{Log } 5.00 = 0.6990$$
$$\text{Log } 0.50 = 9.6990 - 10$$
$$\text{Log } 0.05 = 8.6990 - 10$$

If you looked at a common logarithm table for the log of 500, you would see the mantissa of 0.6990. Then, after you determined the characteristic for the number 500, you could say that $\log_{10} 500$ equals 2.6990. The following two equations show the exponential form and the logarithmic form for the same number.

$$10^{2.6990} = 500 \qquad\qquad 2.6990 = \text{Log}_{10}\ 500$$
$$\text{(Exponential form)} \qquad\qquad \text{(Logarithmic form)}$$

2.6-2   HOW TO USE LOGARITHMIC TABLES

In order to find the logarithm for a particular number, you will need a common logarithm table. Listed across the top will be a column listing numbers normally marked with the capital letter "N" and digits ranging from 0 to 9 which are used to describe the particular number. The numbers begin with the number 10 and continue into the hundreds, or thousands. We will use a small part of a four-place logarithm table to develop the remaining data on table usage.

COMMON LOGARITHM OF NUMBERS EXCERPT

N	0	1	2	3	4	5	6	7	8	9
69	8388	8395	8401	8407	8414	8420	8426	8432	8439	8445
70	8451	8457	8463	8470	8476	8482	8488	8494	8500	8506

We will demonstrate how to find the mantissa for the number 69.5 from the table on page 164 by following two simple steps. These steps are:

1. Find the first two digits of the given number under the "N" column.

2. Follow this line to the column headed by the third digit of the given number and record the mantissa for the three-digit number.

Since the characteristic is positive and equals 1, the common logarithm value for 69.5 is 1.8420. The following logarithms can also be obtained from the previous logarithm table.

$$\text{Log } 699 \quad = 2.8445$$
$$\text{Log } 7.05 \quad = 0.8482$$
$$\text{Log } 0.70 \quad = 9.8451 - 10$$
$$\text{Log } 0.007 = 7.8451 - 10$$

2.6-3   ANTILOGARITHMS

Finding an antilogarithm is just opposite to the process of finding a logarithm. In other words, finding the antilogarithm is finding the number that corresponds to a given logarithm. The antilogarithm process is indicated whenever the term antilog or $\log^{-1}$ is written.

The tables containing the mantissas are used when finding the decimal part of the logarithm and the characteristic of the logarithm tells us the position of the decimal point in the resulting number. The rules for characteristic-decimal point relationships are as follows:

1. If the characteristic of the logarithm is positive, count from the left of the resulting number one more digit then expressed by the characteristic.

2. If the characteristic of the logarithm is negative, such as 9.8451–10, the resulting number will have as many zeros minus one zero between the decimal point and the first significant digit, as the number 10 following the mantissa in our case exceeds the characteristic of 9.

To apply these rules, examine what is happening to the following examples:

$$\text{Antilog } 2.8445 \quad = 699 \text{ (rule 1)}$$
$$\text{Antilog } 0.8482 \quad = 7.05 \text{ (rule 1)}$$
$$\text{Antilog } 9.8451 - 10 = 0.70 \text{ (rule 2)}$$
$$\text{Log}^{-1} \quad 7.8451 - 10 = 0.007 \text{ (rule 2)}$$

2.6-4   LOGARITHM MULTIPLICATION

Since logarithms are exponents of 10, multiplication is accomplished in the same general way as exponents of algebra. Since we add the exponents in algebra when the bases are identical, we can say the logarithm of the product of two or more numbers is equal to the sum of their logarithms. To repeat this in formula form, the results are:

$$10^a \, 10^b = 10^{a+b} \text{ (algebraic form)}$$
$$\text{Log MN} = \text{Log M} + \text{Log N (logarithm form)}$$

The logarithm form illustrated may seem misleading unless you remember that the base of 10 is understood when written as simply a log of a number. For application of multiplication, we will multiply the logarithms of 50 and 500 in the following manner:

$$(50)(500) = \text{antilog of Log 50} + \text{Log 500}$$

Since Log 50 = 1.6990
and Log 500 = 2.6990

then the product is their sum:
$$
\begin{array}{r}
1.6990 \\
+ \; 2.6990 \\
\hline
4.3980
\end{array}
$$

Consulting the log table for the number whose mantissa is 0.3980 we find the number 25. In order to determine the decimal point position, we must consider the characteristic. Recall rule (1) outlined in 2.6-1A for determining the characteristic; in particular that this number was one less than the number of digits to the left of the decimal point. Because of this we must add one more digit to the present characteristic of 4. This new total of 5 tells us that the number 25 must have five digits to the left of the decimal point. This new number is 25000 as shown by:

$$(50)(500) \text{ or } 25000 = \text{antilog of Log 50} + \text{Log 500}$$

2.6-5   LOGARITHM DIVISION

Division by logarithms is accomplished by subtracting the log of the divisor from the log of the dividend. The simplified formula indicating this process is:

$$\text{Log} \frac{N}{M} = \text{Log N} - \text{Log M}$$

For an example, we will divide 25000 into 500.

$$\frac{500}{25000} = \text{antilog of Log 500} - \text{Log 25000}$$

Since Log 500 = 2.6990
and Log 25000 = 4.3979

then the quotient is their difference:

$$\begin{array}{r} 2.6990 \\ -4.3979 \\ \hline 8.3011 - 10 \end{array}$$

After looking at the log table for a number whose mantissa is 0.3011 we find the number 20. This also does not determine the position of the decimal point. Because of rule #2, outlined in 2.6-1B, a number whose characteristic is negative has one less zero to the right of the decimal point than the value of the negative characteristic. Therefore, the characteristic is $8-10 = -2$ minus the one, so there is one zero after the decimal and before the number 20 obtained for the quotient. The final answer is 0.02 and is expressed as:

$$\frac{500}{25000} = 0.02 = \text{antilog of Log } 500 - \text{Log } 25000$$

2.6-6 RAISING POWERS OF LOGARITHMS

Raising any number to a power using logarithms is done by multiplying the logarithm of the number by the exponent of the power. This concept is represented by the following formula:

$$N^x = \text{antilog } (X \text{ Log } N)$$

To show this formula in action we will raise the number 25 to the third power. The process using logarithms is shown below:

$$(25)^3 = \text{antilog of } 3 \text{ (Log } 25)$$
$$\text{Since Log } 25 = 1.3979$$
$$\text{then the result is } 3(1.3979) \text{ or } 4.1937$$

When we look for the number whose mantissa is 0.1937 we find the value of 15625 (the last two digits being found by interpolation). Since the mantissa numbers are 1931 and 1959 and because the 1937 value is about ¼ of the difference, a value of 0.25 is used. The characteristic of 4 provides five digits to the left of the decimal point or 15,625.

2.6-7 EXTRACTING ROOTS OF LOGARITHMS

The logarithm of the root for any number is the logarithm of the number divided by the power of the root. The equation illustrating this process is as follows:

$$\text{Log } \sqrt[X]{N} = \frac{\text{Log } N}{X}$$

We will find the antilog of the cube root of the number 125. The operations necessary are as follows:

$$\sqrt[3]{125} = \text{antilog of } \frac{\text{Log } 125}{3}$$

Since Log 125 = 2.0969

$$\text{Then: } \frac{\text{Log } 125}{3} = = 0.6989$$

Since the characteristic of zero provides one digit to the left of the decimal point, the cube root of 125 is 5. This is logical because $5 \times 5 \times 5$ equals 125.

2.7   ADVANCED MATHEMATICS ANALYSIS

It seems that limits exist for the usefulness of specialized areas of mathematics. For example, in elementary mathematics, the basic limits seem to be adding, subtracting, multiplying, and dividing; algebra confines itself to solving unknown equations; geometry and trigonometry are contained within circles. Now, in all of these areas of specialized math, a dependency exists, between one and the other. In this portion of Chapter 2, combinations of these specialized areas of mathematics result in what might be called analytic geometry. Calculus will also be outlined. In keeping with the thumbnail sketch approach found within the covers of this book, facts, rules and other pertinent data dealing with advanced mathematics will be given in eye-opening, brain-reaching outlines.

2.7-1   FUNCTIONS

Mathematics in general uses two kinds of symbols to represent numbers or numerical quantities. These are called variables and constants. In higher or advanced mathematics, two variables can have a relationship between each other so that for each set of values given to one, there results one or more definite values for the other. When this exists, it is said that one is a function of the other. The first variable is called the *dependent function* or *variable,* while the second variable is termed the *independent variable* or *argument.*

If the letter Y is a function of the letter X and for each value of X there is a value or values for Y, then this can be written in equation or functional notation form illustrating the same. To indicate that Y is a function of X we write $Y = f(X)$. This equation is read Y equals f of X or Y equals a function of X. The symbol $f(X)$ represents any mathematical expression involving only the variable X or any quantity that is a function of X.

If the variable in a functional notation equation is replaced with a number as in the following examples, it indicates that the variable is to be made equal to that number. For example, in the equation $y = x^2 - 2$, the equation has different answers when solved for different functions.

$$\text{(Given Equation) } y = x^2 - 2$$

$$f(x) \text{ function} = x^2 - 2$$
$$f(0) \text{ function} = 0 - 2 = -2$$
$$f(1) \text{ function} = 1 - 2 = -1$$
$$f(3) \text{ function} = 9 - 2 = 7$$
$$f(e) \text{ function} = (e)^2 - 2$$

Inverse functions are also possible when you regard X as the dependent variable and Y as the independent variable. Thus, the function of $y = x^2 - 2$ and $x = \sqrt{y + 2}$ are inverse functions.

2.7-2   INCREMENTS

An increment for mathematics is defined as a variable that changes from one numerical value to another. The increment of the variable is determined by subtracting the first value of the variable from the second value. With this in mind, if current (I) is 5.6 ma for one reading and then 5.8 ma, the increment for I is 0.2. Increments are also taken when variables decrease, such as 5.8 for the first reading to 5.6 ma for the second. The increment for I in this case would be -0.2.

In practice, the word increment is symbolized by the Greek letter delta symbol (Δ). If this symbol is prefixed to the letter X representing the variable, then ΔX denotes an increment of X. When a variable is a function of another variable, the following truths exist. We will use x as a function of y or $x = f(y)$ for illustration purposes. If you let the first value of the function, y in our case, equal y_1 and the second value equal y_2, then $\Delta y = y_2 - y_1$ or $y_2 = y_1 + \Delta y$. Because x is a function of y, and since y is taken on the increment Δy, then x will also have a corresponding increment. The values for x will be represented by x_1 and x_2. All of this means that $\Delta x = x_2 - x_1$ or $\Delta x = f(y_2) - f(y_1)$ or $\Delta x = f(y_1 + \Delta y) - f(y_1)$.

The solution for Δx in the equation $x = y^2 - 6y$ when $y = 2$ and $\Delta y = 3$ is obtained in the following manner:

1. Substitute 2 for y in the equation $x = y^2 - 6y$ solving for $f(x_1)$ when $y_1 = 2$.

$$x_1 = f(y_1) = 2^2 - 6(2)$$
$$x_1 = -8$$

2. Find the "value of y_2 by adding the values given for y and Δy."

$$y_2 = 2 + 3 = 5$$

3. Solve for $f(x_2)$ when $y_2 = 5$ in the equation $x = y^2 - 6y$.

$$x_2 = f(y_1 + \Delta y)$$
$$x_2 = (5)^2 - 6(5)$$
$$x_2 = -5$$

4. Substitute x_2 representing $f(y_1 + \Delta y)$ and x_1 representing $f(y_1)$ into the following equation solving for Δx.

$$\Delta x = f(y + \Delta y) - f(y) \qquad \text{OR:} \qquad \Delta x = x_2 - x_1$$
$$\Delta x = -5 - (-8) \qquad\qquad\qquad \Delta x = -5 - (-8)$$
$$\Delta x = +3 \qquad\qquad\qquad\qquad\quad \Delta x = +3$$

2.7-3   SLOPE

There are three words used in higher mathematics that might seem confusing even to the experienced. These three are: inclination, angle, and slope. The one basic thing they have in common is that they all define lines. An *inclination* is the angle that exists between the given line and the horizontal or X-axis. The *angle* existing between two directed lines is the angle whose sides extend from the angle's vertex. The *slope* of a line is a tangent function of its inclination.

The slope provides a convenient way of telling line direction. The slope normally denoted by a small letter m is written as: $m = \tan \theta$, where theta (θ) or some other symbol represents the angle for the line. The slope may be any real positive or negative number. If the angle is less than 90 degrees, the slope is positive, while if the angle is more than 90 degrees, the slope is negative.

2.7-3A   Slope Formula

The slope is considered to be the rate of change relationships between the Y axis values and the X axis values as shown in Figure 2-27.

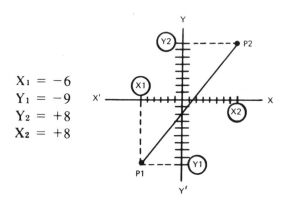

$$X_1 = -6$$
$$Y_1 = -9$$
$$Y_2 = +8$$
$$X_2 = +8$$

Figure 2-27

The slope, considered to be the rate of change of the ordinate (Y-coordinate of the point) with respect to the abscissa (X-coordinate of the point), can be written using increment notation. Thus $m = \dfrac{\Delta Y}{\Delta X}$ where ΔY is the increment of $Y_2 - Y_1$ and ΔX is the increment of $X_2 - X_1$. The slope of the line passing through points P_1 or X_1, Y_1 and P_2 or X_2, Y_2 may also be expressed as:

$$m = \frac{Y_2 - Y_1}{X_2 - X_1} = \frac{8 - (-9)}{8 - (-6)} = \frac{17}{14}$$

$$m = \frac{17 \text{ representing ``Y''}}{14 \text{ representing ``X''}}$$

2.7-3B Point Slope Form

The point slope form provides an easy way for constructing a line that passes through a given point at a given slope. Therefore, an equation for a straight line can be recorded if you want the slope and one point on that line. The equation illustrating the point slope form is:

$$X - X_1 = m (Y - Y_1)$$

X and Y represent the unknown coordinates.

2.7-3C Slope-Intercept Form

You can easily determine the slope and the Y intercept value for a straight line using the slope-intercept equation form. The X intercept is the X coordinate of the point of intersection of the line with the X axis, while the Y intercept is the Y coordinate of the point of intersection of the line with the Y axis. The general slope-intercept formula form is:

$$Y = mX + b$$

The slope and Y intercept for the equation $5y - 25X - 30$ is automatically in the $Y = mX + b$ form upon completion of the following solution for Y:

$$5Y - 25X = 30$$
$$5Y = 25X + 30$$
$$Y = \frac{25X + 30}{5}$$
$$Y = 5X + 6 \text{ (the } mX + b \text{ form)}$$

2.7-3D Two-Point Form

When two points of a straight line are known, an equation representing the two-point form can be written. The equation is:

$$\frac{Y - Y_1}{X - X_1} = \frac{Y_2 - Y_1}{X_2 - X_1}$$

After the two known points represented by their two X and Y coordinate values have been substituted, the results will be in the mX + b form.

2.7-3E   Series RC Circuit Application

Instantaneous values for currents and voltages during specific periods of time can be solved quite easily when techniques of higher mathematics are employed. Figure 2-28 illustrates a series resistive, capacitive circuit and its vectorial graph showing voltage-time charge relationships. Our task will be to find the instantaneous current i value when the 2 microfarad capacitor has charged to 10 volts after 1 microsecond of time. Needless to say, i_c is the instantaneous capacitor current, e_c the instantaneous capacitor voltage, and $t_0 - t_1$ are the time limits.

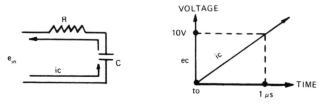

Figure 2-28

If the capacitor voltage is increasing as the time increases, an increment of $\frac{\Delta e}{\Delta t}$ showing a change in voltage with respect to time can be written. A formula representing the slope showing these same effects could be written as:

$$e_c = Kt \text{ where } e_c \text{ is the capacitor voltage}$$

K is the slope
t is the time in seconds.

We will use the equation $i_c = C\frac{\Delta e}{\Delta t}$ to determine the current flowing in the capacitive circuit after finding the slope, *also called the rate of change of voltage with respect to time*. This is accomplished by substituting the values for e_c and t into the equation for e_c as follows:

Given: $e_c = 10$ volts

$\Delta t = 1$ microsecond $= 1 \times 10^{-6}$

Therefore: $e_c = Kt$

$$K = \frac{e_c}{t} = \frac{10}{1 \times 10^{-6}}$$

$$K = 10 \times 10^{+6}$$

Since the slope (K) is the same as $\frac{\Delta e_c}{\Delta t}$, then the values for the capacitor and $\frac{\Delta e_c}{\Delta t}$ can be substituted into the equation describing the current flow in a capacitive circuit. The results are:

$$ic = C \frac{\Delta e_c}{\Delta t} \text{ or CK}$$

$$ic = (2 \times 10^{-6})(10 \times 10^{+6}) = 20 \text{ amperes}$$

$ic = 20$ amperes. This is the instantaneous current flowing for 1 microsecond, thereby causing an instantaneous voltage of 10 volts to exist across the capacitor.

2.7-4 DERIVATIVES

In the examples defining their slopes as $\frac{\Delta Y}{\Delta X}$ in the previous 2.7-3 sections of this chapter, derivatives of the first variable with respect to the second variable were implied. The derivative of the first variable with respect to the second is implied whenever one variable is a function of a second function, and the increment of the first function is divided by the increment of the second, and when the limit of the quotient is as the second increment approaches zero. We will use Y as a function of X to show how this definition looks when in formula form. The formula is:

$$y = f'(x) = \frac{\text{Limit}}{\Delta x \to 0} \frac{\Delta y}{\Delta x} \text{ at } x = x_1$$

The f' simply means the derivative of y with respect to x having the limit of $\frac{\Delta Y}{\Delta X}$ as Δx approaches zero. The derivative process for y with respect to x is also denoted by:

$$\frac{dy}{dx} \text{ or } y' \text{ or } f'(x) \text{ or } \frac{d}{d(x)} f(x)$$

The process used to find the derivatives of functions is called *differentiation*. The following generalized rules will help you differentiate one variable with respect to the other. We will use the $y = f(x)$ form for the following:

1. Give the x variable an increment Δx and substitute $x + \Delta x$ in the equation describing the variable "y."

2. Calculate the value for y + Δ y, expanding the right-hand equation member.

3. Subtract y from y + Δ y, obtaining Δ y in terms of x and Δ x.

4. Divide Δ y by Δ x, obtaining the value for $\dfrac{\Delta\,y}{\Delta\,x}$.

5. Find the limit for the expression found in step 4 as Δ x approaches zero (Δ x → 0).

The result will be the value of $\dfrac{dy}{dx}$, y', f'(x) or $\dfrac{d\,f(x)}{d(x)}$, depending upon which notation for finding the derivative you employed.

For example, we will find the derivative of y for the equation y = x³ − 2x + 4.

Rule 1: substitute x + Δ x for x.

$$y = x^3 - 2x + 4$$
$$y = (x + \Delta\,x)^3 - 2(x + \Delta\,x) + 4$$

Rule 2: Calculate the value for y + Δ y, expanding the right-hand equation member.

$$y + \Delta\,y = (x + \Delta\,x)^3 - 2(x + \Delta\,x) + 4$$
$$y + \Delta\,y = x^3 + 3x^2\,\Delta\,x + 3x(\Delta\,x)^2 + (\Delta\,x)^3 - 2x - 2\,\Delta\,x + 4$$

Rule 3: Subtract y from the left-hand equation member and the value for y (which equals x³ − 2x + 4) from the right-hand equation member, resulting in:

$$\Delta\,y = 3x^2\,\Delta\,x + 3x(\Delta x)^2 + (\Delta\,x)^3 - 2\,\Delta\,x$$

Rule 4: divide Δ y by Δ x, obtaining:

$$\frac{\Delta\,y}{\Delta\,x} = 3x^2 + 3x(\Delta\,x) + (\Delta\,x)^2 - 2$$

Rule 5: Find the limit for the expression of Rule 4. Note that the second and third terms of the right-hand equation member approach zero if Δ x → 0 therefore:

$$\frac{dy}{dx} = 3X^2 - 2$$

2.7-4A   Differentiation Formulas

Rather than deriving formulas by differentiation to show you their origin, etc., we shall give you the conditions and formulas generally used in differential calculus.

1. *Derivative of a constant*
   If the letter c is a constant and if y = c then:

$$\frac{dy}{dx} = 0 \quad \text{or} \quad \frac{dc}{dx} = 0$$

2. *Derivative of a first-order variable*
   This simply means that a derivative of a variable with respect to itself is one. If y = x then:

$$\frac{dy}{dx} = 1$$

3. *Derivative of a variable having an exponent*
   If $y = x^N$, the formula is:

$$\frac{dy}{dx} = Nx^{N-1}$$

4. *Derivative of a sum*
   If u and v are functions of x and if y = u + v then the following formula results:

$$\frac{dy}{dx} = \frac{du}{dx} + \frac{dv}{dx}$$

5. *Derivative of a product*
   When u and v are functions of x and if y = uv then the formula used is:

$$\frac{dy}{dx} = u\frac{dv}{dx} + v\frac{du}{dx}$$

6. *Derivative of a quotient*
   If $y = \dfrac{u}{v}$ and u and v are functions of x, the following formula is used to find the derivative:

$$\frac{dy}{dx} = \frac{v\dfrac{du}{dx} - u\dfrac{dv}{dx}}{(v)^2}$$

7. *Derivative of a function having an exponent*
   The following formula is used when $y = u^m$ if the letter u is a function of x.

$$\frac{dy}{dx} = (mu)^{m-1} \frac{du}{dx}$$

8. *Derivative of higher orders*

This is termed second derivative, third derivative, fourth derivative, etc. Since the derivative $\frac{dy}{dx}$ of the function y is in itself a function, its derivative is termed the second derivative. The second derivative for $\frac{dy}{dx}$ is illustrated below in four general ways.

$$\frac{d (dy)}{dx (dx)} = \frac{d^2y}{dx^2} = y'' = f'' = dx^2 y$$

The third derivative for the same is:

$$y''' \text{ or } f''' = \frac{d^3y}{dx^3}$$

The nth derivative would be:

$$y^n = \frac{d^n y}{dx^n}$$

2.7-5   INTEGRALS

Many mathematical processes essential for calculation are really inverse operations. Some of the mathematical processes illustrating inverse operations include addition-subtraction, multiplication-division, and logarithms and exponents. The inverse operation for differentiation in calculus is *integration*.

When you integrate, you are actually finding the original function when the derivative of the function is known. An example written in symbolic form is: $\int f'(x)dx = f(x)$. This expression is read as the integral of the first derivative of y with respect to x which equals the function of x.

Circuitry having a resistor and a capacitor form a differentiator circuit or an integrator circuit depending upon which component the output is taken across. Figure 2-29 illustrates these two particular circuits.

Electronically speaking, a square wave when applied to the input of an integrator circuit will produce a triangular waveform and is expressed mathematically by using the integration sign. When a triangular wave is applied to the input of a differentiator circuit, the output waveform will resemble a square wave and is expressed mathematically as a differentiation. Hence, these two circuits perform inverse operations in waveforming or waveshaping circuits.

The voltage developed across either capacitor in Figure 2-29 can be expressed mathematically, but before we show you the formula, the following information will prove helpful. Capacitance symbolized by the letter C is the factor by which the voltage (V) measured across the capacitor is multiplied, thereby determining the charge (Q) on the capacitor. This is expressed as:

INPUT OUTPUT INPUT OUTPUT

INTEGRATOR ($\int$) DIFFERENTIATOR $\frac{dy}{dx}$

Figure 2-29

$$Q = CV \text{ where } Q \text{ is in coulombs}$$
$$C \text{ is in farads}$$
$$V \text{ is in volts}$$

The derivative of the charge Q with respect to time (t) describes the charging current flow for the capacitor. This is written as:

$$\frac{dq}{dt} = i = C\frac{dv}{dt} + \frac{dc}{dt}$$

Since capacitance is constant and not a function of time for most problems, dc/dt is zero and results in solving for current using:

$$i = C\frac{dv}{dt} \text{ where i is in amperes}$$

$$\frac{dv}{dt} \text{ is in volts/second}$$

The voltage (V) developed across the capacitor is determined when solving for V in the following process:

since $i = C\dfrac{dv}{dt}$ then: $dv = \dfrac{1}{C}i\,d\,t$

solving for V results in: $V = \dfrac{1}{C}\displaystyle\int_{0}^{t} i\,d \pm E_{o}$

where E_o equals the voltage across the capacitor at zero time.

This equation represents the voltage which is measurable across the capacitor during a time interval from 0 seconds to the instant of time t seconds later. The number zero written at the bottom of the integration symbol is called the *lower limit* and the letter t written at the top is called the *upper limit*.

3 Key Facts and Formulas for Electronic Problem Solving

The tools used in our profession have their intended primary purpose. You know their limitations, advantages, and disadvantages, and therefore select which to use under certain circumstances. It is equally important to know which facts, formulas, or concepts can be relied upon when various conditions are present.

This chapter will enable you to find out which formula, fact, or concept can be used and relied upon, not only when used in DC or AC circuitry application, but also when other variables are present. The following main subject areas are arranged alphabetically while data pertinent to each subject has been logically, but not necessarily alphabetically, listed.

3.1   ADMITTANCE (AC APPLICATIONS ONLY)

Admittance is the measurement of ease with which AC current flows in any circuit. It is the reciprocal of impedance and is expressed in the following ways:

3.1-1   GENERAL

$$Y = \frac{1}{Z}$$

Y = admittance in mhos
Z = impedance in ohms

3.1-2   SERIES CIRCUIT

$$Y = \frac{1}{\sqrt{R^2 + X^2}}$$

Y = admittance
R = resistance in ohms
X = reactance in ohms

3.1-3   PARALLEL CIRCUIT

$$Y = \sqrt{G^2 + B^2}$$

Y = admittance in mhos
G = conductance in mhos
B = susceptance in mhos

Note: The unit of mho describing conductance or admittance is replaced by the metric unit of siemens (S) whose formula is: $S = A/V$ or I/E

3.2   ALTERNATING CURRENT (AC APPLICATIONS ONLY)

Alternating current is a flow of electrons whose movement direction periodically reverses. A complete cycle consists of two alternations: the positive alternation and the negative. Whenever more than one cycle exists, the term hertz is employed, meaning cycles and involving frequency.

3.2-1   TERMINOLOGY AND VALUES

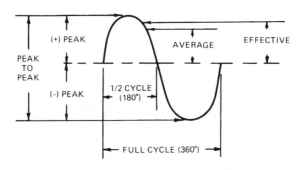

Figure 3-1

Peak to peak—actual voltage swing, measured overall (PP)

Peak voltage—actual voltage swing, positive or negative (PV)

Effective voltage—value read on most meters (rms)

Average voltage—value sine wave is above or below the reference half the time; one peak only.

Period—time required for one complete cycle:

$$t = \frac{1}{f}$$ t is periods (seconds)
        f is frequency (hertz)

3.2-2   CONVERSION FORMULAS (AC APPLICATIONS ONLY)

(A) Peak values

1. Peak value $= \dfrac{\text{peak to peak value}}{2}$

2. Peak value = 1.414 × effective (rms) value
3. Peak value = 1.57 × average value

Note: These values are used to describe peak voltages or currents for maximum instantaneous power calculations.

(B) Peak to peak values

1. Peak to peak value = 3.14 × average value
2. Peak to peak value = 2.828 × effective (rms) value
3. Peak to peak value = 2 × peak value

(C) Effective or rms values

1. Effective or rms value = 0.707 × peak value
2. Effective or rms value = 1.11 × average value
3. Effective or rms value = 0.3535 × peak to peak value

Note: Whenever you see voltage references on schematics, they will be effective or rms values unless otherwise stated. These are used to describe sine wave shapes and serve as calibration reference for meters.

(D) Average values

1. Average value = 0.637 × peak value
2. Average value = 0.9 × effective value
3. Average value = 0.32 × peak to peak value

3.2-3   INSTANTANEOUS VOLTAGE SPECIFICS (AC APPLICATIONS ONLY)

A sine wave is the wave form of an alternating current or voltage in which the amplitude varies as the sine of the phase angle between each instantaneous value and the last previous passage through zero from the negative to positive direction. When determining the actual value of the instantaneous voltage at any particular instant of time, simply multiply the sine function of the desired angle times the peak value of the voltage.

(A) Less than 90 degrees

E inst. sine wave at 70° = ?
E inst. = sine 70° × E peak value

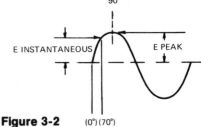

Figure 3-2   (0°) (70°)

(B) Greater than 90 degrees

    * Use sign function of number of
    degree difference to closest
    zero voltage reference point.
    E inst. sine wave at 112° = ?
    * E inst. = sine (180° − 120°) × peak value
    E inst. = sine 68° × E peak value

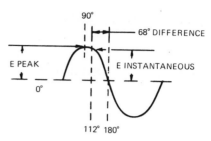

Figure 3-3

(C) Greater than 180 degrees

    E inst. sine wave at 262° = ?
    * E inst. = sine (262° − 180°) × E peak value
    E inst. = sine 82° × E peak value

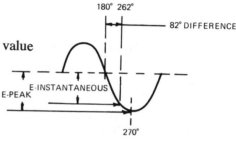

Figure 3-4

3

3.2-4   OHM'S LAW VARIATIONS (AC APPLICATION ONLY)

(A) Voltage

$$E = IZ$$

$$E = IX$$

$$E = \frac{P}{I \cos \Theta}$$

$$E = \frac{W}{Q}$$

(B) Reactance

$$X = \frac{E}{I}$$

E = voltage in volts
I = current in amperes
X = inductive or capacitive
    reactance in ohms
P = power in watts
Θ = phase angle in degrees
Z = impedance in ohms
W = energy in joules
Q = quantity of electrical
    charge in coulombs

(C) Current

$$I = \frac{E}{Z}$$

$$I = \frac{E}{X}$$

(D) Impedance

$$Z = \frac{E}{I}$$

$$Z = \frac{P}{I^2 \cos \Theta}$$

(E) Power

$$P = IE \cos \Theta$$

$$P = I^2 Z \cos \Theta$$

$$P = \frac{E^2}{Z} \cos \Theta$$

3.2-5   PHASE ANGLES (AC APPLICATION ONLY)

The difference in degrees by which current leads voltage in a capacitive circuit, or by which current lags voltage in an inductive circuit, is termed phase angle. The formulas used to determine phase angles in series circuits are as follows:

$$\Theta = ARC \tan \frac{X_L}{R}$$

$$\Theta = ARC \tan \frac{X_C}{R}$$

Θ = angle of lead or lag in degrees
X_L = inductive reactance in ohms
X_C = capacitive reactance in ohms
R = nonreactive resistance in ohms
(ARC tan = TAN^{-1})

3.2-6   POWER FACTOR (AC APPLICATION ONLY)

Power factor is a ratio between the actual power of an alternating or pulsating current, measured by a wattmeter, to an apparent power value as indicated by voltmeter and ammeter readings. Power factor is a cosine function of the phase angle between sinsusoidal voltage and current.

Power factor also indicates loss in an inductor, capacitor, or insulator since it is a ratio of resistance and impedance. The formulas used to determine the power factor are:

$$PF = \frac{R}{Z}$$

PF = Cosine Θ

$$PF = \frac{\text{true power}}{\text{apparent power}}$$

PF = power factor (percentage)
R = nonreactive resistance (ohms)
Z = impedance (ohms)
True power = EI cos Θ (watts)
Apparent power = EI (volt-amperes)

3.2-7   ANGULAR VELOCITY (AC APPLICATION ONLY)

The Greek letter omega (ω) represents the angular velocity of alternating voltage or signal. Instead of writing 2π f in any formula requiring this particular trio, the angular velocity symbol is employed because:

angular velocity (ω) = 2π f

π = 3.14
f = frequency

3.2-8   INSTANTANEOUS VOLTAGE (AC APPLICATION ONLY)

e = Emax sin ω t

e = instantaneous voltage at anytime (t)
Emax = maximum voltage
ω = angular velocity (2πf)
t = given time length

3.2-9 POTENTIAL DIFFERENCE FOR A CHARGING CAPACITOR IN RC CIRCUITS

Refer also to time constants (3.22)

$$e_C = E_A \left(1 - \epsilon \frac{-t}{RC}\right)$$

OR

$$e_C = E_A (1 - \xi^{-X})$$

e_C = voltage across capacitor
E_A = applied voltage
ξ = base of Napierian logarithm equaling 2.718
t = desired time length
RC = circuitry charge time constant
X = time in time constants $\left(\frac{t}{RC}\right)$

3.2-10 POTENTIAL DIFFERENCE FOR A DISCHARGING CAPACITOR IN RC CIRCUITS

Refer also to time constants (3.22) (AC applications)

$$e_C = Ec \left(\xi \frac{-t}{RC}\right)$$

OR

$$e_C = Ec (\epsilon^{-X})$$

e_C = voltage across capacitor
Ec = initial charge on capacitor
ξ = base of Napierian logarithm equaling 2.718
RC = circuitry discharge time constant
X = time to time constants (t/RC)
t = desired time length

3.2-11 VOLTAGE ACROSS A RESISTOR IN RC CIRCUITS (AC APPLICATIONS)

Refer also to time constants (3.22)

$$e_R = E_A \left(\xi^{-t/RC}\right)$$

e_R = voltage across resistor
E_A = applied voltage
ξ = Napierian log base (2.718)
t = any given time length (seconds)
R_C = time constant (seconds)

3.2-12 VOLTAGE ACROSS A COIL IN LR CIRCUITS (AC APPLICATIONS)

Refer also to time constants (3.22)

$$e_L = E_A \left(\xi^{-tR/L}\right)$$

e_L = voltage across coil
E_A = applied voltage
t = any given time length (seconds)
R = circuitry resistance (ohms)
L = circuitry inductance (henrys)

3

3.2-13   VOLTAGE ACROSS A RESISTOR IN LR CIRCUITS (AC APPLICATIONS)

Refer also to time constants (3.22)

$$e_R = E_A \left(1 - \xi^{-tR/L}\right)$$

e_R = voltage across resistor
E_A = applied voltage
ξ = Napierian log base (2.718)
R = circuitry resistance (ohms)
L = circuitry inductance (henrys)
t = any given time length (seconds)

3.2-14   INSTANTANEOUS CURRENT (AC APPLICATIONS)

$$i = I_{max} \sin \omega t$$

i = instantaneous current at any time (t)
I_{max} = maximum current (peak)
$\omega = 2\pi f$

3.2-15   INSTANTANEOUS CURRENT IN LR CIRCUITS (AC APPLICATIONS)

Refer also to time constants (3.22)

$$i = \frac{E_A}{R} \left(1 - \xi^{-tR/L}\right)$$

i = instantaneous current
E_A = applied voltage
R = circuitry resistance (ohms)
L = circuitry inductance (henrys)
t = any given time interval
ξ = Napierian log base (2.718)

3.2-16   INSTANTANEOUS CURRENT IN RC CIRCUITS (AC APPLICATIONS)

Refer also to time constants (3.22)

$$i = \frac{E_A}{R} \left(\xi^{-t/RC}\right)$$

i = instantaneous current
E_A = applied voltage
ξ = Napierian log base (2.718)
t = value of given time
RC = circuitry time constant

3.2-17   TRANSIT TIME PHASE DIFFERENCE (AC APPLICATIONS)

$$\alpha = 2\pi f t$$

OR

$$\alpha = \omega t$$

α = transit time phase difference
π = 3.14
f = frequency
t = value of given time
$\omega = 2\pi f$

3.3   ANTENNAS (AC APPLICATIONS ONLY)

It seems that antenna design and reference data are based upon the fundamental single wire antenna type whose physical length is approximately equal to one-half its transmitting wavelength. The following formulas are listed for quick reference for antenna applications. They are all single wire antenna formulas.

3.3-1   HALF-WAVELENGTH IN FEET (IN SPACE)

$$L = \frac{492}{f}$$

L = length in feet
f = frequency in megahertz

3.3-2   ACTUAL HALF-WAVELENGTH IN FEET

$$L = \frac{492 \times 0.95}{f}$$

OR

$$L = \frac{468}{f}$$

L   = length in feet
f   = frequency in megahertz
0.95 = resonant antenna length factor

3.3-3   PHYSICAL LENGTH (ONE WAVELENGTH)

$$L = \frac{984 \times V}{f}$$

L = physical length in feet
V = velocity factor for particular transmission
     line used
f = frequency in megahertz

3.3-4   ELECTRICAL LENGTH

$$\lambda = \frac{984,000}{f}$$

f = frequency in kilohertz
λ = wavelength in feet
(electrical length is longer than actual length)

3.3-5   LONG WIRE ANTENNA LENGTH

$$L = \frac{492\,(N - 0.05)}{f}$$

L = length in feet
N = number of halfwaves on antenna
f = frequency in megahertz

3.3-6   QUARTER-WAVE ANTENNA LENGTH

$$L = \frac{246(V)}{f}$$

L = length in feet
f = frequency in megahertz
V = velocity factor of transmission line used

3.3-7   ANTENNA RADIATION RESISTANCE

$$R = \frac{P}{I^2}$$

R = radiation resistance
P = radiated power
I^2 = effective current (maximum current point on antenna)

3.3-8   ANTENNA EFFICIENCY

$$EFF = \frac{Rr \times 100}{Rr + Rw + R_L}$$

EFF = antenna efficiency
Rr = radiation resistance
Rw = effective wire resistance
R_L = equivalent resistance (other losses)

3.3-9   TOTAL NUMBER OF ANTENNA LOBES

$$L_T = 2N$$

L_T = total number of lobes
N = number of half-wave lengths on antenna

3.4   CHARACTERISTIC IMPEDANCE (AC APPLICATIONS ONLY)

A transmission line's primary purpose is to carry electrical energy from its source to its antenna or load with minimum loss. Impedance matching, therefore, between the source and load, is most important for maximum power transfer. Since the characteristics of the line may be resistive with either capacitive or inductive reactive elements when alternating current voltages are applied, the characteristics of a line are generally described by its characteristic impedance (Zo).

3.4-1   THEORETICAL VALUE OF PURELY RESISTIVE LINE

$$Zo = \sqrt{\frac{L}{C}}$$

OR

$$Zo = \frac{Ei}{Ii}$$

Zo = characteristic impedance (ohms)
L = inductance per unit length
C = capacitance per unit length
Ei = incident voltage
Ii = incident current

3.4-2 COAXIAL CABLE LINE

Zo = characteristic impedance
K   = dielectric constant for insulating material
* D   = inside diameter of outer conductor
* d   = outside diameter of inner conductor
* Use the same units for measurements

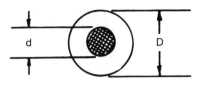

Figure 3-5

Solid Dielectric

$$Zo = \frac{138}{\sqrt{K}} \, Log \, \frac{D}{d}$$

Air Dielectric

$$Z_o = 138 \, log \, \frac{D}{d}$$

3.4-3 COAXIAL CABLE LINE ATTENUATION

$$A = \frac{4.6 \sqrt{f} \, (D + d)}{Dd \left(Log \frac{D}{d}\right)} \times 10^{-6}$$

A = attenuation of line (dB/ft)
f = frequency in megahertz
* D = inside diameter of outer conductor
* d = outside diameter of inner conductor

* Same units of measurement

3.4-4 TWIN LEAD/PARALLEL LINE

Zo = characteristic impedance
K   = dielectric constant for insulating material
* D   = distance between conductor centers
* r   = conductor radius
* d   = diameter of conductor
* Use same measurements

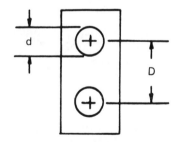

Figure 3-6

Solid Dielectric

$$Zo = \frac{276}{\sqrt{K}} \, Log \, \frac{2D}{d}$$

Air Dielectric

$$Zo = 276 \, Log \, \frac{D}{r}$$

3.4-5　STANDING WAVE RATIO

General

$$SWR = \frac{Emax}{Emin}$$

$$SWR = \frac{Imax}{Imin}$$

$$SWR = \sqrt{\frac{Zmax}{Zmin}}$$

SWR = standing wave ratio
E　= voltage on the line
I　= current on the line
Z　= impedance
Z_L = load impedance
Z_O = characteristic impedance

Resistive Load Only

$$SWR = \frac{Z_L}{Z_O} \text{ (use if } Z_L \text{ is larger)} \quad OR \quad SWR = \frac{Z_O}{Z_L} \text{ (use if } Z_O \text{ is larger)}$$

3.4-6　TRANSFORMER MATCHING

$$Z_O = \sqrt{Z_I \, Z_L}$$

Z_O = characteristic impedance
Z_I = input impedance
Z_L = output impedance

3.4-7　REFLECTION COEFFICIENT

$$\Gamma = \frac{Er}{Ei}$$

$$\Gamma = \frac{Ir}{Ii}$$

$$\Gamma = \frac{Z_L - Z_O}{Z_L + Z_O}$$

Γ　= reflection coefficient
Er = reflected voltage
Ei = incident current
Ir　= reflected current
Ii　= incident current
Z_L = load impedance
Z_O = characteristic impedance

3.4-8　DELAY LINE WAVE TRAVEL TIME

$$t = N \sqrt{LC}$$

t　= the time needed to travel one length
　　of the delay line
N = number of line sections
L = total inductance of one section
C = total capacitance of one section

3.4-9　PULSE FORMING LINE PULSE WIDTH

$$PW = 2N \sqrt{LC}$$

PW = pulse width
N　= number of line sections
L　= total inductance of one section
C　= total capacitance of one section

3.4-10   ARTIFICIAL LINE CUTOFF FREQUENCY

$$F_{CO} = \frac{1}{\pi \sqrt{LC}}$$

F_{CO} = cutoff frequency
π = 3.14
L   = total inductance per section
C   = total capacitance per section

3.4-11   ONE-QUARTER WAVELENGTH MULTIPLE

$$Z_O = \sqrt{Z_s\, Z_r}$$

Z_O = characteristic impedance
Z_s = impedance looking into line source
Z_r = pure resistance load impedance

(line length equals odd multiple of ¼ wavelengths)

3.5   CIRCUITRY COMPARISON (SERIES-PARALLEL)

3.5-1   CURRENT

Series

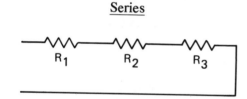

Figure 3-7

$*\, I_T = I_{R1} = I_{R2} = I_{R3}$

Note: Total current *decreases* when adding more resistors.
* Refer also to 2.2-10A

Parallel

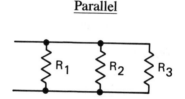

Figure 3-8

$I_T = I_{R1} + I_{R2} + I_{R3}$

Note: Total current *increases* when adding more resistors.

3.5-2   VOLTAGE

Series

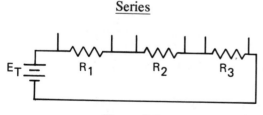

Figure 3-9

$E_T = E_{R1} + E_{R2} + E_{R3}$

Parallel

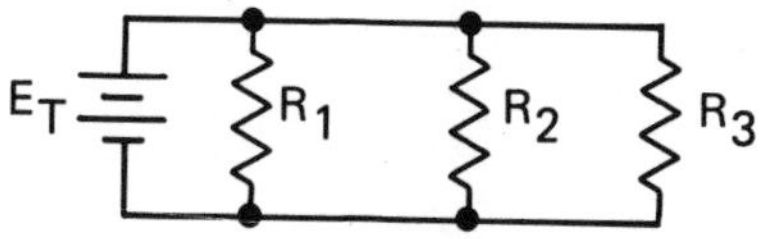

Figure 3-10

$E_T = E_{R1} = E_{R2} = E_{R3}$

3.5-3   RESISTANCE

Series	Parallel

$$R_T = R_1 + R_2 + R_3$$

$$R_T = \frac{1}{\dfrac{1}{R_1} + \dfrac{1}{R_2} + \dfrac{1}{R_3}}$$

Total resistance *is greater* than any one resistor in the circuit.

Total resistance *is less* than lowest value resistor in the circuit.

3.5-4   WATTAGE

Series   Parallel

$$P_T = P_{R1} + P_{R2} + P_{R3}$$

$$P_T = P_{R1} + P_{R2} + P_{R3}$$

3.5-5   KIRCHHOFF'S LAWS

Series   Parallel

Apply the voltage law. (see 3.5-2)   Apply the current law. (see 3.5-1)

3.5-6   NOTES

Series   Parallel

Voltage division   *Current division

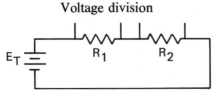

Figure 3-11

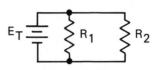

Figure 3-12

$$E_{R1} = E_T \frac{R_1}{R_T}$$

$$I_{R1} = (I_T) \frac{R_2}{R_1 + R_2}$$

$$E_{R2} = E_T \frac{R_2}{R_T}$$

$$I_{R2} = (I_T) \frac{R_1}{R_1 + R_2}$$

* Refer also to 2.2-9A

3.6   CONDUCTANCE

The property of a component allowing current to flow is termed *conductance*. The obsolete unit for conductance is mhos (ohm spelled backwards) and was represented by the letter G, while the new metric unit is siemens and is represented by the letter S.

3.6-1   GENERAL (DC APPLICATIONS)

$$G = \frac{1}{R}$$

OR

$$G = \frac{I}{E}$$

G = conductance in mhos (siemens)

R = resistance in ohms

E = voltage in volts

3.6-2   RESISTORS IN PARALLEL (DC APPLICATIONS)

$$GT = \frac{1}{R_1} + \frac{1}{R_2} + \frac{1}{R_3} + \ldots$$

OR

$$GT = G_1 + G_2 + G_3 + \ldots$$

3.7   DECIBELS (AC AND DC APPLICATIONS)

Our sense of hearing, based upon an almost logarithmic response, serves as a reference for sound levels. You and I can pretty well distinguish degrees of sound loudness while adjusting the radio, phonograph, tape unit, or TV volume control to a position that meets our individual range of comfortable listening. Since each of our listening levels might differ, a standardized expression denoting relative magnitude of sound level change is desirable. The expression we use is termed *decibel* and is abbreviated officially as dB. However, you may see db, or DB in print.

The decibel provides the means of stating ratios of two voltages, two currents, or two powers.

3.7-1   CURRENTS (INPUT AND OUTPUT IMPEDANCES EQUAL)

$$dB = 20 \log \frac{I_2}{I_1}$$

dB = decibel

I_2 = output current

I_1 = input current

3.7-2   CURRENTS (INPUT AND OUTPUT IMPEDANCES NOT EQUAL)

$$dB = 20 \log \frac{I_2 \sqrt{Z_2}}{I_1 \sqrt{Z_1}}$$

dB = decibel

I_2 = output current

I_1 = input current

Z_2 = output impedance

Z_1 = input impedance

3.7-3   POWER (INPUT AND OUTPUT IMPEDANCES EQUAL)

$$dB = 10 \log \frac{P_2}{P_1}$$

dB = decibel
P_2 = output power
P_1 = input power

3.7-4   VOLTAGES (INPUT AND OUTPUT IMPEDANCES EQUAL)

$$dB = 20 \log \frac{E_2}{E_1}$$

dB = decibel
E_2 = output voltage
E_1 = input voltage

3.7-5   VOLTAGES (INPUT AND OUTPUT IMPEDANCES NOT EQUAL)

$$dB = 20 \log \frac{E_2 \sqrt{Z_2}}{E_1 \sqrt{Z_1}}$$

dB = decibel
E_2 = output voltage
E_1 = input voltage
Z_2 = output impedance
Z_1 = input impedance

3.7-6   REFERENCE LEVELS

The decibel also is used extensively in other areas of electronics which do not rely directly upon voltage, current, or power ratios as did the previous formulas. Whenever the decibel unit is used, make certain you know the reference level employed. The television industry, for example, uses a 1-millivolt rms signal across a 75-ohm impedance. If no reference is given, usually a 6-millivolt signal across a 600-ohm impedance is assumed since it is a standard that corresponds to zero decibel (0 dB). Adding decibels is the equivalent of multiplying circuitry gains. The following are some of the more popular decibel references employed.

Symbol	Reference
dBk	1 kilowatt
dBm	1 milliwatt across 600 ohms
dBV	1 volt
dBW	1 watt
dBVg	voltage gain
dBrap	above reference acoustical power
vu	(volume unit) 1 milliwatt across 600 ohms

3.8   DELTA AND WYE CIRCUITS

The data in this section will be valuable when solutions of electrical-electronic networks of the pie (π) or delta (Δ) and the tee (T) or wye (Y) variety are required. Those of you having backgrounds in industrial electricity will probably call these networks "wye" and "delta" whereas those involved in pure electronics will perhaps be more familiar with the "tee" and "pie" names. I'll clarify this by saying that the pie and delta describe the same circuit configuration while the tee and wye references describe their own circuit configurations. Figures 3-13 and 3-14 illustrate these basic networks using resistors in each leg.

3.8-1   TEE OR WYE NETWORK

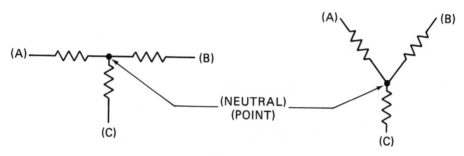

Figure 3-13

The three terminal pairs of A-B, B-C, and C-A provide three-phase power (3 ϕ). The line voltage is $\sqrt{3}$ or 1.7320508+ times the coil voltage. Single phase power is available when taken from neutral to A, neutral to B, or neutral to C.

3.8-1A   Wye/Tee to Delta Conversion

$$R_A = \frac{R_1 R_2 + R_1 R_3 + R_2 R_3}{R_2}$$

$$R_B = \frac{R_1 R_2 + R_1 R_3 + R_2 R_3}{R_1}$$

$$R_C = \frac{R_1 R_2 + R_1 R_3 + R_2 R_3}{R_3}$$

Note: See Figure 3-14 for R_A, R_B, R_C reference.

3.8-2   PIE OR DELTA NETWORK

This network is commonly used since current availability is better than the wye or tee configuration. The current available in a three-phase (3 ϕ) delta is $\sqrt{3}$ or 1.7320508+ times the current capability of any one coil or leg. Single-

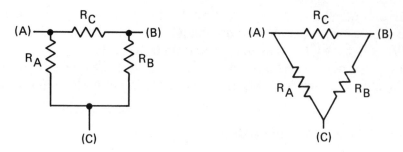

Figure 3-14

phase voltage is also available if taken between A to B or B to C or C to A. Three-phase is possible when using three wires from A, B, and C.

3.8-2A   Pie/Delta to Wye/Tee Conversion

$$R_1 = \frac{R_A R_C}{R_A + R_B + R_C}$$

$$R_2 = \frac{R_B R_C}{R_A + R_B + R_C}$$

$$R_3 = \frac{R_A R_B}{R_A + R_B + R_C}$$

Note: See Figure 3-13 for R_1, R_2, R_3 reference.

3.9   IMPEDANCE (AC APPLICATIONS ONLY)

The laws, formulas, and facts governing current and voltage in direct current circuits seem to be more consistent and less complex than alternating current applications. The main reason for simplicity in DC circuits is that the only opposition offered is that of pure resistance while AC circuit opposition consists of resistance and reactances.

The term describing AC resistance or total opposition to current flow is called *impedance* (Z). Impedance is due mainly to inherent characteristics of inductors, capacitors, and wire-wound resistors whose oppositions become altered somewhat when alternating voltages or frequencies are applied. You will find data you can rely on when dealing with impedance in this portion of Chapter 3.

3.9-1   IMPEDANCE FORMULAS

(A) Polar Form: $Z \angle \Theta$ Z   = impedance

                                                             Θ = direction of angle

(B) Rectangular Forms: $Z = R - jX_C$ R   = resistance

                                       $Z = R + jX_L$ $\pm j$ = "j" operator

(C) Triangular Forms: $Z = \sqrt{R^2 + (X_L - X_C)^2}$ X_C = capacitive reactance

                                       $Z = \sqrt{R^2 + (X_C - X_L)^2}$ X_L = inductive reactance

(D) Trigonometric Forms: $(Z) = (\cos \Theta + j \sin \Theta)$ $\cos$ = function of the angle

                                       $(Z) = (\cos \Theta - j \sin \Theta)$ $\sin$ = function of the angle

3.9-2   IMPEDANCE AND PHASE ANGLES FOR RESISTORS, CAPACITORS AND INDUCTORS

(A) Resistors: $Z = R_1$

                                  $\Theta = 0°$

R_1

Figure 3-15

(B) Inductors: $Z = X_L$

                                  $Z = 2 \pi fL$

                                  $\Theta = 90°$

                                  $\Theta = +j$

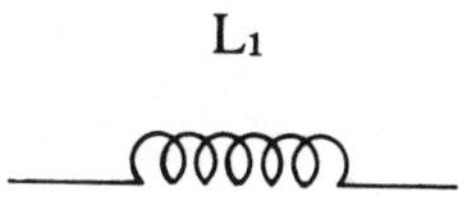

L_1

Figure 3-16

3

(C) Capacitors: $Z = X_C$

                                  $Z = \dfrac{1}{2 \pi fC}$

                                  $\Theta = -90°$

                                  $\Theta = -j$

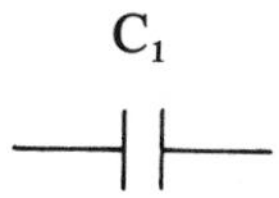

C_1

Figure 3-17

3.9-3   IMPEDANCE AND PHASE ANGLES FOR COMPONENTS IN SERIES

(A) Resistors: $Z = R_1 + R_2 + R_3 + \ldots$

                                  $\Theta = 0°$

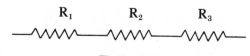

R_1 R_2 R_3

Figure 3-18

(B) Inductors:

$$Z = X_{L1} + X_{L2} + X_{L3} + \ldots$$

$$\Theta = +90°$$

$$\Theta = +j \text{ (no mutual induction)}$$

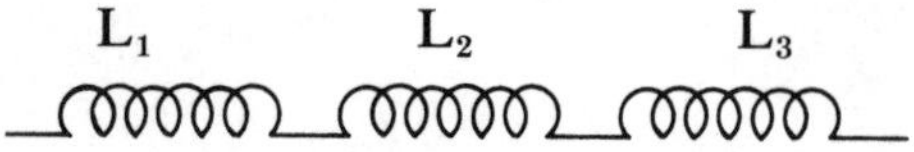

L$_1$ L$_2$ L$_3$

Figure 3-19

(C) Capacitors:

$$Z = X_{C1} + X_{C2} + X_{C3} + \ldots$$

$$\Theta = -90°$$

$$\Theta = -j$$

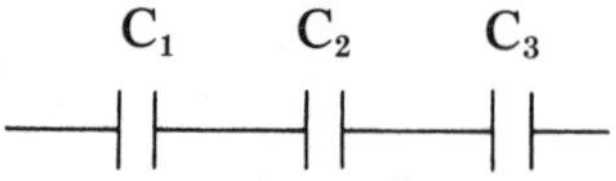

C$_1$ C$_2$ C$_3$

Figure 3-20

3.9-4   IMPEDANCE AND PHASE ANGLES OF SERIES L-R CIRCUIT

$$Z = \sqrt{R^2 + X_L^2}$$

$$\Theta = \arctan \frac{X_L}{R}$$

L   R

Figure 3-21

3.9-5   IMPEDANCE AND PHASE ANGLES OF SERIES R-C CIRCUIT

$$Z = \sqrt{R^2 + X_C^2}$$

$$\Theta = \arctan \frac{X_C}{R}$$

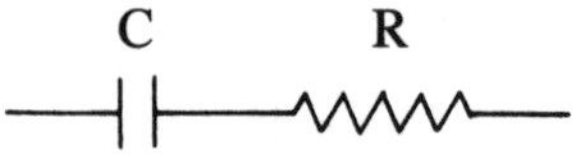

C   R

Figure 3-22

3.9-6   IMPEDANCE AND PHASE ANGLES OF SERIES L-C CIRCUIT

$$Z = X_L - X_C$$
(if X_L is larger)

$$Z = X_C - X_L$$
(if X_C is larger)

$$\Theta = 0° \text{ at resonance}$$
$$(X_L = X_C)$$

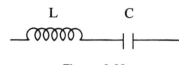

L   C

Figure 3-23

3.9-7   IMPEDANCE AND PHASE ANGLES OF SERIES R-L-C CIRCUIT

$$Z = \sqrt{R^2 + (X_L - X_C)^2}$$

$$Z = \sqrt{R^2 + (X_C - X_L)^2}$$

$$\Theta = \text{arc tan } \frac{X_L - X_C}{R}$$

$$\Theta = \text{arc tan } \frac{X_C - X_L}{R}$$

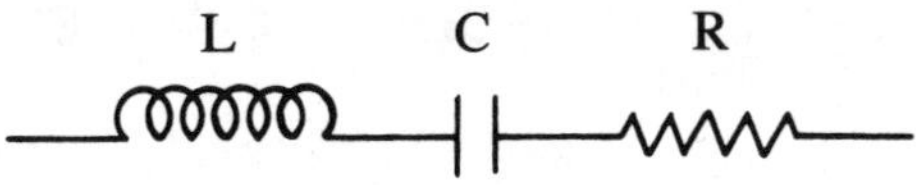

Figure 3-24

3.9-8 REACTIVE CIRCUIT SUMMARY

(A) R-L Circuit:

(Voltage leads current)

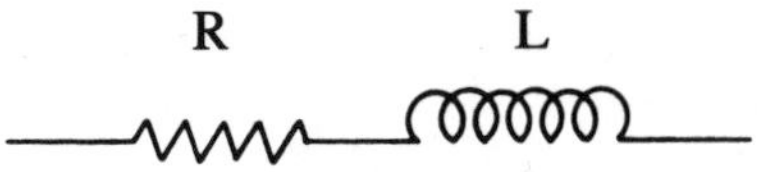

Figure 3-25

$$X_L = \omega L = 2 \pi fL$$

$$Z = \sqrt{R^2 + X_L{}^2}$$

$$I_T = \frac{E \text{ applied}}{Z}$$

X_L = inductive reactance (ohms)
$\omega = 2 \pi f$
R = pure resistance (ohms)
E applied = source potential (volts)
Z = circuitry impedance (ohms)
I_T = total current (amperes)

(B) RC Circuit:

(Current leads voltage)

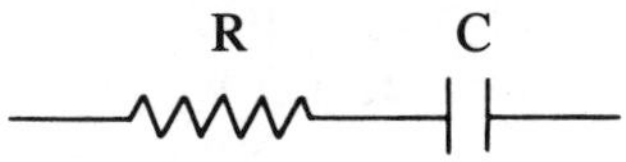

Figure 3-26

$$X_C = \frac{1}{\omega C} = \frac{1}{2 \pi fC} = \frac{0.159}{fC}$$

$$Z = \sqrt{R^2 + X_C{}^2}$$

$$I_T = \frac{E \text{ applied}}{Z}$$

X_C = capacitive reactance (ohms)
$\omega = 2 \pi f$
R = pure resistance (ohms)
E applied = source potential (volts)
Z = circuitry impedance (ohms)
I_T = total current (amperes)

(C) R-L-C Circuit:

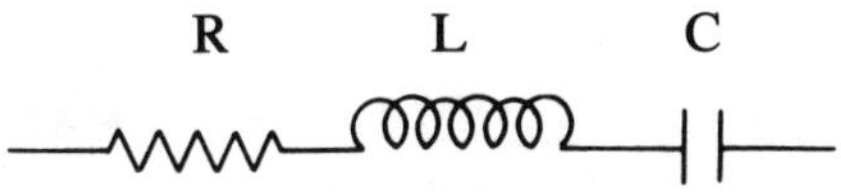

Figure 3-27

$$X_C = \frac{1}{\omega C} = \frac{1}{2 \pi fC} = \frac{0.159}{fC}$$

$$X_L = \omega L = 2 \pi fL$$

$$Z = \sqrt{R^2 + X_T{}^2}$$

$$*Z = \sqrt{R^2 + (X_L - X_C)^2}$$

$$*Z = \sqrt{R^2 + (X_C - X_L)^2}$$

$$I_T = \frac{E \text{ applied}}{Z}$$

X_C = capacitive reactance (ohms)
$\omega = 2 \pi f$
X_L = inductive reactance (ohms)
L = value of inductor (henrys)
C = value of capacitor (farads)
R = pure resistance (ohms)
X_T = total reactance (ohms)
I_T = total current (amperes)
Z = impedance (ohms)
E applied = source potential (volts)

* Subtract smaller reactance from larger (circuit acts inductive or capacitive depending upon largest opposition)

3.9-9   R-L-C RESONANT SERIES CIRCUITRY DATA

$$Fr = \frac{1}{2\pi\sqrt{LC}} = \frac{0.159}{\sqrt{LC}}$$

$$Z = R$$

$$X_L = X_C$$

$$\theta = 0°$$

(current is maximum, circuit acts resistive)

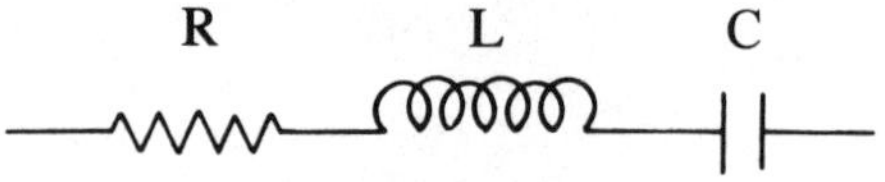

R   L   C

Figure 3-28

Fr = resonant frequency (hertz)
L = value of inductor (henrys)
C = value of capacitor (farads)
Z = impedance (ohms)
R = pure resistance (ohms)
X_L = inductive reactance (ohms)
X_C = capacitive reactance (ohms)

The characteristics of the series R-L-C circuit illustrated in Figure 3-28 will change somewhat when the frequency goes above or below the particular resonant frequency. The following chart summarizes how the circuitry acts at frequencies above, below, and at the desired frequency.

	Above Resonance	At Resonance	Below Resonance
The circuit appears to be:	XL + R	Resistive	XC + R
The circuitry current is:	Low	High	Low
The circuitry impedance is:	High	Low	High
The circuitry current phase is:	Lagging E	In phase	Leading E

3.9-10   IMPEDANCE AND PHASE ANGLES FOR COMPONENTS IN PARALLEL

(A) <u>Resistors:</u>

$$Z = \frac{R_1 \times R_2}{R_1 + R_2} \text{ (when only two resistors)}$$

$$\theta = 0°$$

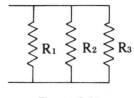

Figure 3-29

$$Z = \frac{1}{\dfrac{1}{R_1} + \dfrac{1}{R_2} + \dfrac{1}{R_3}} \text{ (more than two resistors)}$$

$$\theta = 0°$$

(B) Inductors:

(no mutual induction)

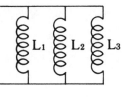

Figure 3-30

$$Z = \frac{(X_{L1})(X_{L2})}{X_{L1} + X_{L2}} \text{ (when only two inductors)}$$

$$Z = \frac{1}{\dfrac{1}{X_{L1}} + \dfrac{1}{X_{L2}} + \dfrac{1}{X_{L3}} + \ldots} \text{ (when more than two inductors)}$$

$\Theta = +90°$

$\Theta = +j$

(C) Capacitors:

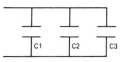

Figure 3-31

$$Z = \frac{(X_{C1})(X_{C2})}{X_{C1} + X_{C2}} \text{ (when only two capacitors)}$$

$$Z = \frac{1}{\dfrac{1}{X_{C1}} + \dfrac{1}{X_{C2}} + \dfrac{1}{X_{C3}} + \ldots} \text{ (when more than two capacitors)}$$

$\Theta = -90°$

$\Theta = -j$

3.9-11   IMPEDANCE AND PHASE ANGLES OF PARALLEL R-L CIRCUIT

$$Z = \frac{(R)(X_L)}{\sqrt{R^2 + X_L^2}}$$

$$\Theta = \text{arc tan } \frac{R}{X_L}$$

Figure 3-32

3.9-12   IMPEDANCE AND PHASE ANGLES OF PARALLEL R-C CIRCUIT

$$Z = \frac{(R)(X_C)}{\sqrt{R^2 + X_C^2}}$$

$$\Theta = \text{arc tan } \frac{R}{X_C}$$

Figure 3-33

3.9-13   IMPEDANCE AND PHASE ANGLES OF PARALLEL L-C CIRCUIT

$$Z = \frac{(X_L)(X_C)}{X_L - X_C}$$

$$Z = \frac{(X_C)(X_L)}{X_C - X_L}$$

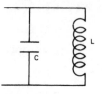

$\Theta = 0°$ at resonance $(X_L = X_C)$

Figure 3-34

3.9-14   IMPEDANCE AND PHASE ANGLES OF PARALLEL L-C-R CIRCUIT

$$Z = \frac{(R)(X_L)(X_C)}{\sqrt{X_L^2 X_C^2 + R^2(X_L - X_C)^2}}$$

$$\Theta = \frac{R(X_L - X_C)}{(X_L)(X_C)}$$

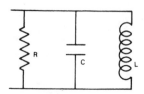

Figure 3-35

The formulas assumed X_L to be larger than X_C. Change values if X_C is larger.

3.9-15   PARALLEL REACTIVE CIRCUIT SUMMARY

(A) R-L Circuit:
       (current lags voltage)

$$X_L = 2\pi fL = \omega L$$

$$.Z = \frac{E \text{ applied}}{I_{Total}}$$

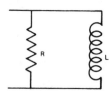

Figure 3-36

$$Z = \frac{(R)(X)}{\sqrt{R^2 + X^2}}$$

$$I_T \sqrt{IR^2 + Ix_L^2}$$

X_L = inductive reactance (ohms)
ω $= 2\pi f$
f   = frequency (hertz)
L   = value of inductor (henrys)
Z   = impedance (ohms)
E applied = source potential volts
I_{Total} = total circuitry current (amperes)
R   = pure resistance (ohms)
X   = total reactance (ohms)

(B) R-C Circuit:
(voltage lags current)

$$X_C = \frac{1}{2\pi fC} = \frac{1}{\omega C} = \frac{0.159}{fC}$$

$$Z = \frac{E \text{ applied}}{I\text{Total}}$$

$$I_T = \sqrt{I_R^2 + Ix_C^2}$$

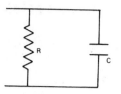

Figure 3-37

X_C = capacitive reactance (ohms)
ω = $2\pi f$
E applied = source potential (volts)
ITotal = total circuitry current (amperes)
R   = pure resistance (ohms)
Z   = impedance (ohms)

(C) R-L-C Circuit:
(circuit acts inductive or capacitive depending
upon which leg has largest current)

$$X_C = \frac{1}{2\pi fC} = \frac{1}{\omega c} = \frac{0.159}{fC}$$

$$X_L = 2\pi fL = \omega L$$

$$Z = \frac{E \text{ applied}}{I\text{Total}}$$

$$I_T = \sqrt{I_R^2 + Ix^2}$$

$$I_T = \sqrt{I_R^2 + (Ix_L - Ix_C)^2}$$

$$I_T = \sqrt{I_R^2 + (Ix_C - Ix_L)^2}$$

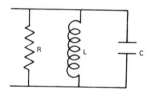

Figure 3-38

X_C = capacitive reactance (ohms)
ω = $2\pi f$
X_L = inductive reactance (ohms)
Z   = impedance (ohms)
E applied = source potential (volts)
ITotal = total circuitry current (amperes)
X   = total reactance (ohms)

3.9-16   PARALLEL RESONANT R-L-C CIRCUITRY DATA

(current is minimum, circuit acts resistive)

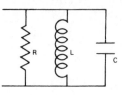

$$Fr = \frac{1}{2\pi\sqrt{LC}} = \frac{0.159}{\sqrt{LC}}$$

$Z = R$

$X_C = X_L$

$I_L = I_C$

$\theta = 0°$

Figure 3-39

Fr = resonant frequency (hertz)
L = value of inductor (henrys)
C = value of capacitor (farads)
Z = impedance (ohms)
R = pure resistance (ohms)
I = current (amperes)
X_C = capacitive reactance (ohms)
X_L = inductive reactance (ohms)

The following chart further summarizes the inherent characteristics the circuit of Figure 3-39 has when the frequency of the circuit goes above and below the desired frequency.

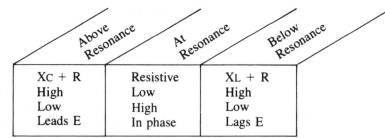

	Above Resonance	At Resonance	Below Resonance
The circuit appears to be:	$X_C + R$	Resistive	$X_L + R$
The circuitry current is:	High	Low	High
The circuitry impedance is:	Low	High	Low
The circuitry current phase is:	Leads E	In phase	Lags E

3.9-17   IMPEDANCE MATCHING

(A) High input to lower value output resistance

when Rin > R₀

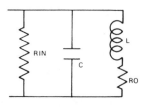

Figure 3-40

$$X_L = \sqrt{R_0 Rin - R_0{}^2}$$

$$X_C = \frac{R_0 Rin}{X_L}$$

X_L = inductive reactance (ohms)
R_0 = output or load resistance (ohms)
Rin = input resistance (ohms)
X_C = capacitive reactance (ohms)

(B) Low input to high value output resistance

when Rin < R_0

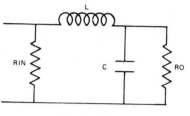

Figure 3-41

$$X_C = R_L \sqrt{\frac{Rin}{R_0 - Rin}}$$

$$X_L = \frac{R_0 Rin}{X_C}$$

Rin = input resistance (ohms)
R_0 = output or load resistance (ohms)
X_C = capacitive reactance (ohms)
X_L = inductive reactance (ohms)

3.10 INDUCTORS
(AC AND DC APPLICATIONS)

   Transformers, chokes, toroidal coils, and ferrite beads all have one thing in common; and that is the family type of grouping called inductors. In its simplest form, an inductor or choke or coil, as it is sometimes called, relies upon magnetic fields produced when alternating current flows through them. The ability of an inductor to oppose current changes causes a smoothing-out action to occur.
   The unit of inductance is the henry, but smaller units of millihenry and microhenry are used extensively in electronic application. Inductance itself is dependent upon the number of turns, cross-sectional dimensions of the coil, length of the winding, and permeability of the coil core. All of the following formulas and facts will aid you when working with inductors.

3.10-1   INDUCTORS IN SERIES

(A) Total Inductance – No Mutual Inductance

   (AC and DC application)

   $$L_T = L_1 + L_2 + L_3 + \ldots$$

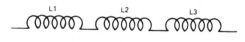

Figure 3-42

L_T = total inductance (henrys)
$L_1 - L_3$ = individual inductor values (henrys)

(B) Total Inductance with Mutual or Coupled Inductance

(AC application only)

Figure 3-43

$$L_T = L_1 + L_2 + 2m$$
$$L_T = L_1 + L_2 - 2m$$

L_T = total inductance (henrys)
$L_1 - L_2$ = individual coil inductance (henrys)
$+ 2m$ = mutual inductance, fields aiding
$-2m$ = mutual inductance, fields opposing

$$m = \frac{L_A - L_B}{4}$$

L_A = total inductance of L_1, L_2 with fields aiding
L_B = total inductance of L_1, L_2 with fields opposing

3.10-2   INDUCTORS IN PARALLEL

(A) Total Inductance of Two Inductors – No Mutual Inductance

(AC and DC application)

$$L_T = \frac{L_1 L_2}{L_1 + L_2}$$

$$* L_T = \frac{L}{N}$$

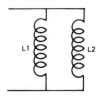

Figure 3-44

L_T = total inductance (henrys)
$L_1 - L_2$ = individual coil inductance (henrys)
L = one inductor's value
N = number of inductors
* used when inductors are the same value (henrys).

(B) Total Inductance of Two Inductors with Mutual Inductance

(AC application only)

$$L_{TA} = \frac{1}{\dfrac{1}{L_1 + m} + \dfrac{1}{L_2 + m}}$$

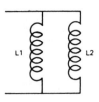

Figure 3-45

$$L_{TB} = \cfrac{1}{\cfrac{1}{L_1 - m} + \cfrac{1}{L_2 - m}}$$

L_{TA} = total inductance with fields aiding
L_{TB} = total inductance with fields opposing
$L_1 - L_2$ = individual coil inductance (henrys)
m = mutual inductance

(C) Total Inductance of Any Number of Inductors – No Mutual Inductance

(AC and DC application)

$$L_T = \cfrac{1}{\cfrac{1}{L_1} + \cfrac{1}{L_2} + \cfrac{1}{L_3} + \ldots}$$

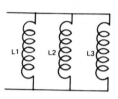

Figure 3-46

L_T = total inductance (henrys)
$L_1 - L_3$ = individual coil inductance (henrys)

(D) Total Inductance of Two Separated Coils with Mutual Inductance

(AC application only)

$$L_T = L_1 + L_2 \pm 2m$$

Figure 3-47

L_T = total inductance (henrys)
$L_1 - L_2$ = individual coil inductance (henrys)
m = mutual inductance

3.10-3   MUTUAL INDUCTANCE (AC APPLICATIONS ONLY)

$$m = \frac{L_A - L_B}{4}$$

$$m = K \sqrt{L_A L_B}$$

L_A = total inductance with fields aiding
L_B = total inductance with fields opposing
K = coefficient of coupling

3.10-4   COEFFICIENT OF COUPLING (AC APPLICATIONS ONLY)

(A) $K = \dfrac{m}{\sqrt{L_A L_B}}$

(B) $K = \dfrac{m}{\sqrt{L_P L_S}}$

K = coupling coefficient
L_A, L_B = individual coil inductance (henrys)
m = mutual inductance
L_P = primary's coil inductance (henrys)
L_S = secondary's coil inductance (henrys)

3.10-5   INDUCTANCE (AC AND DC APPLICATIONS)

(A) General

$$L = \frac{N}{I} \times 10^{-8}$$

L = inductance (henrys)
N = number of turns
I = current in amperes

(B) Single Layer-Air Core

$$L_T = \frac{R^2 N^2}{9R + 19\,(l)}$$

L_T = inductance in microhenrys
R = radius of coil (inches)
N = number of turns
l = length of coil (inches)

3.10-6   NUMBER OF TURNS REQUIRED (AC AND DC APPLICATIONS)

$$N = \sqrt{\frac{L[9R + 10\,(l)]}{R^2}}$$

N = number of turns
L = inductance in microhenrys
R = radius of coil in inches
l = length of coil in inches

3.10-7   NUMBER OF FEET REQUIRED (AC AND DC APPLICATIONS)

$$F = \frac{R_D}{R_G}\,(L)$$

F   = number of feet
R_D = desired resistance
R_G = resistance per given length
       (1000 feet normally)
L   = length used to determine
       resistance

3.10-8   ENERGY STORED IN AN INDUCTOR (AC AND DC APPLICATIONS)

$$W = \frac{LI^2}{2}$$

W = energy in joules
L = inductance in henrys
I = steady current in amperes

3.10-9   AVERAGE INDUCED VOLTAGE (AC APPLICATIONS ONLY)

(A) Into a Coil

$$e_{AV} = \frac{-N\,\Delta\,\Theta}{\Delta t} \times 10^{-8}$$

e_{AV} = average induced voltage
N   = number of turns in coil
$\Delta\Theta$ = change in flux (maxwell)
Δt = time increment given for flux
        change (seconds)

(B) From One Coil into Another

$$e_{AV} = -M \frac{\Delta i}{\Delta t}$$

e_{AV} = average induced voltage
M = coefficient of mutual inductance between coils
Δi = change in current (amperes)
Δt = time increment (seconds)

Note: The minus sign indicates that the induced voltage opposes the force that created it and may or may not be included in the equations.

3.10-10 COUNTER EMF ACROSS AN INDUCTOR (AC APPLICATIONS ONLY)

$$e_L = L \frac{\Delta i}{\Delta t}$$

e_L = instantaneous voltage (volts)
L = value of inductance (henrys)
Δi = change in current (amperes)
Δt = change in time (seconds)

3.11 MAGNETISM—ELECTROMAGNETS (AC APPLICATIONS ONLY)

3

A phenomenon often desirable in electronic circuitry is the generation of magnetic fields created when wire conductors and coils have current flow. The magnetism and electromagnetism terms encountered include magnetic poles, fields, force, flux, permeability, and hysteresis. Some of the formulas relating to these terms are given within this section of Chapter 3.

3.11-1 MAGNETIC FIELD INTENSITY

(A) General

$$H = \frac{F}{m}$$

* H = field strength in oersteds
F = force exerted on pole by the field
m = strength of pole

(B) Around Straight Conductor

$$H = \frac{2(I)}{10R}$$

* H = field strength (oersteds)
I = current flowing (amperes)
R = radius of conductor (centimeters)

(C) Long Coils

$$H = \frac{4 \pi NI}{10L}$$

* H = field strength (oersteds)
N = number of turns
I = current flowing (amperes)
L = length of coil (centimeters)

(D) Short Coils

$$H = \frac{2 \pi NI}{10R}$$

* H = field strength (oersteds)
N = number of turns
I = current flowing (amperes)
R = radius of coil (centimeters)

* Oersted unit is superseded by the metric unit ampere/metre.

3.11-2   FORCE BETWEEN TWO MAGNETIC POLES

$$F = \frac{M_1 M_2}{\mu d^2}$$

F = force
M_1 = strength of one pole
M_2 = strength of second pole
μ = permeability of medium
d = distance between the poles

3.11-3   PERMEABILITY

$$\mu = \frac{\beta}{H}$$

* μ = permeability
β = flux density
H = field density

* indicates ease with which magnetic lines of force flow in a magnetic circuit.

3.11-4   FLUX

$$\varnothing = \frac{mmf}{R}$$

$\varnothing$ = flux in maxwells (webers)
mmf = magnetomotive force in gilberts (ampere turns)
R = reluctance

3.11-5   MAGNETOMOTIVE FORCE

$$mmf = \frac{4 \pi NI}{10}$$

mmf = magnetomotive force
N = number of turns
I = current flowing

3.11-6   RELUCTANCE

$$R = \frac{L}{\mu A}$$

R = reluctance
μ = permeability
A = cross-sectional area in square centimeters
L = coil length in centimeters

3.11-7   FLUX DENSITY

$$\beta = \frac{\varnothing}{A}$$

β = flux density in gauss (Tesla)
$\varnothing$ = flux in maxwells (Webers)
A = cross-sectional area in square centimeters

3.11-8   FORCE EXERTED ON A CONDUCTOR

$$F = \frac{\beta\, IL}{10}\, \sin \Theta$$

F = force in dynes (Newtons)
β = field strength in gauss (Tesla)
I = conductor current in amperes
L = length of conductor in sq. centimeters
Θ = conductor's angle with the flux-field
    strength

3.12   METERS

An ammeter and voltmeter differ mainly in the circuitry design and component positioning within the meter's enclosure. If the meter serves as an ammeter, there will be a resistor or resistors in parallel (shunt) with the meter, while a voltmeter uses a resistor or resistors connected in series with the meter. Since series circuitry forms a voltage divider and parallel circuitry forms a current divider, only additional knowledge of Ohm's law needs to be applied when altering meter ranges. The useful data, formulas, and illustrations found in this section of Chapter 3 will help you design, troubleshoot, or modify your meter when the need arises.

3.12-1   METER SENSITIVITY

Sensitivity, when speaking about meter movements, is a term used to describe the current-voltage required for full-scale deflection. Sensitivity of a voltmeter is the ability a meter movement has that allows a small amount of voltage to be measured without loading or in any appreciable way disturbing the circuitry under test. This sensitivity is measured in units of ohms-per-volt, the amount of resistance required for a one-volt meter movement.

Voltmeters having good sensitivity begin around 20,000 ohms-per-volt. The following formulas can be used when determining meter sensitivity.

(A) Voltmeter

$$\frac{R}{E} = \Omega/V = \frac{Rm}{VF_s} \qquad\qquad \frac{R}{E}\ \text{or}\ \frac{\Omega}{V} = \text{ohms-per-volt}$$

(B) Ammeter

$$\frac{\Omega}{V} = \frac{1}{IF_s}$$

R_m = meter resistance
VF_s = full-scale reading voltage
IF_s = full-scale current reading

3.12-2   DETERMINING METER RESISTANCE

You can determine DC meter resistances using two variable resistors, a dc power source, and an ohmmeter, if you carefully apply the following hints. Construct the circuit illustrated in Figure 3-48, making certain the switch is open and R_1 is set for maximum resistance.

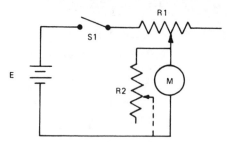

Figure 3-48

After making certain R_1 is set at maximum, close switch S_1 and adjust R_1 until the meter indicates full-scale reading; then connect resistor R_2 in parallel with the meter, adjusting it until the meter deflection is one-half its original full-scale reading. Open switch S_1, disconnect one side of R_2 from the circuit, and then measure the resistance of R_2. The value obtained represents the meter's resistance.

3.12-3   AMMETERS

Ammeter ranges can be extended by shunting the meter with a particular value resistor. To calculate the value for a shunt resistor, we must know the maximum current value to be measured and the maximum current required for full-scale deflection before applying Kirchhoff's current law. These concepts are as follows:

$$RS = \frac{Rm}{N-1}$$

$$RS = \frac{ImRm}{I_T - Im}$$

$$RS = \frac{ImRm}{I_s}$$

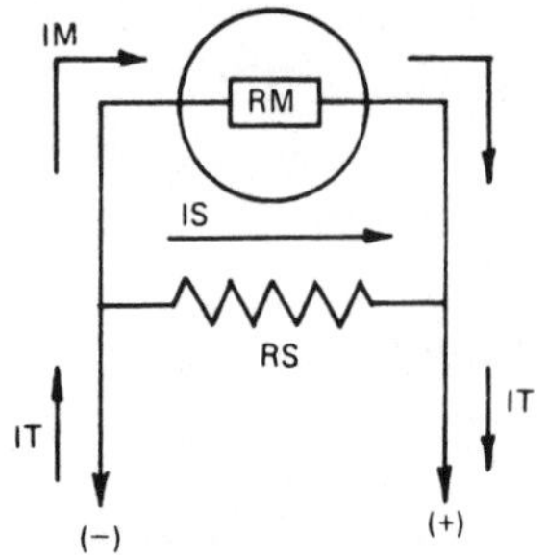

Rs = shunt resistor (ohms)

I_T = total current (amperes)

I_s = shunt resistor's current (amperes)   Rm = meter's resistance (ohms)

I_m = meter's full-scale current (amperes)   *N = scale multiplication factor

Figure 3-49

* This is the new full-scale reading divided by the original full-scale reading (both in same units).

3.12-4   VOLTMETERS

The series resistive circuitry commonly encountered within a voltmeter forms a voltage divider circuit. These resistors, called multipliers, are added to increase or extend the meter's voltage range. Since voltmeters are connected in parallel with voltage potentials, and because all circuitry currents flow through the multiplier resistors and then on through the meter, calculations needed when determining values for multiplier resistors are easily obtained using Ohm's law.

R_1, R_2 = multiplier resistors

R_m = meter resistance

E_{fs} = full-scale voltage

I_{fs} = full-scale current

For example:

R_m = 10 k Ω

E_{fs} = 10 volts

I_{fs} = 0.001 amperes

R_x = resistor for position #1

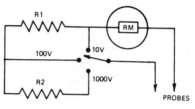

Figure 3-50

(A) General Formula, Position #1 (10 Volts)

$$R_X = \frac{E_{fs}}{I_{fs}} - R_m$$

$$R_X = \frac{10v}{1mA} - 10k\ \Omega = 10k\ \Omega - 10k\ \Omega$$

R_X = 0 ohms (none required because E_{fs} = 10 volts)

(B) General Formula, Position #2 (100 Volts)

$$R_1 = \frac{E_{fs}}{I_{fs}} - R_m = \frac{100v}{1mA} - 10k\ \Omega = 100k\ \Omega - 10k\ \Omega = 90k\ \Omega$$

OR

$$R_1 = R_m\ (N-1) \text{ where } N = \frac{\text{new voltage}}{\text{old voltage}}$$

$$R_1 = 10k\ \Omega\ \frac{(100 - 1)}{10} = 10k\ \Omega\ (9) = 90k\ \Omega$$

(C) General Formula, Position #3 (1,000 Volts)

$$R_2 = \frac{E_{fs}}{I_{fs}} - R_m + R_1 = \frac{1000v}{1mA} - 10k\ \Omega + 90k\ \Omega = 1M\Omega - 100k\ \Omega = 900k\ \Omega$$

OR

$$R_2 = R_m + R_1\ (N-1)\ \text{where}\ N = \frac{\text{new voltage}}{\text{old voltage}}$$

$$R_2 = 10k\ \Omega + 90k\ \Omega\ \frac{(1000-1)}{100} = 100k\ \Omega\ (9) = 900k\ \Omega$$

It should be noted from Figure 3-50, and from the formulas for each of the three positions denoting a voltage range increase from 10 volts to 100 volts and finally to 1000 volts, that the basic formula was modified somewhat for each range. You will need to add additional values of resistances to the basic formulas since a voltage divider action exists. To sum up this section on voltmeters, the third position formula would be:

$$\frac{E_{fs}}{I_{fs}} - R_m + R_1 + R_2\ \text{or}\ R_m + R_1 + R_2\ (N-1).$$

3.13   MODULATION (AC APPLICATIONS ONLY)

The data found in this section of Chapter 3 will highlight amplitude and frequency modulation. Since the terminology for modulation is similar, it will be pointed out prior to AM or FM formula particulars.

Modulation, whether it is amplitude, frequency, or phase, generates a new set or sets of radio frequencies that are symmetrically distributed around a carrier frequency.

When audio frequencies are used to control the amplitude of a carrier radio frequency, the general term used to describe this process is *amplitude modulation*.

Amplitude modulation creates frequencies that are actually sums and differences of the frequencies used. These two particulars, when generated, are called *beat frequencies*. The frequency sum is termed *upper side/sideband frequency* and the difference is the *lower side/sideband frequency*.

When the instantaneous values of the separate frequencies (lower and upper) are added together in modulation, a *modulation envelope* is created. The AM envelope resembles the amplitude variations of the signal used when modulating the carrier frequency. FM does not actually use the term envelope because after modulation there is no amplitude change, only a frequency change within the carrier's frequency amplitude.

The reference for frequency modulation is the unmodulated transmitter oscillator's frequency termed *center frequency*. When the modulating signal causes the frequency of the modulated wave to increase or decrease above or below the center frequency, the effect is called *frequency deviation* or *swing*. *Bandwidth* is the total frequency range that exists between minimal and maximal frequency deviations.

3.13-1   MODULATION FACTOR (AM AND FM)

(A) Amplitude Modulation (General)

$$M = \frac{Es}{Ec} \times 100$$

M = modulation factor (%)
Es = modulating signal amplitude
Ec = carrier signal amplitude

(100% modulation or less)

$$M = \frac{Emax - Emin}{Emax + Emin} \times 100$$

$$M = \frac{Emax - Emin}{2Eav} \times 100$$

M = modulation factor (%)
Emax = maximum amplitude of carrier
Emin = minimum amplitude of carrier
Eav = average amplitude

(more than 100% modulation)

$$M = \frac{Emax - Ec}{Ec} \times 100$$

M = modulation factor (%)
Emax = maximum amplitude
Ec = carrier amplitude

(B) Frequency Modulation

$$M = \frac{\Delta F}{\Delta F \, @ \, 100\% \, m} \times 100$$

M = modulation factor (%)
ΔF = frequency deviation

3.13-2   MODULATION INDEX (FM ONLY)

$$MI = \frac{Fd}{Fm}$$

$$\beta = \frac{\Delta f}{Fm}$$

MI, β = modulation index
Fd = frequency deviation
Fm = modulating frequency
Δf = frequency shift from unmodulated carrier

3.13-3   BANDWIDTH (AM AND FM)

(A) Amplitude Modulation

$$BW = 2FM$$

BW = bandwidth
FM = highest modulating frequency
β = modulation index

(B) Frequency Modulation

$$BW = 2FM (1 + \beta)$$

Note: AM has only one pair of sidebands; FM has several pairs. The modulation index indicates the number of FM sideband pairs; the higher the index, the more sideband pairs there are.

3.13-4   POWER (AM ONLY)

(A) Sideband Power

$$P_{sb} = \frac{M^2}{2} \times P_c$$

P_{sb} = sideband power (both sidebands)
M = percent of modulation
P_c = carrier power

(B) Total Radiated Power

$$P_T = P_{sb} + P_c$$

P_T = total power
P_{sb} = sideband power (both sidebands)
P_c = carrier power

3.14   MOTOR-GENERATOR-ALTERNATOR

The following data represents some of the more popular relied-upon information regarding motors. Delta, Star (Wye), constant horsepower and torque, and variable torque connections are listed, plus some important formulas which, if you have a need, might have instant application. The facts you are expected to know about the Star (Y) and Delta (Δ) configurations are as follows:

Star/Y (Wye)	Delta
$E_{phase} = \dfrac{E_{line}}{1.732}$	$E_{phase} = E_{line}$
$E_{line} = E_{phase} \times 1.732$	$I_{line} = I_{phase} \times 1.732$
$I_{line} = I_{phase}$	$I_{phase} = \dfrac{I_{line}}{1.732}$
$I_T = I_{line} \times 1.732$	$I_T = I_{line} \times 1.732$

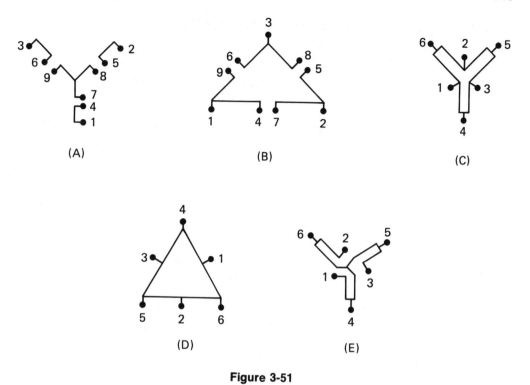

Figure 3-51

FIGURE	SPEED/VOLTAGE	LINE#1	LINE#2	LINE#3	OPEN	TIED
(A)	high voltage	1	2	3	-----	(4+7)(5+8)(6+9)
(A)	low voltage	1+7	2+8	3+9	-----	(4+5+6)
(B)	high voltage	1	2	3	-----	(4+7)(5+8)(6+9)
(B)	low voltage	1+6+7	2+4+8	3+5+9	-----	--------------
(C)	high speed	4	5	6	-----	(1+2+3)
(C)	low speed	2	3	1	4-5-6	--------------
(D)	high speed	4	5	6	1-2-3	--------------
(D)	low speed	2	3	1	-----	(4+5+6)
(E)	high speed	4	5	6	-----	(1+2+3)
(E)	low speed	2	3	1	4-5-6	--------------

3.14-1   ALTERNATOR OUTPUT FREQUENCY

$$F = \frac{P \times S}{60}$$

F = frequency (Hz)
P = number of pole pairs
S = speed of rotor (rpm)

3.14-2 ALTERNATOR VOLTAGE REGULATION

$$E_R = \frac{E_{NL} - E_{FL}}{E_{FL}} \times 100$$

E_R = percent voltage regulation
E_{NL} = no load voltage
E_{FL} = full load voltage

3.14-3 CURRENT RATING THREE-PHASE MOTOR

$$A = \frac{H.P. \times 746}{E \times 1.73 \times E_{FF} \times PF}$$

A = amperes
$H.P.$ = horsepower
E_{FF} = efficiency
PF = power factor
E = motor voltage

3.14-4 HORSEPOWER

$$H.P. = \frac{2\pi F \times R \times S}{33000}$$

OR

$$H.P. = \frac{T \times S}{5250}$$

$2\pi F = 6.28$
F = force (lbs)
R = radius (Ft)
S = speed (rpm)
R = torque (Ft lbs)
$H.P.$ = horsepower

3.14-5 INDUCTION MOTORS

(A) Motor Speed

$$S = \frac{F \times 120}{P}$$

S = speed (rpm)
F = frequency (Hz)
P = number of pole pairs

(B) Slip

$$S = S_S - F_L$$

S_S = synchronous speed (rpm)
F_L = full-load speed (rpm)
S = slip

(C) Percent Slip

$$\% \, S = \frac{S_S - F_L}{S_S} \times 100$$

3.14-6 MOTOR EFFICIENCY (PERCENT)

$$E_{FF} = \frac{P_O}{P_I} \times 100$$

E_{FF} = efficiency
P_O = power out
P_I = power in

3.14-7 SYNCHRONOUS MOTOR

(2 pole)

$$S = \frac{60 \times F}{P}$$

S = speed (rpm)
F = input voltage frequency
P = number of pole pairs

(4 pole)

$$S = \frac{120 \times F}{P}$$

3.14-8 TORQUE

$$T = \frac{H.P. \times 5250}{rpm}$$

T = torque
H.P. = horsepower
rpm = revolutions per minute

3.15 OHM'S LAWS VARIATIONS (DC APPLICATIONS ONLY)

3

3.15-1 VOLTAGE

$E = IR$

$E = \dfrac{I}{G} \; or \; E = \dfrac{I}{S}$

$E = \sqrt{PR}$

$E = \dfrac{P}{I}$

$E = \dfrac{W}{Q}$

E = voltage in volts
I = current in amperes
R = resistance in ohms
G = conductance in mhos
    (new metric unit of siemens)
P = power in watts
W = energy in joules
Q = quantity of electric charge (coulombs)

3.15-2 CURRENT

$I = \dfrac{E}{R}$

$I = EG \; or \; I = ES$

$I = \sqrt{\dfrac{P}{R}}$

$I = \dfrac{P}{E}$

3.15-3 RESISTANCE

$$R = \frac{E}{I}$$

$$R = \frac{P}{I^2}$$

$$R = \frac{E^2}{P}$$

3.15-4 POWER

$$P = IE$$

$$P = I^2R$$

$$P = \frac{E^2}{R}$$

Note: See section 3.2-4 for AC formulas.

3.16 OSCILLATORS (AC APPLICATIONS ONLY)

If one were to group the many existing oscillators into some meaningful classification, four specific groupings would probably evolve. One grouping would be classified according to circuitry, another would be based upon the output waveform obtained, the third would be according to the frequency of the generated wave, and the fourth might be according to the method used to excite the oscillator circuitry. One method, called impulse or shock excitation, produces oscillations when the duration of applied voltage is short in comparison with the duration of current produced. It should be pointed out that sharp contrasting differences defining each group would be very difficult to make because there are so many with similar characteristics.

Amplifiers and oscillators are also similar, since both require the amplification qualities offered by vacuum tubes, transistors or ICs. In order to have an oscillator, an amplifier will have a feedback loop through which positive voltages or currents are coupled back to the amplifier's input circuitry. The formulas relating to oscillators are as follows:

3.16-1 L-C OSCILLATOR

$$F_0 = \frac{1}{2\pi\sqrt{LC}}$$

$$F_0 = \frac{0.159}{\sqrt{LC}}$$

F_0 = output frequency (hertz)

L = value of inductor (henrys)

C = value of capacitance (farads)

3.16-2 PHASE SHIFT OSCILLATOR

$$F_0 = \frac{1}{2\pi \, RC\sqrt{6}}$$

F_0 = output frequency (hertz)
R = value of resistance (ohms)
C = value of capacitors (farads)

3.16-3 WIEN BRIDGE OSCILLATOR

$$F_0 = \frac{1}{2\pi \sqrt{R_1 C_1 R_2 C_2}}$$

$$* \, F_0 = \frac{1}{2\pi \, R_1 C_1}$$

F_0 = output frequency (hertz)
R_1, R_2 = resistances in arms (ohms)
C_1, C_2 = capacitance in arms (farads)

* use when $R_1 = R_2$ and $C_1 = C_2$

3.16-4 SHOCK-EXCITED OSCILLATOR SPECIFICS

(A) Merit of Oscillator Tank Circuit

$$Q = \frac{R_S}{X_L} = \frac{R_S}{X_C}$$

$$Q = \frac{R_S}{L/C}$$

Q = merit
R_S = shunt resistance (ohms)
X_L = inductive reactance (ohms)
X_C = capacitive reactance (ohms)
L = value of inductor (henrys)
C = value of capacitor (farads)

Note: At resonance
$$X_L = X_C = L/C$$

(B) Output Frequency When Q Equals 5 or Greater

$$F_0 = \frac{1}{2\pi \sqrt{LC}}$$

F_0 = output frequency (hertz)
L = value of inductor (henrys)
C = value of capacitor (farads)

(C) Output Frequency When Q Is Less than 5

$$F_0 = \frac{1}{2\pi \sqrt{LC}} \times \sqrt{1 - \left(\frac{1}{2Q}\right)^2}$$

F_0 = output frequency (hertz)
L = value of inductor (henrys)
C = value of capacitor (farads)
Q = merit

3.17 POWER (AC AND DC APPLICATIONS)

An important circuitry design factor used extensively in electronics is power. Some of the formulas used in DC applications do not apply to AC circuitry because of the complex nature of alternating current and circuit component characteristics. The data in this section of Chapter 3 will provide un-mistakable power results when selecting the right formula.

3.17-1   ELECTRICAL WORK

$$W = P \times T$$

W = energy in watt-hours
P = power in watts
T = time in hours

3.17-2   DC FORMULAS

$$P = IE$$
$$P = I^2R$$
$$P = \frac{E^2}{R}$$

P = power in watts
I = current in amperes
E = voltage in volts
R = resistance in ohms

3.17-3   AC FORMULAS

(A) Apparent Power

$$P = IE$$
$$P = I^2R$$
$$P = \frac{E^2}{R}$$

P = effective power in *watts
I = effective current in amperes
E = effective voltage in volts
R = resistance or impedance in ohms
* = (volt amperes)

(B) True Power

$$P = \frac{E^2 \cos \Theta}{Z}$$
$$P = IE \cos \Theta$$
$$P = I^2Z \cos \Theta$$
$$P = P_aP_f$$

P = true power in watts
E = voltage in volts
Cos Θ = power factor
Z = impedance in ohms
I = current in amperes
P_a = apparent power in *watts
P_f = power factor
* = (volt amperes)

(C) Current

$$I = \frac{P}{E \cos \Theta}$$

$$I = \sqrt{\frac{P}{Z \cos \Theta}}$$

I = current in amperes
P = power in watts
E = voltage in volts
Z = impedance in ohms
Cos Θ = power factor

(D) Impedance

$$Z = \frac{E^2 \cos \Theta}{P}$$

Z = impedance in ohms
E = voltage in volts
cos Θ = power factor
P = power in watts

(E) Voltage

$$E = \sqrt{\frac{PZ}{\cos \Theta}}$$

E = voltage in volts
P = power in watts
Z = impedance in ohms
cos Θ = power factor

3.18   POWER SUPPLIES

Power sources or power supply circuitry, being the heart of all electronic devices, tend to be the first place an electronic professional checks when particular symptoms arise. This is rightly so because without voltage applied (AC or DC) to active components, the electronic device is useless. The following facts, figures, and formulas will provide quick access to data necessary for power supply circuitry design or troubleshooting.

3.18-1   TERMINOLOGY

(A) Bleeders: This term describes a resistor whose purpose is to discharge capacitors in the power supply circuitry, thereby avoiding physical shocks when power is turned off. The resistor value is large, so small amounts of circuitry current are consumed. Normally, its value is based upon a current value of 10 percent or less of the total output current value.

(B) Input Resistance: This term is used when analyzing transformer impedances combined with rectifier resistances. Sometimes it is called input impedance or input resistance. The generalized formulas used, providing close approximations for half-wave and full-wave transformer type power supplies, are:

HALF-WAVE
$R_{in} = N^2 R_1 + R_2$

R_{in} = input impedance/resistance (transformer impedance plus rectifier resistance)
R_1 = primary resistance
R_2 = secondary resistance
N   = primary to secondary turns ratio

FULL-WAVE
$R_{in} = N^2 R_1 + R_2$

R_{in} = input impedance/resistance
R_1 = primary resistance
R_2 = one-half secondary total resistance
N   = primary to one-half secondary turns ratio

(C) Load or Output Resistance: This term, when talking about power supplies, defines the overall effect felt at the filter circuit, or specifically at the power supply's output terminals. Since circuitry connected to the output terminals requires so much current at so much voltage, the output resistance is easily calculated using Ohm's law.

$$R_L = \frac{E_O}{I_T}$$

R_L = load or output resistance
E_O = output voltage
I_T = total full-load current

(D) Peak Inverse Voltage: The voltage at which diodes will break down when not conducting is called peak inverse voltage (PIV), peak reverse voltage (PRV), breakdown voltage (BV), or something similar. It is the maximum voltage present or allowable on the anodes and cathodes of diodes when a reversed biased condition normally results. When buying diodes, note that one of the ratings will indicate this maximum potential before destruction.

Peak inverse voltage limits may be extended when diodes are placed in series, but their current limits must be adequate for circuitry demands. When diodes are connected in parallel, the peak inverse voltage is not extended, but additional amounts of current are obtainable.

(E) Ripple: To the untrained, it might seem that all electronic devices that plug into an alternating source operate on alternating current, but this is not always true. Electronic circuitry normally demands some amount of direct current potential to operate as designed; therefore, AC to DC rectification is necessary.

Ripple relates to the pulsations of AC which are superimposed on steady DC potentials. The measurement of power supply ripple tells the effectiveness of the filter circuitry. The ripple frequency depends upon the frequency of the line and the type of rectifier circuitry employed. The frequency for a half-wave power supply, for example, equals the line frequency, while the ripple frequency for a full-wave type circuit equals twice the line frequency.

(F) Voltage Regulations: A power supply not having some sort of voltage regulation is like an automobile not having any shock absorbers. A voltage regulator must absorb any changes in conditions and must try to keep voltage/current constant — without change. All power supply output potentials decrease as additional current is taken. Some design and test factor equations used are:

Percent of Regulation

$$\% R = \frac{E_{NL} - E_L}{E_L} \times 100$$

OR

$$\% R = \frac{E_{NL} - E_L}{I_L R_L} \times 100$$

OR

$$\% R = \frac{R_O}{R_L} \times 100$$

$\% R$ = regulation percent
E_{NL} = no load voltage (MIN I)
E_L = load voltage
I_L = load current (MAX I)
R_L = load resistance
R_O = output resistance

Output Resistance

$$R_O = \frac{E_{NL} - E_L}{I_L}$$

3.18-2   HALF-WAVE—ONE DIODE—TRANSFORMER TYPE

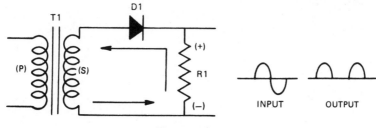

Figure 3-52

3.18-2A   Transformer (T_1) Specifics

(1) Primary Current

$$I_p = 1.57 \times \frac{I_{av} E_s}{E_p}$$

I_p = primary line current
I_{av} = average load current
E_s = secondary voltage
E_p = primary voltage

(2) Primary or Secondary Volt-Ampere Ratings

$$VA = 3.49 \times P$$

VA = volt ampere rating
      (rms voltage × rms current)
P = DC output wattage

(3) Secondary Current

$$I_s = 1.57 \times I_{av}$$

I_s = secondary line current
I_{av} = average output current

(4) Secondary Voltage

$$E_s = 2.22 \times E_{av}$$

E_s = secondary voltage
E_{av} = average output voltage

3.18-2B   Rectifier (D_1) Specifics

(1) Peak Inverse Voltage Rating

$$P_{IV} = 3.14 \times E_{av}$$
OR
$$P_{IV} = 1.41 \times E_s$$

P_{IV} = peak inverse voltage
E_{av} = average output voltage
E_s = secondary rms voltage

(2) Peak Current Value

$$I_D = 3.14 \times I_{av}$$

I_D = peak current of diode
I_{av} = average output current

(3) rms Current Value

$$I_D = 1.57 \times I_{av}$$

I_D = rms current of diode
I_{av} = average output current

3.18-2C   Output Voltage (E_{R_1}) Specifics

(1) rms Voltage

$$E = 1.57 \times E_{av}$$

E = rms output voltage
E_{av} = average output voltage

(2) Peak Voltage

$$E_p = 3.14 \times E_{av}$$

E_p = peak output voltage
E_{av} = average output voltage

3.18-2D   Ripple Frequency

$$F = F_s$$

F = ripple frequency
F_s = source or line frequency

3.18-3   FULL-WAVE—TWO DIODE—TRANSFORMER TYPE

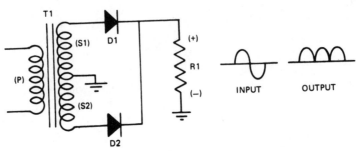

Figure 3-53

3.18-3A   Transformer (T_1) Specifics

(1) Primary Current

$$I_p = \frac{I_{av} \times E_{sl}}{E_p}$$

I_p = primary current
I_{av} = averge output current
E_{sl} = one-half secondary voltage
E_p = primary voltage

(2) Primary Volt-Ampere Rating

$$VA = 1.11 \times P$$

VA = volt-ampere rating
      (rms voltage times rms current)
P = output DC wattage

(3) Secondary Volt-Ampere Rating

$$VA = 1.57 \times P$$

VA = volt-ampere rating
P = dc output power

(4) Secondary Current

$$I_s = 0.707 \times I_{av}$$

I_s = secondary current
I_{av} = average output current

(5) Secondary rms Voltage

$$E_s = 2.22 \times E_{av}$$

E_s = total secondary voltage
E_{av} = average output voltage

3.18-3B   Rectifier (D_1, D_2) Specifics

(1) Peak Inverse Voltage Rating

$$P_{IV} = 3.14 \times E_{av}$$
OR
$$P_{IV} = 2.82 \times E_{sl}$$

P_{IV} = peak inverse voltage
E_{av} = average output voltage
E_{sl} = secondary rms voltage of ½ winding

(2) Peak Current Value

$$I_D = 1.57 \times I_{av}$$

* I_D = peak current value of diode
I_{av} = average output current
* either diode

(3) rms Current Value

$$I_D = 0.785 \times I_{av}$$

I_D = rms current value of either diode
I_{av} = average output current

3.18-3C   Output Voltage (E_{R_1}) Specifics

(1) rms Voltage

$$E = 1.11 \times E_{av}$$

E = rms output voltage
E_{av} = average output voltage

(2) Peak Voltage

$$E_p = 1.57 \times E_{av}$$

E_p = peak output voltage
E_{av} = average output voltage

3.18-3D   Ripple Frequency

$$F = 2 F_s$$

F = ripple frequency
F_s = source or line frequency

3.18-4   FULL-WAVE—FOUR DIODE BRIDGE—TRANSFORMER TYPE

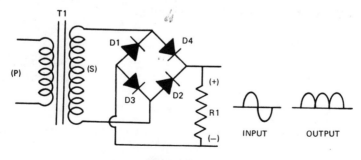

Figure 3-54

3.18-4A Transformer (T$_1$) Specifics

(1) Primary Current

$$I_p = \frac{I_{av} \times E_s}{E_p}$$

I_p = primary current
I_{av} = average output current
E_s = secondary voltage
E_p = primary voltage

(2) Primary and Secondary Volt-Ampere Rating

$$VA = 1.11 \times P$$

VA = volt-ampere rating
    (rms voltage times rms current)
P = output DC wattage

(3) Secondary Current

$$I_s = I_{av}$$

I_s = secondary current
I_{av} = average output current

(4) Secondary rms Voltage

$$E_s = 1.11 \times E_{av}$$

E_s = secondary voltage
E_{av} = average output voltage

3.18-4B Rectifier (D$_1$, D$_2$, D$_3$, D$_4$) Specifics

(1) Peak Inverse Voltage Rating

$$P_{IV} = 1.57 \times E_{av}$$
OR
$$P_{IV} = 1.41 \times E_s$$

P_{IV} = peak inverse voltage
E_{av} = average output voltage
E_s = rms secondary voltage

(2) Peak Current Value

$$I_D = 1.57 \times I_{av}$$

I_D = peak current value of any diode
I_{av} = average output current

(3) rms Current Value

$$I_D = 0.785 \times I_{av}$$

I_D = rms current value of any diode
I_{av} = average output current

3.18-4C Output Voltage (E$_{R_1}$) Specifics

(1) rms Voltage

$$E = 1.11 \times E_{av}$$

E = rms output voltage
E_{av} = average output voltage

(2) Peak Voltage

$$E_p = 1.57 \times E_{av}$$

E_p = peak output voltage
E_{av} = average output voltage

3.18-4D   Ripple Frequency

$$F = 2 F_s$$

F = ripple frequency
F_s = source or line frequency

3.18-5   FILTERS

Power supply filter circuits, designed to provide a practically unvarying DC potential by smoothing out pulsation, are classified into two groups. One group is called *capacitor input* type and the other a *choke input* type. Other terms relating to filter component configuration, such as *pi type, L type,* or *T type*, add variety and other filtering to the two main input capacitor and input choke filter classifications.

3.18-5A   Capacitor Input Types

(Chokes may be used in place of resistors)

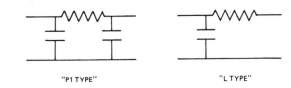

"P1 TYPE"   "L TYPE"

Figure 3-55

(1) Characteristics

Output voltage is high but poor regulation

(2) Input Capacitor Working Voltage

$$E_c = 1.41 \times E_s$$

E_c = working voltage at light or no load
* E_s = second voltage
* Use all of secondary for half-wave or full-wave center tapped transformer types of power supplies. Use one-half of secondary for full-wave bridge power supply.

3.18-5B   Inductor Input Types

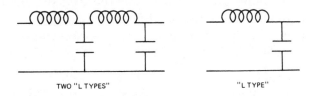

TWO "L TYPES"   "L TYPE"

Figure 3-56

(1) Characteristics

Low output voltage—good regulation

(2) Output Voltage

$$E_0 = \frac{0.9\,E_T - (I_b + I_L)(R_1 + R_2) - E_R}{1000}$$

E_T = rms voltage applied to rectifiers
E_0 = output voltage
I_b = bleeder current
I_L = load current
R_1, R_2 = choke resistance (DC)
E_R = voltage dropped across rectifier

(3) Ripple Value

$$\%R = \frac{100}{LC}$$

$\%R$ = ripple for single filter section with
　　　120 hertz frequency
L = value of inductor (henrys)
C = value of capacitor (farads)

Note: to reduce ripple to 5 percent or less, the product of LC must be 20.

$$\%R = \frac{650}{L_1 L_2\,(C_1 + C_2)^2}$$

$\%R$ = ripple for double filter section with
　　　120 hertz
L_1, L_2 = value of inductors (henrys)
C_1, C_2 = value of capacitors (farads)

(4) Value of Choke

$$L = \frac{R_L}{1000}$$

OR

$$L_1 = \frac{R_L}{1000} \times \frac{120}{F}$$

L = value of choke for 120 hertz filter (henrys)
R_L = load resistance (ohms)
L_1 = value of choke for other frequencies
R_L = load resistance
F = actual frequency value

3.18-6　POWER SUPPLY TROUBLESHOOTING SYMPTOMS

Locating circuitry malfunctions can be simplified by using component cause-effect analysis. The chart on page 230 outlines specific facts that relate to power supply components which might become defective. The chart is based upon two extremes, one of components being shorted and the other of components being open. The letter abbreviation usage is as indicated here:

NOR = normal　　　　　　　　PK (in) = peak of input DC voltage
LTN = lower than normal　　　PK (sec) = peak of secondary DC voltage
GTN = greater than normal　　IN (F) = input frequency

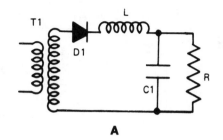

A

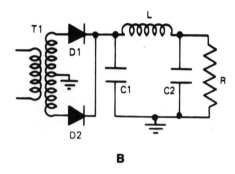

B

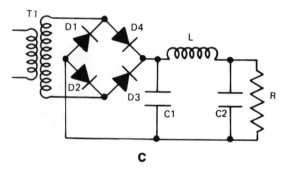

C

Figure 3-57

3.19   REACTANCE (AC APPLICATIONS ONLY)

The opposition to alternating current offered by circuitry having inductance or capacitance is called reactance. The letter symbol used to identify like
grouping of AC oppositions is the letter X. Whenever unlike AC oppositions are
encountered in the same circuitry, the total opposition is termed impedance and
is represented by the letter Z. The important formulas and data regarding reactance are outlined in this section of Chapter 3.

Defective Component	OUTPUT VOLTAGE			PEAK INVERSE VOLTAGE			RIPPLE AMPLITUDE			RIPPLE FREQUENCY		
	(A)	(B)	(C)	(A)	(B)	(C)	(A)	(B)	(C)	(A)	(B)	(C)
T_1 pr/sec open	OV.	OV.	OV.	OV.	OV.	OV.	0	0	0	0	0	0
T_1 pr/sec shorted	OV.	OV.	OV.	OV.	OV.	OV.	0	0	0	0	0	0
½ T_1 sec in Fig. B opens/shorts	—	½ NOR	—	—	NOR for 1 diode	—	—	GTN	—	—	½ NOR	—
D_1 or D_2 or D_3 or D_4 opens	OV.	LTN	filtered ½ wave	PK (in)	NOR	PK (sec)	None	GTN	GTN	None	½ NOR	Equals IN (F)
D_1 or D_2 or D_3 or D_4 shorts	ACV.	Low AC	filtered ½ wave	None	NOR for good diode	PK (sec)	Equals AC	Pk to Pk of output AC	GTN	Equals AC	Equals IN (F)	Equals IN (F)
D_1 and D_2 or D_3 and D_4 opens/shorts	—	—	OV.	—	—	None	—	—	None	—	—	None
"L" opens	OV.	OV.	OV.	None	NOR	None	None	None	None	None	None	None
"L" shorts	GTN	GTN	GTN	2 × PK input	NOR	PK (sec)	GTN	GTN	GTN	IN (F)	NOR	2 × PK input
"C₁" opens	LTN	LTN	LTN	PK (in)	NOR	PK (sec)	GTN	GTN	GTN	IN (F)	NOR	2 × PK input
"C₁" shorts	OV.	OV.	OV.	PK (in)	½ NOR	PK (sec)	None	None	None	None	None	None
"C₂" opens	—	LTN	LTN	—	NOR	NOR	—	GTN	GTN	—	NOR	NOR
"C₂" shorts	—	OV.	OV.	—	½ NOR	½ NOR	—	None	None	—	None	None
R opens	PK of DC	PK of DC	PK of DC	2 × DC PK	NOR	PK (sec)	None	None	None	None	None	None
R shorts	OV.	OV.	OV.	PK (in)	½ NOR	PK (sec)	None	None	None	None	None	None

230

3.19-1   FORMULAS

(A) Capacitive Reactance

$$X_C = \frac{1}{2\pi fC}$$

$$X_C = \frac{1}{\omega C}$$

$$X_C = \frac{0.159}{fC}$$

X_C = capacitive reactance (ohms)
f = applied frequency (hertz)
C = unit of capacitance (farads)
$\omega = 2\pi f$

(B) Inductive Reactance

$$X_L = 2\pi fL$$

$$X_L = \omega L$$

X_L = inductive reactance (ohms)
f = frequency (hertz)
L = value of inductor (henrys)

3.19-2   SERIES

(A) Same Kind

Figure 3-58

General: $X_T = X_1 + X_2 + X_3$ .. X_T = total reactance (ohms)
Capacitors: $X_{CT} = X_{C1} + X_{C2} + X_{C3}$ .. $X_1 - X_3$ = individual reactances (ohms)
Inductors: $X_{LT} = X_{L1} + X_{L2} + X_{L3}$ ..

Note: The letter Z for impedance may be substituted for either X_C or X_L since a combination of reactances is possible.

(B) Opposite Kind

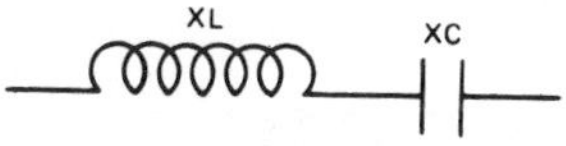

Figure 3-59

$$Z (\text{or } X_T) = X_L - X_C$$
$$Z (\text{or } X_T) = X_C - X_L$$

X_T = total reactance (ohms)
Z = total impedance (ohms)
X_L = inductive reactance (ohms)
X_C = capacitive reactance (ohms)

Note: resultant reactance is smaller than largest individual reactance.

3.19-3   PARALLEL

(A) Same Kind—Two Only

Note:

$$X_{CT} = \frac{1}{2\pi f\,(C_1 + C_2)}$$

$$X_{LT} = 2\pi f\left(\frac{L_1\,L_2}{L_1 + L_2}\right)$$

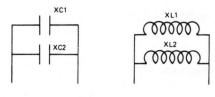

Figure 3-60

$$X_T = \frac{X_1\,X_2}{X_1 + X_2}$$

X_T = total reactance (ohms)
X_1, X_2 = inductive or capacitive reactance of individual components (ohms)

(B) Same Kind—More than Two

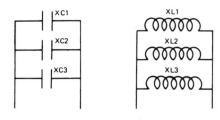

Figure 3-61

$$X_T = \frac{1}{\dfrac{1}{X_1} + \dfrac{1}{X_2} + \dfrac{1}{X_3} + \ldots}$$

X_T = total reactance (ohms)
X_1, X_3 = individual capacitive or inductive reactance of components (ohms)

(C) Opposite Kind

$$X_T = \frac{X_L\,X_C}{X_L - X_C}$$

X_T = total reactance (ohms)
X_C = capacitive reactance (ohms)
X_L = inductive reactance (ohms)

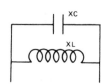

Figure 3-62

Note: resultant reactance is larger than smallest reactance

3.20   RESONANCE (AC APPLICATIONS ONLY)

Tuned circuits have only two components, inductors and capacitors, which are connected in series, parallel, or series-parallel. The inherent opposition characteristics of the reactive components change when the frequency applied increases or decreases. A condition called resonance exists when a specific frequency appears and causes the tuned circuit to lose its reactive property. The resonant frequency is determined by the value of capacitance and inductance in the circuit.

3.20-1   RESONANCE FORMULA

$$fr = \frac{1}{2\pi\sqrt{LC}}$$

$$fr = \frac{0.159}{\sqrt{LC}}$$

fr = resonant frequency (hertz)
L = value of inductor (henrys)
C = value of capacitor (farads)

3.20-2   QUALITY FACTOR (Q OR FIGURE OF MERIT)

(A) Series-Resonant Circuit

$$Q = \frac{X}{Rs}$$

Q = quality factor
Rs = series resistance (ohms)
X = reactance (X_L or X_C in ohms)

(B) Parallel-Resonant Circuit

$$Q = \frac{Z_R}{X}$$

Q = quality factor
Z_R = resistive impedance at resonance (ohms)
X = reactance (X_L or X_C in ohms)

3.20-3   SERIES AND PARALLEL LCR SUMMARY

	SERIES "LCR" CIRCUIT			PARALLEL "LCR" CIRCUIT		
	Above fr	fr	Below fr	Above fr	fr	Below fr
Circuit appearance	XL+R	R	XC+R	XC+R	R	XL+R
Circuit current	low	high	low	high	low	high
Circuit impedance	high	low	high	low	high	low
Current phase	lags voltage	in phase	leads voltage	leads voltage	in phase	lags voltage

fr = resonant frequency
XL = inductive reactance
XC = capacitive reactance
R = resistors resistance

3.21   THEOREMS

When application of Ohm's law, Kirchhoff's laws, and other general laws for series and parallel circuits seem difficult to use on complex circuits or networks, try using a method that will simplify the process—Thevenin's or Norton's theorem. Thevenin's theorem is used for a constant voltage basis, whereas Norton's theorem is used for constant current. When equivalent circuitry impedances are greater than 10 times the load resistance, Norton's equivalent circuit is generally used, and when the equivalent circuit is less than 10 times the load resistance, Thevenin's equivalent circuit is used.

3.21-1   THEVENIN'S THEOREM

Thevenin's equivalent circuit consists of an open circuit voltage called E_{TH} or V_{TH} and an open circuit impedance also called a *look-back resistance*, termed R_{TH}. The Thevenin voltage is divided between the Thevenin resistance and the load resistance. With this in mind, any two-terminal network having resistances and a source or sources may be replaced with a single source and single resistance equivalent. Figure 3-63 illustrates a single and multiple source circuit along with the Thevenin equivalent.

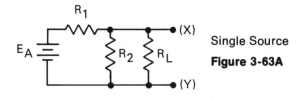

Single Source

Figure 3-63A

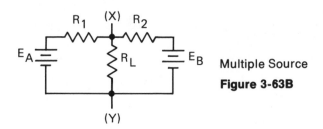

Multiple Source

Figure 3-63B

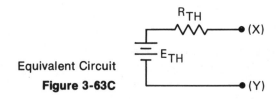

Equivalent Circuit

Figure 3-63C

You will note that the load resistor R_L, normally placed across the output terminals X and Y, is not shown in Figure 3-63C because it is not considered part of the equivalent circuit. This is an advantage, since current calculation using a number of different load resistors is possible without need of recalculation, as is the case using conventional methods. The following procedures and formulas are used when "Theveninizing" circuitry.

(1) Determine the voltage existing between the output terminals when the load resistor R_L is removed from the circuit. This is the Thevenin voltage.

(A) Single Source

$$E_{TH} = E_{R2} = \frac{E_A \times R_2}{R_1 + R_2}$$

(B) Multiple Source

$$E_{TH} = E_B - E_{R2}$$
OR $\quad * E_{TH} = E_A + E_{R1}$
* assuming E_B is larger than E_A potential.

(2) Mentally picture the source voltage or voltages with a short circuit across them with the load resistor R_L still disconnected from the circuit. Then determine the look-back impedance as seen from terminals X and Y.

(A) Single Source

$$R_{TH} = \frac{R_1 \times R_2}{R_1 + R_2}$$

(B) Multiple Source

$$R_{TH} = \frac{R_1 \times R_2}{R_1 + R_2}$$

(3) Determine load currents I_L using the equivalent circuit particulars of voltage (E_{TH}) and resistance (R_{TH}) in series with whatever load resistance you desire. The current formulas and the voltage developed across the load resistor equation are as follows:

(A) Single Source

$$I_L = \frac{E_{TH}}{R_{TH} + R_L}$$

$$E_{RL} = I_{RL} \times R_L$$

(B) Multiple Source

$$I_L = \frac{E_{TH}}{R_{TH} + R_L}$$

$$E_{RL} = I_{RL} \times R_L$$

3.21-2   NORTON'S THEOREM

Norton's theorem is much like Thevenin's in that entire networks consisting of voltages (sources) and resistors having two terminals for its output can be represented by an equivalent circuit. Norton, however, uses a constant current source I_N and one parallel resistance called R_N. The load resistor R_L is treated in the same manner as was the case in the Thevenin equivalent. It is not considered part of the Norton circuit. A single source and multiple source will be used for formula reference. See Figures 3-64A, B, and C.

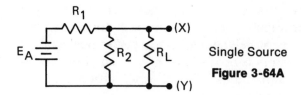

Single Source

Figure 3-64A

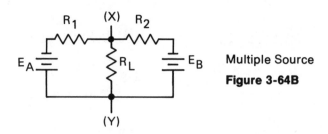

Multiple Source

Figure 3-64B

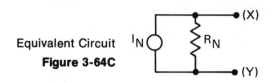

Equivalent Circuit

Figure 3-64C

(1) Determine the short circuit current (I_N) existing if the load terminals X and Y were shorted together.

<u>(A) Single Source</u>   <u>(B) Multiple Source</u>

$$I_N = \frac{E_A}{R_1}$$ $$I_N = \frac{E_A}{R_1} + \frac{E_B}{R_2}$$

(2) Mentally place a short circuit across the source or sources when the load resistor across terminals X and Y (the output) is removed. Determine the look-back impedance as seen from the output terminals.

<u>(A) Single Source</u>   <u>(B) Multiple Source</u>

$$R_N = \frac{R_1 \times R_2}{R_1 + R_2}$$ $$R_N = \frac{R_1 \times R_2}{R_1 + R_2}$$

(3) Using the equivalent circuit, and the I_N and R_N values, determine the current flow through the load (I_{RL}) and the voltage developed across the load (E_{RL}). These formulas are as follows:

(A) Single Source

$$E_{RL} = (I_N) \frac{R_N \times R_L}{R_N + R_L}$$

and $$I_{RL} = \frac{I_N \times R_N}{R_N + R_L}$$

OR $$I_{RL} = \frac{E_{RL}}{R_L}$$

(B) Multiple Source

$$E_{RL} = (I_N) \frac{R_N \times R_L}{R_N + R_L}$$

$$I_{RL} = \frac{I_N \times R_N}{R_N + R_L}$$

OR $$I_{RL} = \frac{E_{RL}}{R_L}$$

3.21-3   THEVENIN-NORTON THEOREM CONVERSIONS

(1) Norton to Thevenin

Resistance: $R_N = R_{TH}$

Voltage: $V_{TH} = I_N \times R_N$

(2) Thevenin to Norton

Resistance: $R_{TH} = R_N$

Current: $I_N = \dfrac{V_{TH}}{R_{TH}}$

3.22   TIME CONSTANTS (AC APPLICATIONS ONLY)

Circuitry having resistors, capacitors, and inductors exhibit charge and discharge time constant characteristics. Normally, these characteristics are based upon the circuit's ability to change from one steady state condition to another, simply termed DC-transient periods. The two general circuitry groups are resistor-capacitor (R-C) and resistor-inductor (R-L).

3.22-1   R-C CIRCUITS

(A) General Formula

TC = RC

TC = time constant (seconds)
R = value of resistance (ohms)
C = value of capacitance (farads)

Resistance Unit	Capacitance Unit	Time Constant Unit
Ohms	Farads	Seconds
Megohms	Microfarads	Seconds
Ohms	Microfarads	Microseconds
Megohms	Picofarads	Microseconds

General Units

The time constants required for the capacitor illustrated in Figure 3-65 to become fully charged (5-time constants) or discharged (5-time constants) as the case may be, are as shown: the calculations were based upon Figure 3-65 circuitry values, and time 0 represents the instant the switch is thrown.

Formula

$T_C = R_C$

$T_C = 1 + 10^{+5} (0.01 \times 10^{-6})$

* $T_C = 0.001$ sec $= 1$ millisecond

* one time constant (requires five time constants for full charge).

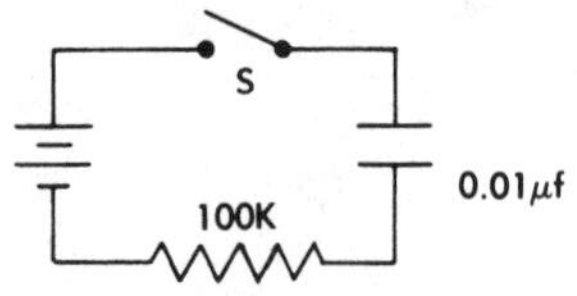

Figure 3-65

Time Constant	Time (milliseconds)	E_C (volts)	E_R (volts)	Current (ma)
0	0	0	100.00	1.000
1	1	63.20	36.80	0.368
2	2	86.46	13.54	0.1354
3	3	95.02	4.98	0.0498
4	4	98.17	1.83	0.0183
5	5	99.32	0.68	0.0068
6	6	99.75	0.25	0.0025

Note: At $T_C = 0$, the capacitor acts like a short circuit. At $T_C = 5$, the capacitor acts like an open circuit.

3.22-2   R-L CIRCUITS

(A) General formula

$$T_C = \frac{L}{R}$$

T_C = time constant (seconds)
L = value of inductor (henrys)
R = value of resistor (ohms)

Note: At $T_C = 0$, the inductor acts like an open circuit. At $T_C = 5$, the inductor acts like a short circuit.

3.23   WAVELENGTH AND WAVEGUIDE SPECIFICS

Different techniques, formulas, and applications are necessary when high frequency, namely frequencies in the microwave region, is employed. At this high frequency, component and circuitry characteristics differ greatly from those encountered in low frequency application. This section of Chapter 3 outlines those facts which adapt themselves readily to high frequency application.

3.23-1   VELOCITY OF PROPAGATION

(A) Meters

$$\lambda = \frac{300,000}{F}$$

OR

$$\lambda = \frac{300}{f}$$

λ = wavelength in meters
F = frequency in kilohertz
f = frequency in megahertz

(B) Feet

$$\lambda = \frac{300,000 \ (3.28)}{F}$$

OR

$$\lambda = \frac{984,000}{F}$$

OR

$$\lambda = \frac{984}{f}$$

λ = wavelength in feet
F = frequency in kilohertz
f = frequency in megahertz

3.23-2   VELOCITY FACTOR

$$V_F = \frac{Vm}{Vs}$$

* V_F = velocity factor
Vm = velocity of material (air, etc.)
Vs = velocity in space

* Always less than one

3.23-3   STANDING WAVE RATIO

$$* \ SWR = \frac{Z_R}{Z_O}$$

OR

$$* \ SWR = \frac{Z_O}{Z_R}$$

OR

$$SWR = \frac{I_{max}}{I_{min}}$$

OR

$$SWR = \frac{E_{max}}{E_{min}}$$

SWR = standing wave ratio
Z_R = impedance of load (pure resistance)
Z_O = characteristic impedance of line
I = maximum or minimum value of current
E = maximum or minimum value of voltage

* Larger value is the numerator

3.23-4   WAVEGUIDES WITH TE$_{01}$ MODES

In either the transverse electric (TE) or transverse magnetic (TM) modes of operation, subscripts are used to define the mode. An example would be TE$_{mn}$ where the m represents the first subscript and the letter n the second. Figure 3-66 should be referred to during waveguide-formula applications.

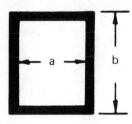

Figure 3-66

(A) Characteristic Impedances

$$Zo = \frac{465\,(a)}{b\sqrt{1 - \frac{(\lambda)^2}{(2b)}}}$$

OR

$$Zo = \frac{930\,(a)}{\sqrt{4b^2 - (\lambda)^2}}$$

OR

$$* \, Zo = 120\,\pi\,\frac{\lambda g}{\lambda}$$

* For TE and TM modes

Zo = characteristic impedance
a = short waveguide dimension
b = long waveguide dimension
λ = wavelength in space (air)
λg = wavelength in waveguide

(B) Waveguide Dimensions

$b = 0.7\,(\lambda)$
$a = 0.35\,(\lambda)$

b = long waveguide dimension
a = short waveguide dimension
λ = wavelength in space

(C) Sine and Cosine Functions for Wavefronts

1. Sine $\Theta = \dfrac{\lambda}{\lambda g}$

2. Sine $\Theta = \dfrac{Vg}{Va}$

Sin = trigonometric sine function
Cos = trigonometric cosine function
Θ = angle wavefront makes with
     waveguide wall

3. $\text{Sine } \Theta = \dfrac{V_a}{V_p}$

4. $\text{Cos } \Theta = \dfrac{\lambda}{2b}$

λ = wavelength in space (air)
λg = wavelength in waveguide
V_g = velocity in waveguide
V_p = phase velocity
b = long waveguide dimension
a = short waveguide dimension

(D) Wavelength

1. At Cutoff

$$\lambda c = \frac{2}{\sqrt{\left(\dfrac{m}{a}\right)^2 + \left(\dfrac{n}{b}\right)^2}}$$

OR

$$\lambda c = 2b$$

λ = wavelength in space
λg = wavelength in waveguide
λc = cutoff wavelength
m = first subscript in TE or TM mode designations
n = second subscript in TE or TM mode designations
b = long waveguide dimension
a = short waveguide dimension

2. In Free Space

$$\lambda = \frac{\lambda g}{\sqrt{1 + \left(\dfrac{\lambda g}{2b}\right)^2}}$$

OR

$$\lambda = \frac{(2b)(\lambda g)}{\sqrt{4b^2 + \lambda g^2}}$$

3. In Waveguide

$$\lambda g = \frac{\lambda}{\sqrt{1 - \left(\dfrac{\lambda}{2b}\right)^2}}$$

OR

$$\lambda g = \frac{2b\,\lambda}{\sqrt{(4b)^2 - (\lambda)^2}}$$

3

4

Technical Assistance Guide— Technology Update

4.1   CAPACITORS

(Refer to Sections 1.3-12, 13, and 14 for Schematic Symbols)

Capacitors are found in all sizes and shapes, all ranges of capacitance and temperature coefficients, and all types of dielectric materials. All of these facts, plus more, contribute to capacitor reputations; reputations established during standardized, agency-approved testing and in actual circuitry operation. The reputation established for each different capacitor type provides for three easy general classification groupings to exist. One classification is low loss-good stability, another is medium loss-medium stability, and the third is electrolytics. Capacitors found within the low loss-good stability and medium loss-medium stability groups are nonpolarized. It will not make any great electrical difference as to which end of these are connected where, unless circuitry shielding is important. If shielding is desired, keep the band-marked end at the negative-most part of its circuit function. Generally, capacitors with capacitances of less than one microfarad will be nonpolarized or not electrolytics. Electrolytics, which are polarized and have definite polarity, range from about one microfarad into the hundreds of thousands.

You will have several opportunities to practice the EIA color codes we had to memorize for resistors, since many capacitors also employ color coding methods. The capacitors use the same color-digit assignment, number of zeros to add (multiplier) and similar tolerance references. The following generalized data will be of assistance when encountering several different capacitor types.

Most capacitors present few problems when deciphering their capacitive value and working voltage rating. Ceramic types, paper types, plastic film types, and electrolytic types all have capacitive values in microfarads. All mica types and some disk-packaged type capacitors have capacitance values in micromicro-

Generalized Capacitor Data Meaning

Color	1st and 2nd Digit	Multiplier	Tolerance	Voltage	Characteristics	
Black	0	1	± 20%	—	A	NP0 **
Brown	1	10	± 1%	100V	B	N033
Red	2	100	± 2%	200V	C	N075
Orange	3	1000	± 3%	300V	D	N150
Yellow	4	10,000	± 4%	400V	E	N220
Green	5	—	± 5%	500V *	F	N330
Blue	6	—	—	600V		N470
Violet	7	—	—	700V		N750
Gray	8	0.01	—	800V	—	—
White	9	—	—	900V	—	—
Gold	—	0.1	± ½%	1000V	—	—
Silver	—	0.01	± 10%	—	—	P100

* Assume 500 volt rating if color is missing or voltage value is not imprinted on the capacitor.

** Three temperature characteristics exist: N = negative, P = positive, NPO = negative-positive-zero. N150 means minus or negative 150, which indicates that for every degree centigrade the temperature increases, the capacitance will decrease 150 parts per million, N570 rating produces a decrease of 750 parts per million per degree increase, etc.

Characteristic	Temp. Coefficient	Voltage Rating	Tolerance	Operating Temp.
A (NPO)	0 to +0	100	—	—
B (N033)	———————	250	—	—
C (N075)	−200 to +200	300	1pF	—
D (N150)	−100 to +100	500	0.5pF	—
E (N220)	− 20 to +100	600	—	—
F (N330)	0 to + 70	1,000	1%	—
G	———————	1,200	2%	—
H	———————	1,500	3%	—
J	———————	2,000	5%	—
K	———————	2,500	10%	—
L	———————	3,000	—	—
M	———————	4,000	—	−55 to +70
N	———————	5,000	—	−55 to +85

farads (mmF), now called picofarads (pF). The disk type capacitors generally can be separated into mF or pF after examining the printed data found on the capacitor. Normally, if a disk capacitor has a number equaling 1 or greater, the capacitor is rated in picofarads. If the disk has a number in decimal form less than one, the capacitor value is in microfarads. If you were to examine micro-farad-picofarad equivalents, you would see the reasoning in marking since different values require more space. Obviously it would take less space to print 1 or 1pF than 0.000001mF or 820pF instead of 0.00082mF. As the decimal equivalent approaches unity, you may find either 0.001mF or 1000pF used, but the division line exists here because 0.01mF is easier than its 10,000pF equivalent.

4.1-1   LOW LOSS—GOOD STABILITY

Capacitors grouped within this classification include mica, glass, some ceramics, and plastics. The variations within each specific type allow choices of manufactured capacitors because they are: small, temperature-stable, tubular, disk, multiple-sectioned, or a substriate, a plug in, a monolithic, a trimmer, a feed-through or have spark gaps, axial leads, specific, or general purpose applications.

It would be almost impossible to cover all characteristics pertinent to every low loss-good stability capacitor type, but the following data provides the capacitive value and normal DC operating voltages for each type listed.

4.1-1A   Mica

Capacitance Range—1pF to 100,000pF (0.01μF)
Voltage Range—50V to 35K VDCW

Normally, if packaging is dipped or encapsulated, manufacturer identification, capacitor value in pF, voltage rating, and temperature coefficient are stamped on the capacitor if space allows. Sometimes, letters and numbers are used; if so, the letters denote fixed mica-dielectric, while the numbers describe dimensions and physical size. The standard tolerance is J ($\pm$ 5%) while the minimum standard is F ($\pm$ 1%).

When molded case styles of packaging are used, color code interpretation is necessary. Figure 4-1 illustrates which dot-color positioning means what.

4.1-1B   Glass/Quartz

Capacitive Range—50pF to 0.005mF
Voltage Range—1 V to 300 V

This particular type, mostly used for trimmers, may be rectangular or cylindrical in shape, having axial leads if rectangular, and special lead design if for panel mounting or printed circuit mounting. Typical temperature coefficients range from 0 to 140.

4.1-1C   Ceramics

Often, these capacitors are called disk, penney, or simply ceramics. Some of the various types include low voltage, high voltage, general purpose, across line, spark arrestors, RF, feed-through or monolithics. Each is rated in

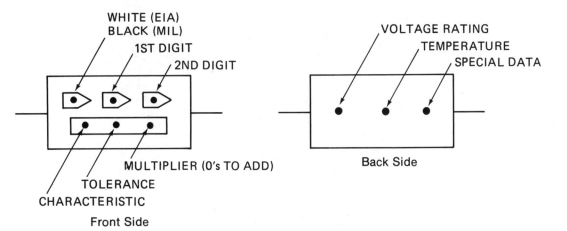

Front Side

Note: Sometimes they will have number codes to identify capacitive value. For example, 391 = 390pF, 100 = 10pF.

The 1st and 2nd digits are significant digits; the 3rd digit indicates how many zeros to add.

Sometimes the letter R will appear; this indicates where the decimal point will appear. For example, 4R7 = 4.7pF.

Figure 4-1

picofarads (pF) and usually follows a three-digit code. The first two digits represent the first two significant numbers, while the third digit indicates the number of zeros to add; IE 683 = 68000pF = 0.068mF. Sometimes, when the value of capacitance is less than 10, the first digit is a zero or a letter R will be used to indicate decimal point position; IE 075 = 0.75pF or R75 = 0.75pF whereas 3R3 = 3.3pF, etc. Sometimes manufacturers express capacitance values in microfarads and if so, the first digit indicates the number of zeros that proceed the significant figure; IE 382 = 0.00082mF = 820pF. Confusion may result unless you have a pretty good idea of popular capacitance values.

	Capacitive Range	Voltage Range
General Applications	0.5pF to 0.1mF	3V to 7.5KV
High Voltage	100pF to 1000pF	10K V to 40KV
RF (transmitting)	3pF to 1000pF	5K V to 40KV
Feed Through	0.5pF to 3000pF	100 V to 600 V
Multi-layer/monolithic	1pF to 6.8mF	50V to 200V

Markings for ceramic dielectric capacitors normally include company trademarks, capacitance value, temperature coefficient, voltage, and tolerances on disk and tubular capacitors if space permits. Feed-through capacitors, being of the symmetrical, eyelet, bushing, or tubular variety, are normally marked by

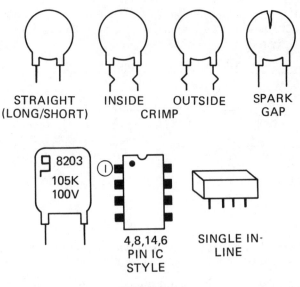

STRAIGHT   INSIDE   OUTSIDE   SPARK
(LONG/SHORT)   CRIMP   GAP

8203
105K
100V

4,8,14,6   SINGLE IN-
PIN IC   LINE
STYLE

Figure 4-2

colors instead of printed data. A single band at one end of ceramic tubular capacitors indicates the inner electrode connection. Some popular packaging styles are illustrated in Figure 4-2.

4.1-1D   Plastics

	Capacitive Range	Voltage Range
Polystyrene	5pF to 10mF	100V to 2KV
Polystyrene-Polyester	0.001mF to 1mF	50V to 1KV

Generally speaking, capacitor type plastics within these capacitive ranges have excellent characteristics that are independent of applied frequencies. Packaging styles vary somewhat among manufacturers, but company trademarks, capacitances, tolerance and voltage ratings are usually printed on the capacitor body. The color coded end, or black band end, normally identifies the outside foil lead, but this same marking has also been used for inner lead identification.

4.1-2   MEDIUM LOSS—MEDIUM STABILITY

This grouping includes paper, plastic film, and high K ceramic capacitor types. The paper type has been largely replaced by plastic film varieties, but still is excellent for high AC and DC voltage applications. The plastic film types include polystyrene, polyester, and polycarbonates, the latter being smaller in physical size. High K type ceramics, sometimes called temperature-compensating ceramics, were designed mainly for bypass and coupling applications since their use for these purposes would not affect normal circuitry operation.

4.1-2A   Paper Types

	Capacitive Range	Voltage Range
General Application	0.001mF to 200mF	50V to 200KV
Paper-Polyester	0.001mF to 30mF	100V to 15KV
Paper-Metallized	0.001mF to 125mF	50V to 600V
Metallized Paper-Polyester	0.001mF to 20mF	200V to 600V

Paper types usually cost less than other capacitors suitable for the same applications. The physical size, however, may limit their use in electronic circuitry. Normally, their shapes are tubular. Manufacturer identification, capacitance, voltage rating, and other possible markings will be found printed on their bodies.

4.1-2B   Plastic Film Types

	Capacitive Range	Voltage Range
Polyester	100pF to 20mF	50V to 1KV
Metallized Polyester	0.01mF to 20mF	50V to 600V
Polycarbonate	0.001mF to 20mF	50V to 600V
Metallized Polycarbonate	0.01mF to 5mF	50V to 600V
Epoxy Coated	0.001mF to 2mF	100V to 2KV
Polystyrene	100pF to 0.2mF	25V to 500V

Capacitor types using plastic film dielectrics have dipped, film wrap, molded, or ceramic encasements. Printed data on each capacitor identifies the manufacturer, capacitance (PF), and voltage range plus tolerances. Outer foil lead is usually identified by a color coded end or black line. Polystyrene types may have a color band end whose color indicates its working voltage limits. Black represents 500V DC, red = 125V DC, yellow = 50V DC and blue = 25 Volts DC.

4.1-2C   High K Ceramics

	Capacitive Range	Voltage Range
General Application	1.5pF to 0.001mF	500V to 1000V

High K or temperature compensating capacitors usually are manufactured as disk types, having specific temperature change ratings. Temperature coefficients identification of NPO (negative, positive, zero) designate the amount of temperature changes in parts-per-million-per-degree centigrade or ppm / °C. This particular reference is for stable types having negligible temperature effects.

The letter N or a minus sign indicates a decrease in capacitance, while a P or plus sign means an increase. A positive temperature coefficient of 450 means the capacitance will increase 450/1,000,000 or 0.045 percent for each degree Celsius temperature rise. A negative temperature coefficient means a decrease in capacitance with a rise in temperature. Capacitance value (PF), voltage, capacitive and temperature tolerances are usually found imprinted on the capacitor.

4.1-3   ELECTROLYTICS

Some of the options available for electrolytic capacitor selection are as follows: choice of low or high terminal posts, with screw or solderable connectors or a bus type terminal; phenolic or metal case; cylindrical, tubular or rectangular shape; military or nonmilitary; polarized or nonpolarized; twist prong or printed circuit mount; single, dual, triple or quad section; axial, radial, insulated or noninsulated leads; liquid or solid; color coded or stamped; hermetic or elastomeric seal.

Capacitors normally having the highest capacitance per volume unit rating are called electrolytics. This term is given to any capacitor whose dielectric layer is formed using electrolytic methods. Some of the capacitors within this group may not contain an electrolytic as such, but manufacturing processes common to both are used.

Two distinct types of electrolytic capacitors are commonly found in electronic circuitry, they are:

1. Aluminum oxide dielectric capacitors, being 99.9 percent reliable, have a shelf life from about 6 months to 5 years, after which reforming is necessary.

2. Tantalum oxide dielectric capacitors, smaller physically and not having shelf life limitations. *All electrolytic capacitors are polarized and must be installed properly to avoid damage.*

4.1-3A   Aluminum Oxide

	Capacitive Range	Voltage Range
cylindrical	1mF to 600,000mF	3V to 1000V
tubular	0.047mF to 100,000mF	3V to 7.5KV

The electrolytic capacitors of the aluminum oxide dielectric type are obtainable with axial leads, tubular or cylindrical in shape, having plug-in sockets, pins which can be soldered, (twistlock) or screw-tightened connections. Cylindrical types can be single capacitors, double, triple, quadruple, or quintuple. At any rate, polarity of potentials must be observed: negative reference voltages to the negative leads, and positive potentials to the positive leads.

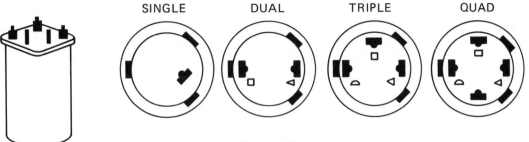

Figure 4-3

Stamped or printed data found on electrolytic capacitors denote manufacturers by name or trademark, identification numbers used in stocking or catalog use, possible temperature rating, capacitance and voltage values, plus polarity markings.

Single element electrolytics usually do not have any reference markings on the terminal end (as evidenced in Figure 4-3). For the others, we must interpret imprinted values on the can and match them to specific terminals on the underside. Dual, triple and quadruple element capacitors usually follow a systematic identification method which also matches imprinted capacitor value data found on the case. The symbols ◠ and ☐ normally represent the highest voltage or highest capacitance value housed in the dual, triple and quadruple cans. The symbols used to denote the next highest voltage or capacitance terminal in the dual, triple, or quad capacitor is the △ and ☐. The lowest value of voltage or capacitance in the triple element can is a blank —, just a line, or the △, whereas the third capacitive element in a quad section can is usually the △. The fourth capacitive element in the quad type electrolytic can capacitor is usually a blank — or line, and is normally the lowest value of voltage or capacitance.

4.1-3B   Tantalum Oxide

	Capacitance Range	Voltage Range
Epoxy dipped	0.1mF to 1000mF	3V to 100V
Molded-solid	0.001mF to 330mF	2V to 200V
Nonpolarized	0.001mF to 160mF	6V to 200V
Liquid	1mF to 2,400mF	6V to 1000V
Foil (polarized)	0.25mF to 2,500mF	2V to 500V
Foil (nonpolarized)	0.01mF to 2,000mF	2V to 300V

Tantalum dielectric electrolytic capacitors vary in size, shape, and encasement styles. You will encounter cylindrical, tubular, rectangular, domino, or taper type shapes plus epoxy dipped, metal encased, hermetically sealed, or foil types. The epoxy dipped solid tantalum capacitor offers tough epoxy coating, low cost, long life electrical stability, smallness in size, high capacitance per given unit size, and low impedance. These capacitors are generally rated in picofarads (pF) and are generally color coded, although some have values imprinted on their cases. If a three-digit numbering system is employed, the first two numbers represent the first two digits having significant value, while the third digit represents the number of zeros to add to the multiplier. Therefore, 563 on a capacitor of this type indicates 56,000pF which, of course, equals 0.056mF. Figure 4-4 illustrates physical size, shapes, and color coding methodology commonly employed.

The liquid electrolyte tantalum capacitor is also called a "wet slug," "gelled electrolyte," or "sintered anode," and may be cylindrical in style, having base metal or plastic film insulation with a hermetic seal. It should be noted with caution that the dielectric may be sulfuric acid under pressure and SHOULD NOT be opened or dismantled. DO NOT apply reverse voltage; DO

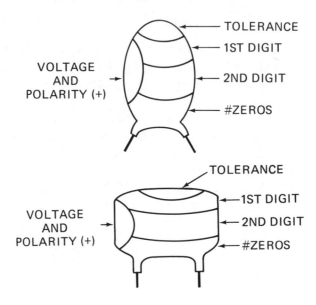

Color Code	Voltage @ 85°C	1st digit	2nd digit	Multiplier
Black	4VDC	0	0	——
Brown	6VDC	1	1	——
Red	10VDC	2	2	——
Orange	15VDC	3	3	——
Yellow	20VDC	4	4	$\times 10^4$
Green	25VDC	5	5	$\times 10^5$
Blue	35VDC	6	6	$\times 10^6$
Violet	50VDC	7	7	$\times 10^7$
Gray	——	8	8	——
White	——	9	9	——

Note: If no tolerance dot exists, the tolerance is ± 20%; silver dot is ± 10%; gold dot is ± 5%

Figure 4-4

NOT exceed temperature ratings; DO NOT exceed rated working and surge voltages, and DO NOT apply ripple or current in excess of specified limits.

Some of the present manufactured solid tantalum type capacitor styles and deciphering information is shown in Figure 4-5.

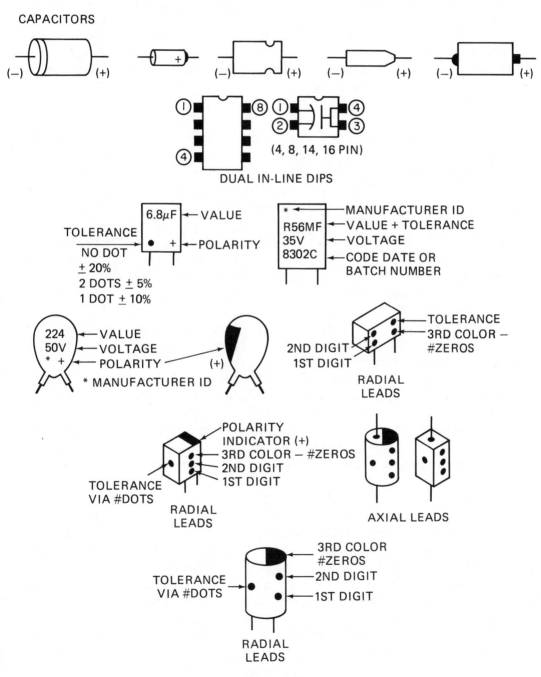

Figure 4-5

4.1-4   CAPACITOR TESTING

Two vitally important characteristics of capacitors provide common sense troubleshooting methods. The characteristics common to DC capacitors are: blocking action offered to DC voltages, and passing action offered to AC voltages.

The DC blocking characteristic is possible because, once the capacitor charges to the applied potential, it remains at that potential. The AC passing characteristic is a result of capacitor discharge and recharge when varying signals affect circuitry operation.

4.1-4A   Ohmmeter Testing

Ohmmeter circuitry design, consisting of a DC voltage source and voltage divider (resistive) circuitry, enables us to use the time constant or charge time—discharge time meter readings as a primitive capacitor test. If a capacitor, one lead removed from the circuit with power off, is discharged and then checked with an ohmmeter, a meter needle rise and fall (kick) should be observed when charging and discharging the capacitor via ohmmeter battery supply voltage. To do this, connect the ohmmeter leads across the capacitor to charge, then reverse the leads to discharge. A small rise-fall meter needle indication should result for small-valued capacitors. Electrolytic capacitors will provide greatest meter deflection because of their large capacitive value.

As a general rule, since the larger the capacity, the larger the kick, smaller-valued capacitors from 0.1mF into picofarads will require higher ohms multiplier settings, while higher capacitances would require lower multiplier settings because of charge-discharge times and meter deflection responses. It is normal, when electrolytic capacitors are checked, for the needle to peg because of discharge (lead reversal), but do not allow it to remain pegged. Drop to a smaller multiplier (another time constant) to avoid meter damage. Normally, a capacitor is defective when it does not show a rise-fall indication, or indicates a constant resistance (providing the multiplier is not in megohms, etc). A better test naturally is using a capacitor tester, or by substitution.

4.1-4B   Voltmeter Testing

Capacitors usually fail in three general ways: (1) failure because of break in leads inside encasement, (2) failure because of dielectric breakdown causing shorting action, (3) failure because of leakage due to dielectric deterioration, a step just before shorting action. Naturally, capacitor failure symptoms cause various things to happen depending upon their use in the circuit. Voltage checks will aid when troubleshooting circuitry if your theory is up to date.

If you suspect a leaky capacitor, DC voltages will no doubt be passed through the capacitor. One way to find out is by removing one end of the capacitor from the circuit (keep the hot DC lead connected), and then connect a DC voltmeter from the free end to the circuitry ground. Any DC voltage present indicates a leaky condition because capacitors are supposed to block DC voltage. Bypass capacitors going to ground can mess up voltage checks because of shorts or leaky conditions also, so to be sure which one is guilty; cut or unsolder one of its leads, thereby removing any doubt.

4.1-4C   Capacitor Shunting

The best way to check a capacitor thought to be defective is by substitution with a known good one, but this requires added work and perhaps a loss in valuable time. Capacitor shunting is a method often used to verify a defective capacitor. Since capacitors connected in parallel in effect add capacitance, leaky or open capacitors can be found quicker. All capacitors used when shunting other capacitors must have the same working voltage rating or higher. It is necessary to observe and match polarity markings for all electrolytic capacitors. Capacitors of the nonelectrolytic types need not be polarity matched. However, to be professional, replace the capacitor with the same value and in the same polarity connection.

4.1-5   CAPACITORS (AC AND DC APPLICATIONS)

The one component used in electronics, that has the ability "to pass alternating current or pulsating direct current voltages and blocks unchanging or direct current voltages" is the capacitor. The capacitor can and does store energy in the form of an electric field which exists between its plates when voltage is applied. The following rules, facts, and formulas are those we rely upon daily in the electronics profession.

4

4.1-5A   Total Capacitance for Two Series Capacitors (AC and DC Applications)

$$C_T = \frac{C1 \times C2}{C1 \times C2}$$

The same unit of capacitance must be be used; microfarads, micromicrofarad (now pF), etc.

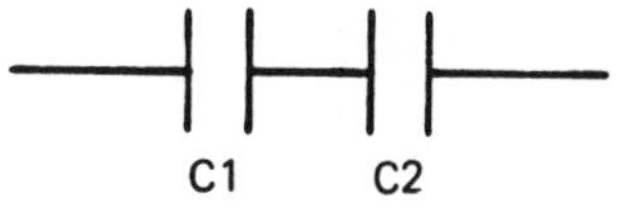

C1   C2

Figure 4-6

4.1-5B   Total Capacitance for Any Number of Capacitors in Series (AC and DC Applications)

$$C_T = \cfrac{1}{\cfrac{1}{C1} + \cfrac{1}{C2} + \cfrac{1}{C3} + \ldots}$$

Same unit of capacitance must be used.

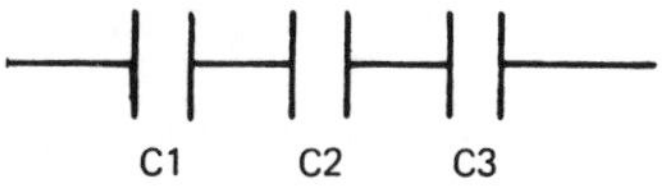

C1   C2   C3

Figure 4-7

4.1-5C   Voltage Across Capacitor When Capacitors Are in Series (DC Applications Only)

$$E_{cx} = \frac{E_A\,(C_T)}{C_x}$$

E_{cx} = desired capacitor's voltage
E_A = applied DC voltage
C_T = total circuitry capacitance
C_x = desired capacitor's value

E_{cx} is inversely proportional to its capacitive value.

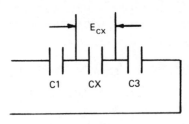

Figure 4-8

4.1-5D   Total Capacitance for Capacitors in Parallel (AC and DC Applications)

$C_T = C_1 + C_2 + C_3 + \ldots$
C_T = total capacitance
C_1-C_3 = individual capacitances

Largest voltage safely applied equals smallest voltage rating of the capacitors.

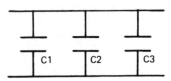

Figure 4-9

4.1-5E   Capacitor's Plate Capacitance (AC and DC Applications)

When area of one plate (A) and dielectric thickness (D) are both in inches, use the first formula.

$$C = 0.2235\,\frac{(KA)(N\text{-}1)}{D}$$

C = plate capacitance in picofarads
K = dielectric constant
A = area of one plate (Sq. inches)
D = dielectric thickness (inches)
N = number of plates

When the area of one plate (A) and dielectric thickness (D) are both in centimeters, use this formula:

$$C = 0.0884\,\frac{(KA)(N\text{-}1)}{D}$$

C = plate capacitance in picofarads
K = dielectric constant
A = area of one plate (square centimeters)
D = dielectric thickness (centimeters)
N = number of plates

4.1-5F   Energy Stored in a Capacitor (DC Applications)

$$W = \frac{CE^2}{2}$$

W = energy in joules (watt-seconds)
C = capacitance in farads
E = applied voltage

4.1-5G   Charge Stored in a Capacitor (DC Applications)

$$Q = CE_c$$

Q = charge in coulombs
C = capacitance in farads
E_c = voltage across capacitor

4.1-5H   Total Charge on Capacitors in Series (DC Applications)

$$Q_T = Q_1 = Q_2 = Q_3$$

Q = charge in coulombs

4.1-5I   Total Charge on Capacitors in Parallel (DC Application)

$$Q_T = Q_1 + Q_2 + Q_3 + \ldots$$

Q = charge in coulombs

4.1-5J   Quality Factor, Q, or Figure of Merit for Capacitors (AC Applications)

For single capacitor:

$$Q = \frac{X_c}{R}$$

Q = reactance-resistance ratio
X_c = capacitive reactance in ohms
R = resistance which acts in series
with capacitor (in ohms)

For a capacitor in series with a resistor:

$$Q = \frac{1}{2\pi f RC}$$

OR

$$Q = \frac{1}{\omega RC}$$

Q = reactance-resistance ratio
f = frequency in hertz
R = total resistance in ohms
C = total capacitance in farads
ω = $2\pi f$

For a capacitor in parallel with a resistor:

$$Q = 2\pi f RC$$

OR

$$Q = \omega RC$$

Q = reactance-resistance ratio
f = frequency in hertz
R = total resistance in ohms
C = total capacitance in farads
ω = $2\pi f$

4

4.1-5K   Capacitive Circuit Steady Current Flow (AC Applications)

$$I = \frac{E_A}{X_C}$$

OR:

$$I = \frac{E_A}{\dfrac{1}{2\pi fC}}$$

OR: $I = E_A (2\pi FC)$

I = steady current flow in amperes
E_A = applied voltage in volts
X_C = capacitive reactance in ohms
C = capacitance of applicator

ω may be substituted for $2\pi f$ in the formulas

4.1-5L   Force Between Two Charges (AC and DC Applications)

$$F = \frac{Q_1 Q_2}{KD^2}$$

F = electrostatic force between plates
Q_1, Q_2 = magnitude of charges
K = dielectric constant
D = distance between plates

4.1-5M   Electric Field Intensity (AC and DC Applications)

$$E = \frac{Q}{KD^2}$$

E = electric field intensity
Q = quantity of charge
K = dielectric constant
D = distance between plates

4.1-5N   Electric Field Strength (AC and DC Applications)

$$F_s = \frac{V}{D}$$

F_s = field strength
V = potential difference
D = distance moved

4.1-5O   Force on Q in Electric Field (AC and DC Applications)

$$F = EQ$$

F = force
E = strength of electric field
Q = magnitude of charge

4.1-5P   Potential Energy of Charged Capacitor (AC and DC Applications)

$$PE = \frac{1}{2} CV^2$$

OR

$$PE = \frac{Q^2}{2C}$$

PE = potential energy
C = value of capacitance
V = potential difference
Q = quantity of charge

4.1-5Q   Value of Capacitance (AC and DC Applications)

$$C = \frac{Q}{V}$$

C = value of capacitance
Q = quantity of charge
V = potential difference

4.1-5R   Tuning Capacitor's Shunt Capacitance (AC Application Only)

$$C_S = \frac{C_1 F}{2W}$$

C_S = shunt capacitance
C_1 = tuning capacitor's capacitance
(change range)
F = low frequency band limit
W = width of frequency band

4.2   DIACS
(Refer to Section 1.10-14 for Schematic Symbols)

The unique solid state device commonly called *Diode Alternating Current*, or DIAC, is basically a two-terminal, bidirectional device which has several schematic symbols. One symbol uses two anodes like emitters in a transistor, but having no base terminal, while other symbols use two diode-like lead configurations. The diac is manufactured in one of two forms called: (1) biodirectional diode thyristor and (2) biodirectional trigger diode. Regardless of the manufactured form, both have almost identical characteristics and will be grouped together for clarity.

4.2-1   VOLTAGE DROP

The diac allows current to flow in either a forward or reverse direction when its breakover voltage (V_{BR} or V_{BO}) is reached. Once breakover is reached in either direction, the diac offers a negligible amount of resistance. In other words, the diac voltage drop decreases rapidly once at breakover voltage, since its resistance changes and thereby allows large amounts of current to flow.

4.2-2   PACKAGING
(Refer to Section 1.9 for Standards)

Among the many triggering applications for diac employment is a usefulness for a surge or transient voltage suppressor. The diac might also be called a "triac trigger." This term, however, may limit its usefulness since it also is used to trigger SCRs. The diac physically would resemble a common diode packaged in the DO-15 packaging style for the triac and SCR trigger type, while a TO-92, or TO-98 packaging would be typically found when the diac is used for phase control applications. The TO-92 and TO-98 styles resemble a transistor, except that only two leads protrude and are used. Diac specifications follow a somewhat uniform standard, meaning that the terminology is almost common.

4.2-3   SPECIFICATION SHEET TERMINOLOGY

1. Material listing — silicon
2. Diac dissipation called P_D in watts.
3. Breakover voltage — both forward and reverse minimum and maximum values called V_{BO}, V_{BR}.
4. Peak breakover current called I_{BO} measured in microamps.
5. Peak output current called ipK measured in milliamps.
6. Case style — (DO-15, TO-92, TO-98, etc.)

4.3   DIODES

Semiconductors in the particular diode family grouping may be made of copper sulfide, selenium, germanium, silicon, and perhaps other materials, depending upon their electronic circuitry function. (Refer to Sections 1.3-27, 1.10-6, 9, 10, 15, 28, 36, 39, 42, 46, 51, and 57 for Schematic Symbols.)

4.3-1   IDENTIFICATION — GENERAL PURPOSE

General purpose diodes are normally identified by an IN letter prefix, either understood, or in print on the diode, plus a series of numbers. Germanium diodes of the glass variety use the resistor color code to describe its number. The IN letter prefix is not usually printed on the diode, nor is its numerical value. The color code relates the numerical value. In some cases, suffixes added to the end (fifth band color position) of the diode, i.e., IN5885A denote voltage tolerances. In most cases, if no suffix is used, a ±20 percent tolerance is indicated. A suffix means ±10 percent (color-brown); B suffix means ±5 percent (color-red), C means ±2 percent (color-orange), and D suffix means ±1 percent (color-yellow). The glass type color code and suffix meanings are found in Figure 4-10.

4.3-2   TESTING

Testing general purpose diodes can be accomplished using an ohmmeter since high resistance should result when reversed-biased (negative on the anode and positive on the cathode), and low resistance is measured when forward-biased (cathode is negative and the anode is positive). The greater the difference in forward and reverse bias when testing via ohmmeter, the more often than not the better the diode. Normally, a ten-to-one ratio when on RX1000 is acceptable. Be sure of your ohmmeter polarity of the probes, because in some meters,

DIODES

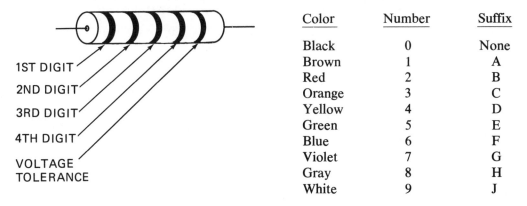

Color	Number	Suffix
Black	0	None
Brown	1	A
Red	2	B
Orange	3	C
Yellow	4	D
Green	5	E
Blue	6	F
Violet	7	G
Gray	8	H
White	9	J

1ST DIGIT

2ND DIGIT

3RD DIGIT

4TH DIGIT

VOLTAGE
TOLERANCE

Figure 4-10

the black lead normally thought to be negative may not be the negative side of the battery used for ohmmeters in present use. To accomplish this, take a diode that you know to be good, one that has the cathode end clearly marked, and place the black lead on the cathode, and the red lead on the anode. If your meter uses battery negative for the black lead and battery positive for the red lead, then the good diode's resistance will be low. If, however, this is not the case on your meter, the red lead must go to the cathode and its black lead to the anode. This knowledge is a must when evaluating a transistor for NPN or PNP—good or bad conditions.

4.3-3   PACKAGING
(Refer to Section 1.9 for Standards)

In the past, diodes have seldom been confused with other components. Today, however, because of packaging standards or the lack thereof, some confusion exists. Common diode case styles are:

(1) DO-1, DO-7, DO-8, DO-9, DO-21, DO-27, DO-41 (standard, little confusion)

(2) DO-4 and DO-5—diodes, also Schottky

(3) DO-15—diodes, also diacs

(4) DO-35—diodes, also varactors

(5) TO-92—diodes, also diacs

4.3-4   IN SERIES

Diodes may be placed in series to increase the peak-inverse-voltage rating; the current rating stays the same.

4

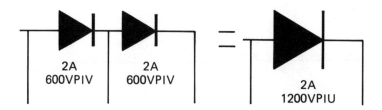

Figure 4-11

4.3-5   IN PARALLEL

Diodes may be placed in parallel to increase the current rating; the peak-inverse-voltage stays the same.

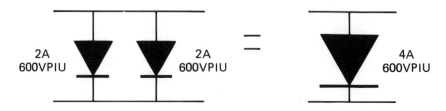

Figure 4-12

4.3-6   TYPICAL ELECTRICAL CHARACTERISTICS—GENERAL PURPOSE

V_{RRM}, V_{RM} – also called peak reverse voltage (PRV) or peak inverse voltage (PIV). This means what the maximum repetitive value of voltage the diode can withstand when it is *not* conducting (V_{RSM} is nonrepetitive).

V_{BR} – also known as reverse breakdown voltage (R_{BV}). This indicates the *minimum* reverse voltage at which the diode may break down.

I_O, I_{FAV}, I_F – also known as "steady state forward current," or "average rectified forward current." This is a value telling of *maximum* continuous currents for which the diode can be used. (I_{FAV} is average current.)

I_{FSM}, I_{FM} – also known as "peak surge current" or simply "surge current." It describes the surge current capability for the diode. (I_{FSM} is maximum surge.)

I_R – also called "static reverse current" or "reverse saturation current." These are facts for a diode under controlled temperature and bias voltage (in μA).

V_F – this is the static forward voltage drop across the diode. It is a value representing the *maximum* forward drop at a specified temperature and at a selected *maximum* continuous current value.

P — also termed "continuous power dissipation." It is the value of maximum wattage—power the diode can dissipate safely.

S_1 — silicon material.

Ge — germanium material.

4.4 FIELD-EFFECT TRANSISTORS
(Refer to Sections 1.10-17, 18, 21, and 31 for Schematic Symbols)

The unipolar device called field-effect transistor (FET) offers more advantages for today's technology than do conventional bipolar junction transistors of the NPN or PNP variety. The FET, to begin with, offers lower noise effects, has higher input impedances, requires fewer biasing components, and has lasted longer with few burnout failures. The conventional NPN and PNP bipolar junction type transistors depend on electron charge carriers and hole charge carriers for circuitry operation, whereas the FET has but one charge carrier which may be either positive or negative. Even the action by which current is controlled is different from that of the bipolar PNP or NPN junction variety. The FET controls current by way of an electric field—hence the name field effect.

4.4-1 TERMINAL IDENTIFICATION

The basic FET has three terminals or elements: a gate (G), drain (D), and source (S). There are, however, FETs with more than one gate, making them ideal for special circuitry functions. The gate acts like the control grid in a triode vacuum tube or the base in a conventional PNP or NPN transistor. It affects current flow between the source and drain terminals or vice versa. The element from which current flows is termed the "source." When thinking about this, picture a water faucet—*the source of water*—and then picture *the drain in the sink catching the water*. The drain of the FET is the element through which current is gathered and passed onto the rest of the circuitry. Often, the drain and source terminals may be interchanged with no direct change in the device's normal operation. This is common in junction field-effect transistors (JFET) and is referred to as being symmetrical. Nonsymmetrical FETs indicate that the drain and source cannot be interchanged.

4.4-2 TESTING

Ohmmeter readings for JFET testing are good for gate identification, since diode type resistance readings will appear high or low depending on lead polarity when one of the three leads happens to be the gate. Ohmmeter indications, preferably VTVM types, should tell, via resistance readings, source and drain terminals of an FET, since their resistances between each other will be the same regardless of lead switching. The remaining lead (out of three) will be the gate.

4.4-3 TYPES

The field-effect transistor types normally are referred to by general gate structure. There are two basic types: junction field effect (JFET) for one, and metal-oxide-semiconductor field-effect transistor (MOSFET) along with the insulated gate field-effect transistor (IGFET) for the second type. Each type has two family groups further divided into the N-channel FET, which requires a negative voltage for gate biasing, and the P-channel FET, which requires a positive voltage for gate biasing. FETs also have three modes of operation: (1) depletion only, (2) enhancement only, and (3) enhancement and depletion combination. To clarify these two family groups (N-channel and P-channel) and the three modes of operation, consider these:

1. In an N-channel FET, the gate requires a positive bias to increase current flow (enhancement) and requires a negative bias to decrease current flow (depletion).
2. In a P-channel FET, the gate requires a negative bias to increase current flow (enhancement) and requires a positive bias to decrease current flow (depletion).
3. The *depletion only* mode is referred to as type A on data sheets. It indicates that no forward gate voltage is used for a maximum drain current.
4. The *enhancement only* mode is referred to as type C on data sheets. It essentially means that little or no drain current flows at zero gate voltage; drain current is allowed when a forward bias gate voltage is applied; a point called its threshold voltage (whose symbol is $V_{GS(TH)}$).
5. The *depletion and enhancement* mode is referred to as type B on data sheets. It has considerable amounts of drain current at zero gate voltage, but not as much as for type A. Forward gate voltage increases current flow while reverse gate voltage reduces current flow.

4.4-4 PACKAGING
(Refer to Section 1.9 for Standards)

Some of the common TO prefix numbers for FET packaging styles that you will find in use today are: TO-18, TO-71, TO-72, TO-76, TO-92, TO-98, and TO-202. Most of these are used for general FETs as well as JFETs while VMOS (vertical metal-oxide-semiconductors) have used the TO-92 and TO-202 structures. The VMOS is essentially a power FET having high impedance and voltage drive capabilities plus elimination of most thermal runaway conditions. It has been past practice, although not standardized, to have the vertical metal-oxide-semiconductor (VMOS) begin with the letter V or Vn prior to part numbers. In like manner, the JFET usually begins with the 2N prefix, whereas the IGFET begins with a 3N prefix. In each case, these semiconductors may use the letter N or P for channel designations, meaning that the gate bias is different, depending upon the channel type.

4.4-5 JFET CIRCUITRY CONFIGURATIONS

The JFET, like vacuum tubes, and the junction type NPN or PNP transistors, may be connected in three different modes of operation or circuitry configurations. As you will recall, vacuum tubes used the common cathode, common grid, and common plate (cathode follower), while the transistors of the PNP and NPN variety used the common emitter, common base, and common collector (emitter follower). Three similar amplifier configurations are used with FETs, each one having advantages and disadvantages, as did each configuration in tubes and junction transistors. The circuitry and notes for the FET amplifier configurations are as follows:

4.4-5A Common Source

C_1, C_4 = coupling capacitors
C_2, C_3 = bypass capacitor
R_2 = source resistor
R_3 = drain load resistor

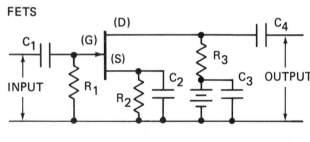

Figure 4-13

The common source (CS) is the equivalent of a common emitter (CE) transistor circuit, offers high input impedance, and a moderately high output impedance. It is by far the most widely used FET amplifier configuration. The common source amplifier produces a 180-degree phase shift between input and output. The P-channel FET has the same characteristics.

4.4-5B Common Gate

C_1, C_4 = coupling capacitors
C_3 = bypass capacitor
R_1 = source resistor
R_2 = drain load resistor

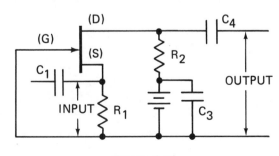

Figure 4-14

The common gate (CG) is the equivalent of the common base (CB) junction transistor configuration. It has a very low input impedance but a high output impedance. The voltage gain is approximately equal to that of the common source. The common gate FET amplifier offers *no* phase inversion; that is, the input and output signals are in phase. It also offers low circuit capacitance, which makes it useful as a high frequency amplifier.

4.4-5C   Common Drain

C_1, C_4 = coupling capacitors
R_2, R_3 = voltage divider
C_3 = bypass capacitor

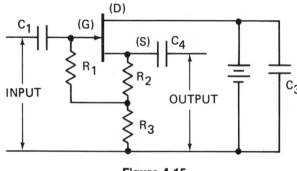

Figure 4-15

The common drain (CD), called the source follower, is the equivalent of a common collector (CC) junction transistor circuit. It offers a gain of nearly unity, has a high input impedance with a low output impedance, thus making it an excellent impedance-matching device. The input and output signals are in phase.

4.4-6   IGFET

The insulated gate field effect transistor (IGFET) offers a very high impedance regardless of the gate voltage polarity, whereas the junction field-effect transistor (JFET) depended upon reverse bias at the gate junction for its high impedance. This type and MOS types are very easily damaged via electrostatic charges; they require special handling. Handle them by the case, not the leads; also, ground the soldering iron. They are normally shipped with the leads shorting together, or grounded by a shorting ring. Some manufacturers build in zener diodes to protect the gate from static discharge, but don't assume complete protection.

4.4-7   SUBSCRIPT NOTATION

Subscripts must be thoroughly understood, since this will prove to be invaluable when working with FETs. It is common for subscripts to denote specific pieces of data or facts. It is also common to see the drain-source voltage indicated by V_{DS} or the gate-source voltage as V_{GS}. It is obvious we are speaking of voltage—the letter V and letters D (drain) and G (gate). You will also note that the second subscript for each is the letter S for the source. You will sometimes find that three subscripts may be used; I_{GSS} will be used to define the triple subscript idea. Letter I indicates we are speaking of currents; the first subscript letter G tells us gate, the second letter S tells us it is the source, and finally, the third subscript, letter S, indicates to the trained individual that it is shorted condition. But shorted to what? Note that the I_{GGS} referred to the gate and source (first and second subscripts) while the Drain (letter D) was not used in any way. This is the secret! It is to the *not mentioned* element to which connections are made. Hence, I_{GGS} means we are talking about gate leakage or gate-source current with the drain (letter not shown) tied or shorted to the source.

4.4-8   JFET TERMINOLOGY

BV_{DGO}	drain to gate breakdown voltage (V)
BV_{GSO}	gate to source breakdown voltage (V)
BV_{GSS}, $BR(GS)$	gate to source breakdown voltage (V)
C_{dgo}	drain to gate capacitance (pF)
C_{gso}	gate to source capacitance (pF)
C_{ISS}	input capacitance (pF)
C_{is}/C_{rs}	gate capacitance (pF)
C_{RSS}	reverse transfer capacitance (pF)
E_n	input noise voltage (pV)
$g_{FS}/R_e(Y_{FS})$	forward transconductance (μ mhos)
G_m	transconductance (μ mhos)
I_D/I_G	forward gate/drain max. current (nA)
I_{DGO}	drain to gate leakage current (nA)
I_{DSS}	drain current at zero gate volts (mA)
I_{DSX}	drain current under specific conditions (μA-mA)
I_{GSO}	gate to source leakage current (nA)
I_{GSS}	gate leakage-reverse current (nA)
I_{GX}	gate leakage under specific conditions (nA)
I_n	input noise current (pA)
MMHOS	common source forward transfer current
N_F	common source noise figure (dB)
O_{TC}	zero temperature coefficient
P_T/P_D	maximum device dissipation
R_{DS}	*ON* resistance-zero gate voltage (Ω)
td$_{(OFF)}$	turn off delay time
td$_{(ON)}$	turn on delay time
V_A	avalanche voltage
V_{DS}	drain to source voltage
V_{GSS}/V_{GS}	gate to source voltage

4

$* V_{GS (OFF)}$ .... gate to source cutoff voltage
$* V_p$ .... pinch-off voltage
Y_{FS} .... forward transadmittance
Y_{is} .... common source input admittance
Y_{OS}/G_{OS} .... output admittance

* Essentially the same — measured differently.

4.4-9   JFET FORMULAS

4.4-9A   Voltage Gain

$$A = \left(\frac{G_m}{I_{DSS}} \right) \left(\frac{BV_{DGO}}{V_p} \right)$$

A = voltage gain
G_m = transconductance
I_{DSS} = maximum drain current
BV_{DGO} = drain to gate breakdown
                voltage
V_p = pinch-off voltage

(Common Gate)

$$A \cong gm\ R_D$$

gm = transconductance also called
        transadmittance (Y_{FS}) *
R_D = drain load resistor resistance
Y_{FS} = transadmittance
$\triangle I_D$ = drain current change
$\triangle V_{GS}$ = gate-source voltage change

$$* Y_{FS} = \frac{\triangle I_D}{\triangle V_{GS}}$$

(Common Source)

$$A \cong -gm\ R_D$$

Note: The unit mho or siemens is generally too large for most Y_{FS} specifications, therefore μ mho or μ siemens (μS) is used. Since Y_{FS} specification for a FET is similar to transconductance (gm) of a vacuum tube, some manufacturers use gm instead of Y_{FS} to represent transadmittance (forward transfer admittance). The higher the value, the greater the amplification ability of the FET.

4.4-9B   Amplification Factor (μ)

$$\mu = \frac{\triangle V_{DS}}{\triangle V_{GS}} \text{ with } I_D \text{ constant}$$

μ = amplification factor
$\triangle V_{DS}$ = drain-source voltage change
$\triangle V_{GS}$ = gate-source voltage change

Note: Often, the amplification factor is *not* given on FET data sheets; this is calculated by using $\mu = \dfrac{Y_{FS}}{Y_{OS}}$

The output impedance can be calculated in like manner since output impedance equals: $Z_{out} = \dfrac{1}{Y_{OS}}$

4.4-9C   Distortion

$$D = \frac{V_p}{V_S}$$

D = distortion
V_p = pinch-off voltage
V_S = signal voltage

4.4-9D   Drain Resistance at Pinch-off

$$r_d = \frac{\Delta V_{DS}}{\Delta I_D} \text{ with } V_{GS} \text{ constant}$$

r_d = drain resistance
ΔV_{DS} = drain-source voltage change
ΔI_D = drain current change

4.4-9E   Frequency Cutoff

$$F_{co} = \frac{Gm}{Crs}$$

F_{co} = cutoff frequency
Gm = transconductance
Crs = gate capacitance

4.4-9F   Input Impedance

$$Z_{IN} = \frac{1}{I_{GSS}} + \frac{1}{C_{is}}$$

Z_{IN} = input impedance
I_{GSS} = gate leakage
C_{is} = gate capacitance

4

4.4-9G   *ON* Resistance

$$R_{DS} \cong \frac{V_p}{I_{DSS}}$$

R_{DS} = *ON* resistance
V_p = pinch-off voltage
I_{DSS} = maximum drain current

4.4-9H   Output Admittance

$$Y_{OS} = \frac{\Delta I_D}{\Delta V_{DS}} \text{ with } V_{GS} \text{ constant}$$

Y_{OS} = output admittance
ΔI_D = drain current change
ΔV_{DS} = drain-source voltage change

Note: Like transadmittance (Y_{FS}), the output admittance (Y_{OS}) is commonly expressed in micromhos or microsiemens.

4.4-9I   Pinch-off Voltage

$$V_p \cong \frac{2\, I_{DSS}}{Gm}$$

V_p = pinch-off voltage
I_{DSS} = maximum drain current
Gm = transconductance

4.4-9J   Switching Efficiency

$$S_E = \frac{R_{DS}}{I_{GSS}}$$

S_E = switching efficiency
R_{DS} = *ON* resistance
I_{GSS} = gate leakage

4.5   FUSES AND CIRCUIT BREAKERS

An inexpensive insurance investment for any electronic device is a properly selected and installed fuse or circuit breaker. Like most insurance policies, there is one just right for your particular need. Fuses are described according to their relationship between the current value flowing through them and the time it takes for its interrupt function to occur. The common terminology used to describe fuse types is (1) "fast acting," "quick acting," "high speed" or "instrument"; (2) "standard," "non-time delay", "normal lag," "normal" or "medium lag"; (3) "time delay," "time lag," "slow acting," or "slow blow." Each type, obtainable in differing current carrying capacities, will protect electronic circuitry if the fuse interrupt-time element is fast enough.

4.5-1   VOLTAGE-CURRENT FUSING RATINGS

All fuses have specific voltage and current and fusing ratings. All of these ratings apply to each group—the slow-acting, medium-acting, fast-acting and very fast-acting—regardless of physical size variations. These fuses are placed in series with the device or circuitry intended to be protected. They all basically are for overcurrent protection. Whenever the current-carrying ability of the fuse is exceeded, the fuse opens and will stop overcurrents and will withstand the arcing voltage and open circuit voltages. A defective fuse will have very high resistances (infinity—open) while a good fuse will measure very low resistance—nearly zero ohms when using a X1 multiplier.

You will find letters and numbers etched, printed, or in some way indicated on the fuse body. The letters denote a particular package style (AGX, MDL) whereas the number relates to amperage expressed in amperes (rms), although not always indicated as amps (A). For example, AGC 1¼A indicates it is a 1¼ amp fuse and the MDL 20 is a 20 amp fuse. Usually, you will find the voltage for the particular fuse imprinted on the opposite end. This voltage is not the ability the fuse has to withstand its rated voltage, but is a maximum or less than maximum voltage expressed in volts. *Do not, under any circumstances,* use a fuse rated at lower voltages than the voltage applied to the fused circuitry, regardless of its amperage rating. The voltage rating for the fuse should be equal to or greater than the circuit voltage. Also, *do not* assume a fuse is rated at the "same past-practice" or the "one you always use" value of voltage, because it may have changed with new technology demands. Perhaps you could have bought a 3AG10 rated at 125 volts, but now it is called AGC10, rated at 32 volts.

The voltage rating is an Underwriters Laboratory (UL) guarantee for fire risk. It indicates that the fuse will safely open without arcing or exploding in a short circuit situation when the voltage is equal to or less than the rated voltage. The UL test generally includes both amperage and short circuit conditions; normally when 110%, 135%, and 200% of their rated amperage values are met. The fuses must carry 110% of their amperage rating, they must open at 135% of their amperage value within one hour and open within two minutes at 200% of the rated current. The time delay or the slow blow types must open in a period of time of not less than twelve seconds at the 200% amperage value. Most of the time our circuitry protectors are based upon overload and short circuit concerns. With this in mind, select a fuse rated at 125% of the circuitry full-load value when dealing with overload concerns, and use a fuse having a current value of 150% to 300% of total load current for any short circuit protection.

4.5-2   FUSE STANDARDIZATIONS
(Refer to Section 1.3-28 for Schematic Symbols.)

It seems that technological growth has pushed aside logical standardization of fuses by physical size or number-letter combination. Efforts to prevent overfusing by adding to fuse length or differing diameter sizes, etc., further add to the confusion. Some of the more popular fuse manufacturers identify fuses by letter, a number-letter combination, or a number identification plus fuse values. Physical sizes, amperage range, and voltage range, are illustrated in the following data:

4.5-2A   Slow-Acting Fuses

Common Identification	Packaging	Amperage	Voltage	Physical Size (inches)
FNM (5AB)	Fiber / Ferrule	1/10-30A	32, 125, 250V	$^{13}/_{32} \times 1\frac{1}{2}$
FNQ	Fiber/Tube/Ferrule	1/10-30A	500V	$^{13}/_{32} \times 1\frac{1}{2}$
GDC	Glass/Ferrule	30MA-7A	250V	0.205×0.787
MDA (3AB)	Ceramic/Ferrule	1/100-30A	125, 250V	$\frac{1}{4} \times 1\frac{1}{4}$
MDL (3AG)	Glass/Ferrule	1/100-30A	125, 250V	$\frac{1}{4} \times 1\frac{1}{4}$
MDQ (3AG)	Glass/Ferrule	1¼-10A	250V	$\frac{1}{4} \times 1\frac{1}{4}$
MDV (3AG)	Glass/Radial Lead	1/100-10A	125, 250V	1¼, 1½ leads
MDX (3AG)	Glass/Ferrule	1¼-10A	125, 250V	$\frac{1}{4} \times 1\frac{1}{4}$

4

4.5-2B   Medium- and Fast-Acting Fuses

Common Identification	Packaging	Amperage	Voltage	Physical Size (inches)
ABC (3AB)	Ceramic/Ferrule	1/8-30A	125, 250V	1/4 × 1 1/4
AGA (1AG)	Glass/Ferrule	1/16-30A	32, 125V	1/4 × 5/8, 7/8
AGC (3AG)	Glass/Ferrule	1/500-30A	32, 250V	1/4 × 1 1/4
AGU (5AG)	Glass/Ferrule	1-30A	250V	$^{13}/_{32}$ × 1 1/2
AGW (7AG)	Glass/Ferrule	1/4-30A	32V	1/4 × 7/8
AGX (8AG) (MJB) (MJW)	Glass/Ferrule	1/500-30A	32, 125, 250V	1/4 × 1
BAF	Laminated/Ferrule	1/2-30A	125, 250V	$^{13}/_{32}$ × 1 1/2
BAN (5AB)	Fiber/Ferrule	2/10-30A	250V	$^{13}/_{32}$ × 1 1/2
GDA	Ceramic/Ferrule	50MA-7A	250V	0.205 × 0.787
GDB	Glass/Ferrule	30MA-10A	250V	0.205 × 0.787
GFA	Glass/Axial Lead	1/200-15A	32, 125V	0.145 × 0.30
GJV	Glass/Radial Lead	1/16-10A	250V	1/4 × 1 1/4
GLH (3AG)	Glass/Ferrule	7-10A	125V	1/4 × 1 1/4
GLN	Glass/Radial Lead	1/200-15A	32, 125V	0.145 × 0.30
GLX	Glass/Radial Lead	15/100-5A	125V	0.145 × 0.30
GMA (GJU)	Glass/Ferrule	1/32-15A	125, 250V	0.197 × 0.769
KTK	Malamine/Ferrule	1/10-30A	600V	$^{13}/_{32}$ × 1 1/2
MGB (3AG)	Glass/Ferrule	1/16 *or* 1/8A	250V	1/4 × 1 1/4
MKB (8AG)	Glass/Ferrule	1/16 *or* 1/8A	250V	1/4 × 1
MTH (3AG)	Glass/Ferrule	4-6A	250V	1/4 × 1 1/4
SFE	Glass/Ferrule	4-30A	32V	1/4 inch Diameter Lengths- 5/8 to 1 $^{7}/_{16}$

4.5-2C   Very Fast-Acting Fuses

Common Identification	Packaging	Amperage	Voltage	Physical Size (inches)
ANN	Flatbody	10-800A	130V	——————
FBP	Ceramic/Ferrule	1-100A	200, 250V, 500, 700V	—————— $^{9}/_{16}$ × 2
FWP	Ceramic/Ferrule	15-30A	200, 250V, 500, 700V	—————— $^{9}/_{16}$ × 2
GBB (3AB)	Ceramic/Ferrule	1/4-30A	60V	1/4 × 1 1/4
KAA	Melamine/Ferrule	1/2-30A	130V	$^{13}/_{32}$ - 1 1/2
KAB + KAX	Melamine/Ferrule	1/2-30A	250V	$^{9}/_{16}$ × 2
KAC	Melamine/Studs	1-30A	600V	$^{9}/_{16}$ Diameter
KAW	Melamine/Ferrule	1-30A	130V	$^{13}/_{32}$ × 1 1/2
KBC	Melamine/Ferrule	1-30A	600V	$^{13}/_{16}$ × 5

4.5-2D   Older Style Fuses

ABS	ACH	ACT	MDC	MDM	MS
ACF	ACO	AGS	MDF	MDR	

Note: These are not recommended for today's technology.

4.5-3   CIRCUIT BREAKERS
(Refer to Section 1.3-16 for Schematic Symbols)

Electronic circuitry having manual or automatic resetting circuit breakers enables you and me to save time since the device need not be taken apart simply to re-fuse the circuit. Circuit breakers have definite current-carrying capabilities and often are described by normal current rating, break current, and hold current ratings. The break current value describes the amount of current the breaker will trip at, thereby protecting the circuit of greater current values. The hold current value indicates the minimum value of current allowable for that particular breaker. Any value under the hold current amount will not allow the circuit breaker to reset as designed.

Typical manual reset circuit breakers, normally rated at 125 volts, are listed next, while in the second listing, typical automatic resetting types, rated normally at 6 volts to 24 volts, are indicated.

4.5-3A   Manual Reset

Current Rating	Break Current	Hold Current
0.650A	0.86A	0.49A
0.80A	1.05A	0.60A
1.00A	1A-1.20A	0.65A
1.25A	1.63A	0.93A
1.50A	1.5A-1.75A	1.00A
1.75A	2.10A	1.20A
2.00A	2A-2.60A	1.25A-1.50A
2.25A	2.90A	1.65A
2.50A	2.5A	1.60A
2.75A	3.30A	1.90A
3.00A	3A-3.67A	1.90A-2.10A
3.25A	3.85A	2.20A
3.50A	3.5A-4.03A	2.20A-2.30A
3.75A	4.20A	2.40A
4.00A	4A-4.40A	2.50A
4.50A	4.5A-5.25A	3.00A
5.00A	5A-5.70A	3.25A
5.50A	5.50A	3.60A
6.00A	6A-6.82A	3.9A
7.00A	7A-7.25A	4.14A

4

4.5-3B   Automatic Reset

<u>Typical Current Ratings</u>

5A, 6A, 8A, 10A, 12A, 15A, 18A, 20A, 25A, 30A, 35A, 40A, 45A, 50A

<u>Breaking Time</u>

100% load; no breaking—arcing
125% load; open within one hour
200% load; open within thirty seconds, resets within ten seconds

4.6   INTEGRATED CIRCUITS (ICs)

The Electronic Industries Association (EIA) defined an IC as "the physical realization of a number of electrical elements inseparably associated on or within a continuous body of semiconductor material to perform the function of a circuit." This statement is perhaps the only thing holding the IC technology together. The presupposed JEDEC standards you and I expected to see, like those of earlier technology years, the ones designed to govern IC technology, went by the wayside because they were too long in coming. Manufacturers in industry were and are bursting out with newer, faster, smaller, and cheaper IC devices. Rather than smothering technology growth and any competitive edge, each manufacturer adopted his own precise device-numbering sequence and packaging preference. It seemed as if the only thing remaining standardized was physical pin size, space, and other physical dimension-related characteristics. This is not totally true, because IC fabrication is standardized in that it is categorized according to sophistication of component density or the number of gates each IC has. At first, small scale integration (SSI) came on the scene with about 12 gates or less, then medium scale integration (MSI) with about 12 to 100 gates, and then the large scale integration (LSI) with about 100 to 1000 gates, and finally, or at least temporarily, the very large scale integration (VLSI) with about 1000 to 50,000 or more gates. Undoubtedly, as the IC technology continues to change, there will be a restructure in gate totals within each fabrication category.

4.6-1   CLASSIFICATION

Microelectronics is the electronic technology associated with the concept of microminiaturization—the smallness in size that somehow governs electronic parts and components. Because of the IC revolution, with the fabrication techniques of SSI, MSI, LSI, and VLSI encompassing every facet of electronics (even the discrete component area), a method of organization arose. The ICs of today are organized and classified by three general specifications: one dealing with construction, one describing operation modes, and last, the packaging particulars. Figure 4-16 illustrates IC subdivisions which are subjected to construction, operating mode, and packaging specifics.

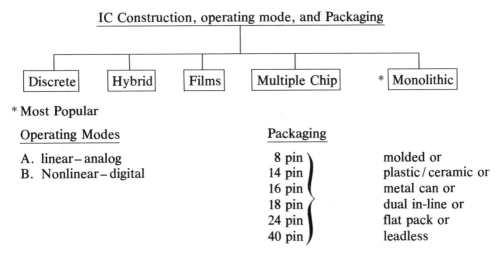

Figure 4-16

4.6-2 PREFERRED REFERENCING

All IC devices have a definite identification code although you and I, at various times, are not aware of what means what. As an end result, we are often confronted with "manufacturing mysticism." I say mysticism because each company uses its own identification code in describing its own special, different, and best IC device ever manufactured. Much of the identification code confusion can be cleared up because many manufacturers of IC devices are using some of, if not all of, a recommended or preferred referencing code. The code preference data includes a *prefix area,* usually used for the manufacturer's logo or letter identification, a *device family* area, *device numbering* area and additional spaces for *packaging* and *temperature* specifications. This coding system is illustrated in Figure 4-17.

Integrated circuits manufactured by some companies can be identified by the letter or number sequence used before the three-, four-, or five-digit number used to describe the IC purpose or function. Suffixes are also used to describe packaging style or specific purpose data. The letter A, for example, means improved electrical specifications to some, while the letter C may imply commercial temperature range, etc. More often than not, the suffixes used resemble those relating to packaging styles as illustrated in Section 4.6-2, preferred referencing. The best thing one can do when using IC devices is to get the manufacturer's specifications sheets and several cross-reference manuals, since industry standards do vary considerably. The LM741CF OP-AMP (741) used in the preferred referencing illustration is a good example of industry variations, since the metal can version for the 741 is identified as being SK3514/941 by RCA, GEIC 263 by GE, TCG941 by Technician Control Group, MC1741CF by Motorola and SN7241Z by Texas Instruments.

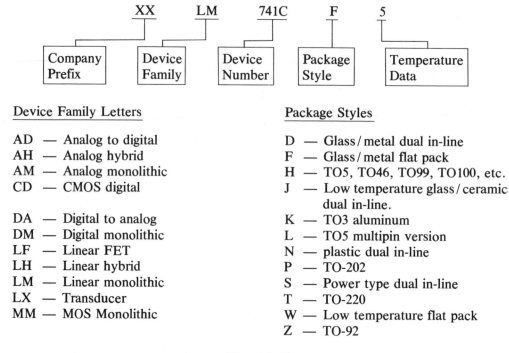

Figure 4-17

4.6-3　LOGIC FAMILIES

All of the IC families that came into existence after Mr. Jack Kilby invented the integrated circuit at Texas Instruments in 1958, have contributed to IC terminology and standards relating to fabrication techniques, construction, operating modes, and packaging. Perhaps you had a preference as to diode logic (DL), resistor-transistor logic (RTL), diode-transistor logic (DTL), resistor-coupled transistor logic (RCTL), or direct-coupled transistor logic (DCTL), but as history indicates, preferences do change when newer families are developed. Now, IC families of the emitter-coupled logic (ECL) equaling the current mode logic (CML), transistor-transistor logic (TTL) equaling the transistor-coupled logic (TCL) integrated injection logic (I^2L), metal-oxide-semiconductors (MOS) and complementary metal-oxide-semiconductors (CMOS) plus others, are making their advances in technology history.

Each family has identification codes. Each, however, differs somewhat in voltage levels, power, speed, fan-out, and other operating mode characteristics. Some notes you will recall concerning some of the logic families are as follows:

DCTL — advantage was simplicity.
　　　　disadvantage was current usage (Hog) and transistor matching limitations.

RTL — advantage was current usage was reduced.
disadvantage was poor noise immunity and slow speeds.
high noise margin is independent of fan-out; low noise margin is affected by fan-out.

DTL — advantage was good noise margin for medium speed switching. Its speed was better than RTL, but was still not too fast. It is more expensive than RTL while low and high noise margins are not affected by fan-out.

TTL — is very widely used although "current hog" possibilities do exist. It has better speed than DCTL, RTL, and DTL. TTL voltage range (0 to +5 volts). Fan out and noise margins characteristics are similar to DTL. Bipolar TTL is about 10 times faster than MOS.

TTL   high region (2 to 5 volts)
undefined region (0.8 to 2 volts)
low region (0 to 0.8 volts)

ECL/CML — is faster than DTL or TTL.

CMOS — is faster than MOS and offers low power consumption. It, however, is physically larger than MOS. The NMOS is more popular than PMOS.

CMOS voltage range (4 to 15 volts). Use fast rise-fall clocks. Avoid static. All inputs must go somewhere.

I^2L — advantage is smaller size (an advancement in monolithic LSI technology) with increased functional density, lower voltage (1 volt), lower current (nA range) and NO electrostatic burnout.

4.6-4   TTL NOTES

Perhaps one reason why the transistor-transistor logic (TTL) logic family has had great success is because it is easily adaptable to all forms of IC logic. Perhaps, also, it is because of increased popular usage industrywide that standardizations are actually being observed worldwide. TTLs have all of the IC advantages of a simplified final result circuitry design in comparison to those of earlier years, fewer interconnections, faster speed, less power consumption, smallness in size, and improved life reliability.

The TTL logic family has for the most part three generalized areas of application. One is military or space application, one is industrial application and one is commercial usage. The identification numbering sequence for TTLs generally begin with a 54 or 74 prefix. The commercial and industrial TTL-ICs, I believe, are those identified by the 74XX number, while the 54XX identification relates to military applications. I do not mean to imply that 54XX or 74XX are solely used for that single purpose, since a 54XX and 74XX IC could have the same identical purpose, voltages, pin count or other important characteristic and would be identical in every detail except for one, and that is of specific temperature range. The temperature range is pretty much the deciding factor for use. Those TTL ICs which meet or surpass a temperature range of −55° to −125°C are those qualifying for military application, the 54XX series.

Those meeting or surpassing a temperature range of −25° to 80°C are set aside for industrial use (74XX), and those meeting or surpassing a temperature range of 0° to 70°C are used for commercial applications — also the 74XX identification reference.

TTL logic ICs are identified generally by a 54XX and 74XX number sequence, and are further subdivided into five group types. They may be termed "regular," "high power," "low power," "Schottky," and "low power Schottky." Those classified as regular TTL chips are identified by a 54XX or 74XX number; low power TTL chips are identified by the letter L as in 54LXX or 74LXX; high power are identified by the letter H as in 54HXX or 74HXX; the Schottky use the letter S as in 54SXX or 74SXX; and low power Schottky use the letters LS as in 54LSXX or 74LSXX.

4.6-5   PACKAGING STYLES AND NOTES

Once it was common practice to accept voltage variations of ten to twenty percent when troubleshooting resistor, capacitor, inductor, solid state, diode, transistor, or vacuum tube circuitry, but today this tolerance is unacceptable. Troubleshooting IC circuitry demands accuracy using digital technology equipment and closer tolerance voltage variations of, say, less than ± five percent. The technology has changed. IC circuits require special care when manufactured, special care when handled, and special understanding when troubleshooting. Imagine a tiny piece of semiconductor material on which microscopic electronic components are etched to form circuits, and then, after connection of leads, a case encapsulating the chip (also called die or dice) ends the manufacturing process. It now is an IC, and is (we hope) identified by standardized JEDEC referencing. You and I don't really know what is inside, and schematics seldom show any internal IC features. The only thing we can do is make educated guesses, or we can rely upon our own knowledge in dealing with IC particulars and past practice industry standards. The following are those facts that will provide knowledge as evidenced by industry past practices.

4.6-5A   ID Numbers and Code Dates

More often than not ICs will have a manufacturer's logo or some other reference imprinted on each IC case whether it is a flat pack, dual in-line, or other package style. Each will also identify the IC by the particular reference number (see preferred referencing 4.6-2), depending upon its particular purpose or function. You may or may not be able to find and decipher a code date that indicates the week and year the device was made. This code is used for callbacks (as in automobiles) in that sometimes a fault is found in manufacturing and

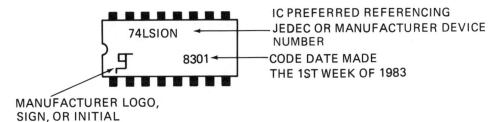

IC PREFERRED REFERENCING
JEDEC OR MANUFACTURER DEVICE
NUMBER

CODE DATE MADE
THE 1ST WEEK OF 1983

MANUFACTURER LOGO,
SIGN, OR INITIAL

Figure 4-18

it can be more easily traced and corrected. This data may resemble the data found in Figure 4-18.

The flat package comes in a variety of sizes, each having differing number of leads or terminals. Normal flat packaging sizes are about ¼ × ¼ having ten and fourteen leads: ¼ × ⅜, with sixteen and twenty-four leads; and ⅜ × ⅝, with twenty-four leads. The flat pack illustrated in Figure 4-19 indicates a reference marking system normally used to point out terminal number one.

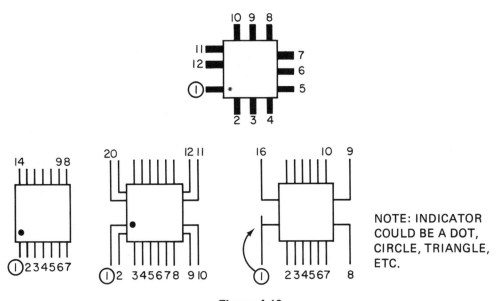

NOTE: INDICATOR
COULD BE A DOT,
CIRCLE, TRIANGLE,
ETC.

Figure 4-19

Dual in-line (DIP) packages differ in style, measurements, and lead number. However, somewhat standardized sizes are available. Some of the approximate shape measurements include the $\frac{9}{32} \times \frac{25}{32}$ having fourteen and sixteen leads; the $\frac{33}{64} \times \frac{55}{64}$ with sixteen leads, or $\frac{33}{64} \times 1\frac{55}{64}$ having thirty-six leads; other size variations are packaged with eight, fourteen, sixteen, twenty, twenty-four, up to sixty-four or more leads. The dual in-line package illustrated

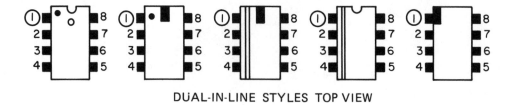

DUAL-IN-LINE STYLES TOP VIEW

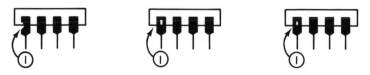

(UNIQUE) SIDEVIEW OF DUAL-IN-LINE STYLES

NOTE: PIN COUNT IS NORMALLY
COUNTER-CLOCKWISE

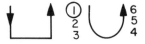

Figure 4-20

in Figure 4-20 indicates a marking system commonly employed, denoting the number one terminal, thereby providing standardized pin count.

Integrated chips—beam lead microelectronic circuits—are normally mounted with glue or paste. Their very fragile packaging sizes range from approximately $1/32 \times 1/32$ to about $1/16 \times 3/32$. As in the previous two integrated circuitry packages, a marking system is employed to identify pin or lead references. Packaging styles and pin referencing are quite similar to those used for flat pack identification.

4.7   OPERATIONAL AMPLIFIERS

An operational amplifier is commonly called an op amp. The op amp is a two-input and one-output linear IC. It is often described as being direct-coupled, high quality, high AC and DC gain, high ability to reduce noise, high stability, high input impedance, low output impedance, or a wide frequency band amplifier. The op amp is noted for its high gain; open loop gains between 100,000 (10^5) and 1,000,000,000 (10^9).

4.7-1   SCHEMATIC IDENTIFICATION

The schematic symbol used extensively throughout the electronic technology field is the two-input, one-output triangle denoting amplification. Figure 4-21 illustrates the preferred references.

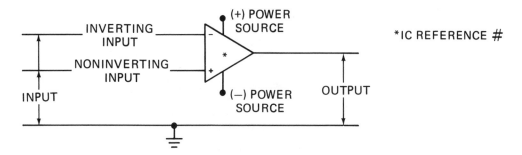

INVERTING INPUT

NONINVERTING INPUT

INPUT

(+) POWER SOURCE

(−) POWER SOURCE

OUTPUT

*IC REFERENCE #

Figure 4-21

It is normal to find no references to +V or −V power sources on actual schematic diagrams. You are supposed to be well enough informed to use them because of common sense and out of pure necessity. Both positive and negative supply voltages are needed since the output must be able to produce either positive or negative outputs. Ground or a zero-volt potential is used for reference for all input, output, and power supply voltages. The minus sign (−), positioned always on the *invert* input terminal and the positive sign (+), always placed on the *noninvert* terminal, do not reference themselves to a positive (+) or negative (−) voltage. These refer to whichever will invert or will not invert the input signal by 180 degrees. The positive (+) terminal does not invert while the negative (−) terminal inverts.

4.7-2   CONFIGURATIONS

An almost limitless application of special and often unique electronic functions are made possible when using one or more of the basic op amp circuitry configurations. You have choices of *open loop, closed loop, inverting,* or *noninverting* configurations, all of which are identified in Figure 4-22.

The open loop configuration has no feedback and acts like a switch, going from zero volts to saturation. The closed loop, also called a voltage follower, does have a feedback, but its gain is only near unity. However, it is ideal for a buffer or an isolator. The noninverting configuration has the advantage of a higher impedance characteristic. The most popular configuration is the inverting type, therefore requiring most emphasis in the remaining op amp data.

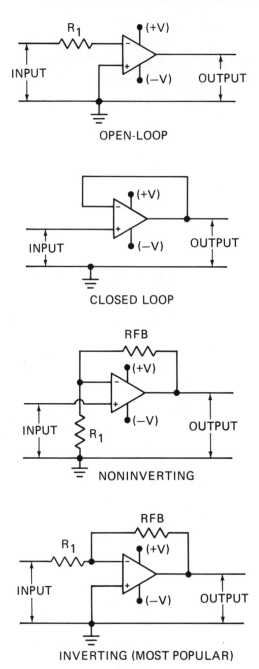

Figure 4-22

Op amps have two characteristics: one is *actual* and the other is *ideal*. For our purposes, and for most applications, the ideal rules and facts will satisfy most all nonengineering needs. These ideal characteristics include:

1. infinite gain (A) ranging from DC to ∞.
2. infinite input impedance (Z_{in}), (Z_I).
3. zero output impedance (Z_{OUT}), (Z_O).
4. zero offset voltage and current (V_{os}), (I_{os}).
5. infinite common mode rejection ratio (CMRR)
6. infinite bandwidth (BW)
7. zero response time.

Generally, in op amp usage, a negative feedback is employed. The negative feedback essentially decreases the gain, but improves sensitivity. It also prevents immediate saturation and increases the bandwidth. Closed loop gain (A_C) is the gain for an op amp having negative feedback applied.

4.7-3   INVERTING SPECIFICS

* (IC 741 number reference)
R_{FB} = feedback resistor
R_1 = offset minimizer resistor
        (noninvert input lead)
R_2 = Input resistance/impedance

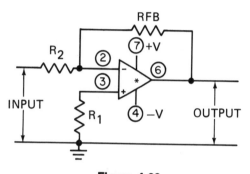

Figure 4-23

4

4.7-3A   Closed Loop Gain

$$A_C = -\frac{V_{out}}{V_{in}}$$

OR

$$A_C = -\frac{R_{FB}}{R_{IN}}$$

OR

$$A_C = -\frac{Z_{FB}}{Z_{IN}}$$

A_C = closed loop gain
V_{out} = output voltage
V_{in} = input voltage
Z_{in}, R_{in} = input resistance/impedance
Z_{FB}, R_{FB} = output impedance

Note: The minus sign ($-$) indicates invert.

4.7-3B   Input Current

$$I_{in} = \frac{V_{in}}{R_{in}}$$

OR

$$I_{in} = \frac{V_{out}}{Z_{in}}$$

I_{in} = input current
V_{in} = input voltage
V_{out} = output voltage
R_{in}, Z_{in} = feedback resistance/impedance

4.7-3C   Feedback Current

$$I_{FB} = \frac{V_{out}}{R_{FB}}$$

OR

$$I_{FB} = \frac{V_{out}}{Z_{FB}}$$

OR

$$I_{FB} = I_{in}$$

I_{FB} = feedback current

V_{out} = output voltage

$* R_{FB}, Z_{FB}$ = feedback resistance/impedance

$*$ = output

4.7-3D   Input Impedance

$$Z_{in} = R_{in}$$

Z_{in} = input impedance

R_{in} = input resistance

4.7-3E   Input Voltage

$$V_{in} = \frac{V_{out}}{A_C}$$

V_{in} = input voltage

V_{out} = output voltage

A_C = closed loop gain

4.7-3F   Output Voltage

$$V_0 = -A_C V_{in}$$

OR

$$V_0 = -\left(\frac{Z_{FB}}{Z_{IN}}\right) V_{IN}$$

OR

$$V_0 = -\left(\frac{R_{FB}}{R_{IN}}\right) V_{IN}$$

V_0 = output voltage

V_{IN} = input voltage

A_C = closed loop gain

$* Z_{FB}, R_{FB}$ = feedback resistance/impedance

Z_{IN}, R_{IN} = input resistance/impedance

$*$ = output

4.7-3G   Noninvert Input Lead Resistor

$$R_1 = \frac{R_2 \times R_{FB}}{R_2 \times R_{FB}}$$

Note: See Figure 4-23. The value is equal to the parallel resistance total.

4.7-3H   Typical Values

Desired gain	R_1 Value	R_{FB} Value
10	1 kΩ	10 kΩ
100	1 kΩ	100 kΩ
1000	100 kΩ	100 kΩ

4.7-4   NONINVERTING SPECIFICS

* (IC741 number reference)
  R_{FB} = feedback resistor
  R_1 = part of voltage divider ($+R_{FB}$)
  R_Z = offset minimizer resistor
       (noninvert input lead)

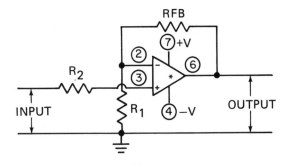

Figure 4-24

4.7-4A   Closed Loop Gain

OR

$$A_C = \frac{V_{out}}{V_{in}}$$

OR

$$A_C = \frac{R_1 + R_{FB}}{R_1}$$

$$A_C = 1 + \frac{R_{FB}}{R_1}$$

A_C = closed loop gain
V_{out} = output voltage
V_{in} = input voltage

4.7-4B   Input Current

$$I_{in} = \frac{V_{in}}{R_{in}}$$

I_{in} = input current
V_{in} = input voltage
R_{in} = input resistance/impedance

4.7-4C   Feedback Current

$$I_{FB} = I_{in}$$

I_{FB} = feedback current
I_{in} = input current

4.7-4D   Input Voltage

$$V_{in} = I_{in} R_{in}$$

OR

$$V_{in} = \frac{V_{out}}{A_C}$$

V_{in} = input voltage
I_{in} = input current
R_{in} = input resistance/impedance
V_{out} = output voltage
A_C = closed loop gain

4

4.7-4E   Output Voltage

$$V_O = A_C \times V_{in}$$

OR

$$V_O = I_{FB} (R_{in} + R_{FB})$$

OR

$$V_O = I_{in} (R_{in} + R_{FB})$$

OR

$$V_O = E_{R1} + E_{RFB}$$

OR

$$V_O = \frac{R_1 + R_{FB}}{R_1} (V_{IN})$$

V_O = output voltage
A_C = closed loop gain
V_{in} = input voltage
I_{FB} = feedback current
I_{in} = input current
R_{in} = input resistance/impedance
R_{FB} = feedback resistance
E_{R1}, E_{RFB} = voltage developed across each resistor

4.7-4F   Noninvert Input Lead Resistor

$$R_Z = \frac{R_1 \times R_{FB}}{R_1 + R_{FB}}$$

Note: See Figure 4-24. The value is equal to the parallel resistance total.

4.7-4G   Typical Values

Desired Gain	R_1 Value	R_{FB} Value
11	1 kΩ	10 kΩ
111	100 kΩ	11 kΩ
1001	100 kΩ	100 kΩ

4.7-5   SUMMING AMPLIFIER (AVERAGING OR MIXER) SPECIFICS

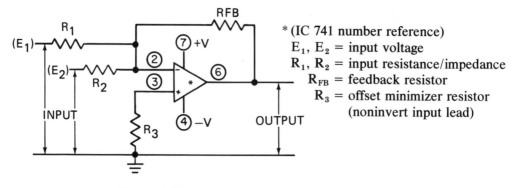

*(IC 741 number reference)
E_1, E_2 = input voltage
R_1, R_2 = input resistance/impedance
R_{FB} = feedback resistor
R_3 = offset minimizer resistor
(noninvert input lead)

Figure 4-25

Note: (1) Each (all) input is isolated and is treated as independent signal and appears simultaneously at the output.

(2) If R_{FB} and R_1 and R_2 are the same value, a gain of unity results, for gains larger than one, make R_{FB} value larger, and then $V_o = \dfrac{R_{FB}}{R_1} (E_1 + E_2)$ is usable.

4.7-5A   Gain Per Channel

$$A_1 = (-) \frac{R_{FB}}{R_1} \text{ (for } E_1 \text{ channel)}$$

A_1 = channel #1 gain
A_2 = channel #2 gain
R_{FB} = feedback resistance
R_1, R_2 = input resistance/impedance

$$A_2 = (-) \frac{R_{FB}}{R_2} \text{ (for } E_2 \text{ channel)}$$

$(-)$ = invert function

4.7-5B   Input Currents

$$I_{R1} = \frac{E_1}{R_1}$$

I_{R1}, I_{R2} = currents flowing through input resistors

$$I_{R2} = \frac{E_2}{R_2}$$

E_1, E_2 = input voltage
R_1, R_2 = input resistance/impedance

$$I_T = I_{R1} + I_{R2}$$

I_T = total input current

4.7-5C   Feedback Current

$$I_{FB} = \frac{V_o}{R_{FB}}$$

I_{FB} = feedback current
V_o = output voltage
R_{FB} = feedback resistance

4.7-5D   Input Impedance

$$Z_{E1} = R_1$$
$$Z_{E2} = R_2$$

Z_{E1}, Z_{E2} = input channel impedance
R_1, R_2 = input resistances

4

4.7-5E   Output Voltage

$$V_o = -R_{FB} \left(\frac{E_1}{R_1} + \frac{E_2}{R_2} \right)$$

OR

$$V_o = -(A_1 E_1) + (A_2 E_2)$$

OR

$$* V_o = - \left[\left(\frac{R_{FB}}{R_1} \right) E_1 + \left(\frac{R_{FB}}{R_2} \right) E_2 \right]$$

V_o = output voltage
A_1 = channel #1 gain
A_2 = channel #2 gain
E_1, E_2 = input voltages
R_{FB} = feedback resistance
R_1, R_2 = input resistance/impedance

* Expanded as input channels are added

4.7-5F   Noninvert Input Lead Resistor

$$R_3 = \frac{1}{\dfrac{1}{R_1} + \dfrac{1}{R_2} + \dfrac{1}{R_{FB}}}$$

Note: See Figure 4-25. The value is equal to the parallel resistance total.

4.7-6   DIFFERENCE AMPLIFIER SPECIFICS

* (IC741 number reference)

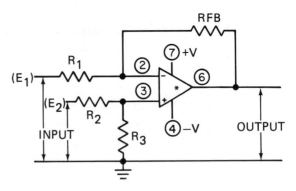

Figure 4-26

Note: (1) Generally, $R_1 = R_2$ and $R_{FB} = R_3$
(2) Has three modes of operation: (A) single-ended input and output inverting
(B) single-ended input and output noninverting
(C) differential input, single-ended output
(3) If the same signal is applied to each input, the output is zero.

4.7-6A   Closed Loop Gain

$$A_C = \frac{R_{FB}}{R_1}$$

OR

$$A_C = \frac{R_{FB}}{R_2}$$

A_c = closed loop gain
* R_1, R_2 = input resistance/impedance
* R_{FB} = feedback resistance
* See Figure 4-26, note (1)

4.7-6B   Output Voltage

$$V_0 = \frac{R_{FB}}{R_1}(E_2 - E_1)$$

OR

$$V_0 = \frac{R_{FB}}{R_2}(E_2 - E_1)$$

OR

$$V_0 = A_C(E_2 - E_1)$$

V_0 = output voltage
E_1, E_2 = input voltage
* R_{FB} = feedback resistor
* R_1, R_2 = input resistance/impedance
A_C = closed loop gain
* See Figure 4-26, note (1)

$E_2 - E_1$ is the differential input voltage amplified by op amp

4.7-6C   Common-Mode Ratio

$$CMRR = \frac{A_V \text{ Diff}}{A_V \text{ Com}}$$

CMRR   = common mode rejection ratio (dB)
A_V Diff = voltage gain for differential signals
A_V Com = voltage gain for common mode signals

Note: (1) Common mode operation is the simultaneous signal application to both inputs of the differential amplifier.
(2) A_V Diff and A_V Com equals signal out divided by signal in.

4.7-7   OP-AMP—UNIQUE LETTER REFERENCES

A_c	— closed loop gain / common mode voltage gain
A_d	— differential voltage gain
A_o	— open loop gain (no feedback)
A_{VO}, A_{VOL}	— large signal voltage gain
BW	— unity gain; closed loop bandwidth
C_{in}	— input capacitance
CMRR	— common mode rejection ratio
$\triangle$ CMRR	— common mode rejection ratio match
CMVR	— common mode voltage range
e_n	— equivalent input noise voltage (density)
e_{np-p}	— input noise voltage
GBW	— gain bandwidth product
I_B	— input bias current
$I_B{}^+$	— average noninverting bias current
i_F	— feedback current
i_I	— input current
i_n	— equivalent input noise current (density)
i_{np-p}	— input noise current
I_{os}	— input offset current
$I_{os}{}^+$	— noninverting input offset current
$I_{os}{}^-$	— inverting input offset current
I_s, I_{sy}	— supply current
i_{SJ}	— summing junction current
IVR	— input voltage range
Pd	— power dissipation
P_{SRR}	— power supply rejection ratio
$\triangle P_{SRR}$	— supply voltage rejection ratio match
R_F, R_{FB}	— feedback resistor
R_{in}	— input resistance-differential mode
$R_{in} - CM$	— common mode input resistance
R_o	— open loop output resistance
SR	— slew rate
TCI	— average bias current drift

4

TCI_B^+ — average drift of noninverting bias current
TCI_{OS} — average offset current drift
TCI_{OS}^+ — average drift of noninverting offset current
TCV_{OS} — average offset voltage drift
TCV_{OSN} — average offset voltage drift with external timing
$TC\triangle V_{OS}$ — input offset voltage tracking
V_{CM} — input common mode voltage
V_{in} — input voltage
V_O, V_{out} — output voltage swing
V_{OS} — input offset voltage
$\triangle V_{OS}$ — input offset voltage match
Z_F, Z_{FB} — feedback impedance
Z_I, Z_{in} — input impedance

4.7-8   DEFINITIONS OF OP AMP TERMS

Average bias current drift – A ratio of input bias current change to the change in temperature.

Average offset current drift – A ratio of input offset current change to the change in temperature.

Average offset voltage drift – A ratio of input offset voltage change to the change in temperature.

Common mode input resistance – A ratio of input voltage change (range) to the change in input bias current.

Common mode rejection ratio – A ratio of differential open-loop gain to common mode open-loop gain.

Full power bandwidth – The maximum frequency over which full output voltage swing is obtainable.

Gain-bandwidth product – The frequency at which open-loop gain equals unity.

Gain margin – The amount the voltage gain is below unit level (0dB) at the frequency where 180° phase shift is found.

Input bias current – The average of the two input terminal currents when the output is 0 volts with no load.

Input common mode range – The maximum input voltage range applied simultaneously without saturation or cutoff of amplifier gain stages.

Input noise current – The p-p noise current within a specific frequency band.

Input noise current —equivalent / density – The rms noise current in a one H_z band centered on a specific frequency.

Input noise voltage – The p-p noise voltage within a specific frequency band.

Input noise voltage density – The rms noise voltage in a one H_z band centered on a specific frequency.

Input offset current – The difference between both input terminal currents when the output is 0 volts without a load.

Input offset voltage – The voltage required across the input terminal to obtain 0 volts as an output without a load.

Input resistance —differential mode – A ratio of change in input voltage to the change in input current on either input with the other grounded out.

Input voltage range – The input voltage range which allows linear operation.

Large signal voltage gain – A ratio of change in output voltage over a specific range to the input voltage change producing it.

Output voltage swing – The peak output voltage obtainable without clipping.

Overload recovery time – The time required for the output stage to return to an active region after driven into deep saturation.

Power dissipation – The total power dissipated with the output at 0 volts with no load.

Power supply rejection ratio – The inverse ratio of input offset voltage change to power supply changes.

Slew rate – The maximum rate of change time of output voltages to respond to input voltage changes.

Supply current – The current required from the power supply when the amplifier has 0 volts out with no load.

Unity gain —closed loop bandwidth – The frequency at which the voltage gain for a unity gain follower amplifier is 3dB below unity.

4.8   OPTOELECTRONICS

Electronic technology, infiltrated by the photodiode, phototransistor, photodarlington, photo SCR, fiber optics, and intermingled with emitters and detectors, along with other photo-type amplifier combinations, have helped create a new field of specialized electronics — optoelectronics. This field has a great deal of subject matter requiring understanding for application. It seems that one needs the basics in electronics, plus a workable blend of photometry, physics, optics, radiometry, and some statistical analysis. Evidence of optoelectronics is found everywhere; automobile headlight dimmers, photography flash units, home nightlights and smoke detectors, furnace flame detectors, telephone communication systems, copy machines, tape readers, motor-speed controls, motion detectors, counters of all sorts, along with microprocessor control devices, are just a few examples.

Optoelectronic devices are manufactured by several companies. Standards exist, but are not well defined at this particular time. Each manufacturer seeks approval of its own logical packaging and identification codes. There are common TO-18 and TO-92 structures, along with dual in-line devices manufactured, that do seem to comply with lead spacing-dimension, etc. to aid in interchangeability. Some devices begin with IN prefixes, some with 2N, 4N, and most with manufacturing letter selections. The one thing to remember is that each device should be analyzed separately, using its own specification sheet.

Optoisolator generalized schematic symbols are found in Chapter 1, Section 1.10-34 for ready reference.

4.8-1 OPTOELECTRONIC SYMBOL GLOSSARY

Some of the specialized symbols you will find when using infrared emitters, detectors—phototransistors and darlingtons, coupled modules—phototransistors and darlingtons, fiber optics—detectors and emitters, optocouplers—phototransistors, darlingtons, photo SCRs, triacs, programmable couplers, FETs, or Schmitt triggers are as follows:

A	– area
Å	– angstrom
B_L	– luminous
B_r	– radiant intensity
C_{CB}, C_{cb}	– collector to base capacitance (pF)
C_{EB}, C_{eb}	– emitter to base capacitance (pF)
C_{CE}, C_{cb}	– collector to emitter capacitance (pF)
C_i	– capacitance (pF)
C_J	– junction capacitance (pF)
CT	– color temperature
CTR	– current transfer ratio
di/dt	– critical rate of rise current
dv/dt	– critical rate of rise voltage
E_e, H_E	– irradiance—effective
F	– lens focal length/illumination
f/#	– lens parameter
GaAs	– gallium arsenide
$GaAlA_s$	– gallium aluminum arsenide
h_{FE}	– forward current transfer ratio
I_C	– continuous collector current (mA)
I_{CEO}	– photodetector leakage current/dark current
I_D	– dark current (nA)
I_e	– radiant intensity
I_F	– IRED forward bias current (mA-A)
I_{FT}	– input trigger current (mA)
I_L	– light current (mA), luminous intensity (nA)
I_R	– infrared/reverse leakage current (μA-nA)
IRED	– infrared-emitting diode
L	– luminance
LASCR	– light-activated SCR (photo SCR)
LED	– light-emitting diode
m	– meter/lense magnification
n.a.	– numerical operature of a lens
P_D, P_E, P_T	– power dissipation (mW-W)
PPM	– pulse rate modulation
P_o	– power out (μW-mW)
PPS	– pulse per second
R_{IO}, r_{io}	– input-output isolation resistance (giga ohms)

Si	– silicon
T_A	– ambient temperature (°C)
T_C	– case temperature (°C)
t_d	– delay time (μ sec)
t_f	– fall time (μ sec-n sec)
T_J	– junction temperature / operating temperature (°C)
T_L	– lead soldering temperature (°C)
t_o	– operating time
t_{OFF}	– turn-off time (μ sec)
t_{ON}	– turn-on time (μ sec)
t_p	– propagation time (μ sec)
t_r	– rise time (μ sec-n sec)
t_s	– storage time (μ sec)
T_{STG}	– storage temperature (°C)
UCL	– upper confidence level
$V_{(BR)CBO}$	– collector to base breakdown voltage (V)
$V_{(BR)CEO}$	– collector to emitter breakdown voltage (V)
$V_{(BR)EBO}$	– emitter to base breakdown voltage (V)
$V_{(BR)R}$	– radiant intensity
V_{CBO}	– collector to base dark voltage (V)
$V_{CE(SAT)}$	– saturation voltage (V)
V_{CEO}	– collector to emitter dark voltage (V)
V_{EBO}	– emitter to base dark voltage (V)
V_F	– forward voltage (V)
V_R	– reverse voltage (V)
W	– radiant emittance
λ	– wavelength / predicted failure rate
λp	– peak emission wavelength (nm)
$\triangle \lambda$	– spectrical bandwidth (nm)
Θ_{HI}	– half intensity beam angle (degrees)
η	– conversion efficiency

4

4.9   RESISTORS

Resistors are or may be grouped by type of basic construction or manufacturing process. This particular section of the book will focus on five of these groups:

1. composition type (standard and hot mold)
2. glazed metal and metal-oxide type
3. film type
4. wire-wound (power and precision) type
5. variable type

Before we continue, it should be noted that resistors are not polarity conscious; don't worry about which end goes where. Another thing is that neither the physical size nor its particular manufacturing process has anything to do with the resistor's resistance. You will find identical resistive values, say 100 ohms, in all five types, and will find it available at various differing wattage ratings. The resistor's physical size does, however, normally suggest its current carrying capability as denoted by wattage rating. This rating indicates that a low-wattage resistor is capable of handling small amounts of current safely, whereas a higher-wattage resistor is capable of much more current activity. (Refer to Sections 1.3-7, 10, 58, 59, 60, 61, and 62 for schematic symbols.)

All resistors, whether insulated or noninsulated, composition, metal glazed, glass-tin-oxide, wire-wound, adjustable or variable, fusable, fixed film, linear or nonlinear taper, have specifications that must be met by manufacturers before standardization agencies will approve their use. These standards provide us with reliable facts regarding identification by codes, sizes, and shapes. They also insure chances of greater interchangeability, since uniform methods and specifications are used when testing before selling. Often, standards are referred to on resistor packaging and/or on data sheets. Two of the abbreviations often used are EIA (Electronic Industries Association) and MIL (Military). There are several more agencies involved, and page after page of specifications that must be met to rate special letter-number coding.

4.9-1   COMPOSITION RESISTORS

The resistive element for the composition resistor is a carbon or graphite mixture formed into a ceramic core. You can recognize it by way of the standard EIA-MIL color coding. If it is an axial lead *insulated* resistor, the body color is *usually tan,* but other colors, except for black, are also used. If it is an axial lead *noninsulated* type, the body color is *usually black.*

TYPE	RESISTIVE RANGE	TOLERANCE RANGE	WATTAGE RANGE
carbon composition (standard)	0.1 Ω to 22M Ω	±5 to ± 20%	1/8 to 2 watts
carbon composition (hot mold)	1 Ω to 100M Ω	±5 to ± 20%	1/8 to 5 watts

Normal wattage is 1/8, 1/4, 1/2, and 1 and 2 watts. If MIL specifications are used, the physical size determines wattage assignments. The MIL letter-number designating the 1/8 watt resistor is RCR05; the 1/4 watt is RCR07; the 1/2 watt is RCR20; one watt is designated by RCR32, and the two-watt resistor by RCR42. The suggested voltage rating for each is: 1/8 watt equals 150 volts, 1/4 watt equals 250 volts, 1/2 watt equals 350 volts, and the one watt has a maximum voltage of 500 volts as does the two-watt rating.

4.9-2   FIXED RESISTOR—PREFERRED RESISTIVE VALUES

Fixed composition resistors normally have three general tolerance groupings which are manufacturer established and agency approved. The three groupings of ± five percent, ± ten percent, and ± twenty percent tolerances assigned to specific quality controlled resistors eliminate manufacture of resistors in a sequential resistive progression. This is possible since resistance of the ± twenty percent nature would duplicate the 10 percent resistive values, and in like manner, the ten percent values would overlap into the five percent values.

To prevent resistive value duplication, a system called "preferred value" controls resistor value production. The preferred value system uses a specific multiplier which, when multiplied times the beginning resistive value within that tolerance group, equals or closely equals the next preferred resistive value. After multiplication by the given multiplier, the end result value is a rounded off, two-significant-figures digit. For example, one multiplier for a five percent resistor is 1.58 and the beginning resistive value is 10 ohms, so the next preferred value is: 10 × 1.58, equaling 15.8 ohms or rounded off equals 16 ohms. This data is outlined within the following chart (Chart 4-1).

TOLERANCES	5%		10%		20%
Two U.S. Standard Multipliers (A) *Z17.1 (B) **C83.2	*1.58	**1.10	*1.26	**1.21	1.46
	10	10	10	10	10
	—	11	—	—	—
	—	12	12	12	—
	—	13	—	—	—
	—	15	—	15	15
	16	16	16	—	—
	—	18	—	18	—
	—	20	20	—	—
	—	22	—	22	22
	—	24	—	—	—
	25	—	25	—	—
	—	27	—	27	—
	—	30	—	—	—
	—	—	32	—	—
	—	33	—	33	33
	—	36	—	—	—
	—	39	—	39	—
	40	—	40	—	—
	—	43	—	—	—
	—	47	—	47	47

NOTE:

(1) For resistances under 100 ohms, multiply by one.

(2) For resistances under 1000 ohms, multiply by ten. IE: 160 ohms may be bought having 5- and 10-percent tolerances.

(3) For resistances under 10,000 ohms, multiply by one hundred. IE: 2,200 ohms can be bought having 5-, 10-, and 20-percent tolerances.

(4) For resistances under 100,000 ohms, multiply by one thousand. IE: 62,000 ohms is available only in a 5-percent resistor.

Chart 4-1

TOLERANCES	5%		10%		20%
Two U.S. Standard Multipliers (A) *Z17.1 (B) **C83.2	*1.58	**1.10	*1.26	**1.21	1.46
(5) For resistances greater, multiply by 10k, 100k, etc.	—	—	50	—	—
	—	51	—	—	—
	—	56	—	56	—
	—	62	—	—	—
	63	—	63	—	—
	—	68	—	68	68
	—	75	—	—	—
	—	—	80	—	—
	—	82	—	82	—
	—	91	—	—	—
	100	100	100	100	100

Chart 4-1 (continued)

4.9-3   THREE-, FOUR-, AND FIVE-BAND COLOR CODED RESISTORS

Before buying any resistor, you need to know two things: the desired wattage rating and the required resistance necessary. If you are professional, determining wattage is an easy enough task, but the value calculated does not grant much of a safety factor since resistors of the composition type change in resistive value when hot. A good safety design factor that professionals use to prevent overheating is doubling the *calculated* power rating.

Circuitry demands dictate values of resistance required because of Ohm's law applications, but these calculations can be quickly made as were those required in determining wattage. The next step is to select the resistor having the desired resistance, wattage rating, temperature coefficients, failure rates, and tolerances acceptable for your circuit. This is where we may have difficulty, because often even we professionals forget some of the important facts concerning color coded resistors. The following notes, figures, and charts will aid those of us who know, but have forgotten.

Color coded resistors must be read correctly and therefore have standardized color positioning, color digit or meaning assignments, and color pigmentation requirements. Although it does not make any difference as to which end is connected how in a circuit, it does make a difference at which end you begin interpreting the color codes.

4.9-3A   First Color Code Band

This is the band physically closest to the physical end of the resistor. It will not be black, silver, or gold. It will be followed by at least two other close color bands. The first color band represents an assigned color digit (illustrated

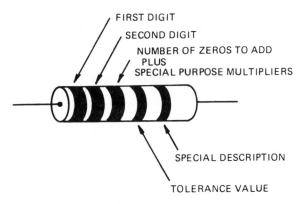

FIRST DIGIT

SECOND DIGIT

NUMBER OF ZEROS TO ADD
PLUS
SPECIAL PURPOSE MULTIPLIERS

SPECIAL DESCRIPTION

TOLERANCE VALUE

Figure 4-27

in Chart 4-2) which is the first number of the resistor's resistance. *Note:* If the first band appears to be double the normal color banding width, it is a wire-wound resistor.

4.9-3B   Second Color Code Band

This band is next to the first color. It indicates the second number of the resistor's resistance. It will not be gold or silver, but can be any of the ten colors listed in Chart 4-2.

Color	1st color digit value	2nd color digit value	3rd color # o's	4th color tolerance	5th color special
Black	0	0	0	20%	—
Brown	1	1	1	1%	1.0 / 1khr (M)*
Red	2	2	2	2%	0.1 / 1khr (P)*
Orange	3	3	3	3%	0.01 / 1khr (R)*
Yellow	4	4	4	4%	0.001 / 1khr (S)*
Green	5	5	5	GMV	tested after load cycle
Blue	6	6	6	6%	—
Violet	7	7	7	7%	—
Gray	8	8	8 (X0.01)	8%	—
White	9	9	9 (X0.1)	9%	solderable terminals**
Gold	—	—	X0.1	5%	—
Silver	—	—	X0.01	10%	—
No color	—	—	—	20%	—

 * Reliable types only
** Film types
   GMV—Guaranteed Minimum Value
   Note: You may find gray or silver and white or gold used in the third band. Gray = silver; white = gold in the third band.

EIA-MIL Color Codes
Chart 4-2

4.9-3C   Third Color Code Band

This band is used for two general purposes. The first purpose is to tell via color digit assignment the number of zeros to add to the first and second band digits. The colors used defining the number of zeros to add are black through white or zero-zeros to nine zeros. All color coded resistors will have at least three color bands.

The second purpose is to define resistive values that are less than ten ohms and those less than one ohm. The two colors representing this second purpose are gold and silver. When silver appears in the third color band, the resistance will be under one ohm because this color means multiply the first two digits by 0.01, which also equals division by 100. If gold appears in the third color band, the resistance will be less than ten ohms because it implies multiplication of the first two digits by 0.1 or division by 10, its equivalent.

4.9-3D   Fourth Color Code Band

The fourth band may or may not be included on color coded resistors. Normally, this band, if present, will be separated from the first three bands by a wider space, to discourage misreading. If no fourth band exists, the tolerance indicated is 20 percent. Sometimes a black band is found where the fourth band would be; this also means 20 percent tolerance. All other colors, with the exception of green, in most cases represent a tolerance value equaling their color digit assignment. Resistors having a 10-percent tolerance value are identified by silver and 5 percent tolerance resistors by gold when positioned in the fourth band. If green is used a guaranteed minimum value of 0 to 100 percent tolerance is implied.

4.9-3E   Fifth Color Code Band

The fifth color band may or may not be present. Normally, if used, there will be four preceding bands also. This band tells us three specific things: a failure rate, type of terminal, and test sequence.

The failure rate is for "established reliability" resistors which is actually a failure rate guarantee. These particular resistors are rated for 1000 hours of use. Although colors are used indicating a percent per 1000 hours, a letter is also assigned and might be mentioned instead of its percentage. If brown is found (letter M) the rating is 1.0; red (letter P) means 0.1; orange (letter R) means 0.01; and yellow (letter S) means 0.001 which is the percentage given for 1000 hours.

The type of terminal, indicated for film types, uses the color white which says the terminals are solderable.

If green is found in the fifth band, this signifies that it was tested after the load cycle test.

Temperature coefficients are related in print by "MIL" characteristic letters being K, H, and J. The letter K equals a change of ± 100 parts per million per degree centigrade (ppm/°C). H means ± 50ppm/°C and J means 25ppm/°C.

4.9-4 METAL-GLAZE/GLASS TIN-OXIDE RESISTORS

The resistive element for this type consists of a layer of films of glass and metal fused into a crystalline ceramic core or tin-oxide deposits fused to a glass or ceramic surface in spiral paths. They use standard EIA-MIL color coding, having tin-electroplated copper leads, a solvent-resistant molded body, and will have their resistive values printed on them.

TYPE	RESISTIVE RANGE	TOLERANCE RANGE	WATTAGE RANGE
glazed metal	1 Ω to 500 M Ω	± 2 to ± 5%	1/10 to 10 watts
metal-oxide	10 Ω to 15 M Ω	± 1 to ± 5%	1/4 to 120 watts

Normal wattage ratings of 1/8, 1/4, 1/2 and 2 watts are common. The MIL letter-number assigned to this type begins with RN. Closer tolerances because of manufacturing processes, along with more stability throughout operating temperature ranges, are advantages for their use.

4.9-5 FILM RESISTORS

The resistive elements for film type resistors consist of thin layers of resistive material deposited on insulated cores which make up low resistance values. Resistances equivalent to those found in wire-wound resistors are possible by using spiral patterns; coarse patterns are used for intermediate resistances and close spirals are used for high resistances. They are somewhat easy to recognize since they are generally smaller in physical size and more stable than the carbon type resistors. Carbon film resistors also have greater heat dissipation abilities than carbon composition types. A 1/2 watt film resistor may be nearly the same physical size as a 1/4 watt carbon film resistor but a side by side comparison will show the larger wattage resistor (film type) as being slightly longer. The body may be molded (letter M) or conformally coated (letter C). If color codes are employed in the manufacturing process, the EIA-MIL color coding method is used with modification. For example, if you feel confident with resistor color code knowledge, then decipher this color code found on a 1/2 watt film type color coded axial lead resistor: First color—*yellow*, second color—*violet*, third color—*black*, fourth color—*red*, and fifth color—*red*.

If you mentally said 47 ohms plus and minus 2 percent having a 0.1/KHR failure rate, then you and I would have agreed before I became educated. Educated by the fact that film resistors manufactured by someone, somewhere use five color bands to do what four bands did before. The yellow, violet, black, red, red resistor is not a 47 ohm resistor, but is 47,000 ohms (47K ohms) having a tolerance of ± 2 percent. Film resistors use the first two color bands for the first and second digits just as before. The third band adheres to the EIA color code number assignment. If black is found in the third band, then add the zero to the first two digits. If a color through white is observed, then add its digit value to the previous two-digit number. To clarify this, suppose you had a yellow, violet, green, red, red resistor; its resistive value would be 47,500 ohms ± 2 percent or 47.5K ohms ± 2 percent. As you no doubt guessed, the fourth band indicates how many zeros to add, while the fifth band tells us the tolerance. For confusion's sake, both color coding methods (Charts 4-2 and 4-3) will be encountered in your daily work.

If you are still confused, look at the metal film color code data in Chart 4-3 or hope that the value is printed or stamped on the resistor body as it sometimes is.

TYPE	RESISTIVE RANGE	TOLERANCE RANGE	WATTAGE RANGE
carbon film	1 Ω to 200 M Ω	± 5 to ± 10%	1/10 to 100 watts
cermit film	10 Ω to 500 M Ω	± 0.5 to ± 5%	1/10 to 2 watts
film (bulk property)	30 Ω to 10 M Ω	±0.01 to ± 1%	1/20 to 3/4 watts
metal film	0.27 Ω to 100 M Ω	±0.01 to ± 2%	1/20 to 20 watts

Wattage ratings vary depending upon temperature, resistance, and the standards agency or manufacturer. What the manufacturer calls 1/4 watt, MIL standards say is perhaps 1/30 watt. Maximum voltages are also given for specific resistances at the manufacturer's suggested value of wattage. For example, resistors rated at 1/8 and 1/4 watt have 200 volts maximum rating; 1/2 to 3/4 watt have 250 volts maximum; 1 to 1½ watts have 350 volts maximum, and 2 watts have up to 700 volts maximum ratings. To be safe, make certain of wattage and/or voltage limitations for your particular use.

4.9-6   WIRE-WOUND RESISTORS

Wire-wound resistors normally have low resistances and are capable of carrying high amounts of current. There are many different techniques used in manufacturing and, therefore, physical size is of little importance. The resistive element normally employed is a nickel-chromium or a copper-nickel alloy wound around a tubular ceramic material. They are quite easy to recognize because resistive values and wattage ratings are often printed on the cases. The cases are usually rectangular or circular, and made of ceramic materials, but metal heat-sink types are also popular. Sometimes they are color coded using the standard EIA-MIL color codes. If this is the case, the first color band is about twice the width of the other bands.

TYPE	RESISTIVE RANGE	TOLERANCE RANGE	WATTAGE RANGE
wire-wound (power)	0.1 Ω to 1 M Ω	± 1 to ± 10%	1 to 1500 watts
wire-wound (precision)	0.001 Ω to 60 M Ω	± 0.001 to ± 1%	1/25 to 250 watts

COLOR	1st COLOR DIGIT VALUE	2nd COLOR DIGIT VALUE	3rd COLOR DIGIT VALUE	4th COLOR # ADDITIONAL ZEROS TO ADD	5th COLOR TOLERANCE
Black	0	0	0	—	—
Brown	1	1	1	1	1%
Red	2	2	2	2	2%
Orange	3	3	3	3	—
Yellow	4	4	4	4	—
Green	5	5	5	5	0.5%
Blue	6	6	6	—	0.25%
Violet	7	7	7	—	0.1%
Gray	8	8	8	—	0.05%
White	9	9	9	—	—
Gold	—	—	—	X0.1	5%
Silver	—	—	—	X0.01	10%

* Always black

FILM TYPE COLOR CODED RESISTORS

Chart 4-3

4

The wattage rating can be extended somewhat if their heat can be dissipated by their positioning or mounting. Each specific manufactured wattage group may have its own preferred or standard resistive values.

4.9-7   VARIABLE RESISTORS

When purchasing variable resistors, several options are available other than a material choice between carbon or wire-wound. You can buy variable resistors (potentiometers) having a bushing or tab mount, with or without a switch (and if with a switch, the selection of rotary or push-pull), plug in or snap in shaft having nylon, plastic, or a metal shaft, size of shaft choice, shaft out front or out rear, blade or Phillips screwdriver adjust, regular size or miniature, trimmers, etc. Whatever the purchase, their resistive values range from about 100 ohms to around 10 million ohms, having 1/5 watt carbon or conductive plastic, 1/8 watt linear taper, 1/2 watt audio taper, 3/4 watt linear taper or even cermet types. Generally, the working voltage range is from 250 volts to 4000 volts.

Definitions for variable resistors called rheostats and potentiometers are as follows: the *rheostat* is a variable resistor which uses only two terminals and finds its primary use in *current control*. The *potentiometer,* also a variable resistor, uses three terminals and finds its primary use in *voltage control*. The potentiometer can be used as a rheostat, but a rheostat cannot be used as a potentiometer. Conventional practice also dictates that a rheostat or potentiometer be connected in a circuit so that a clockwise rotation of the shaft produces an increase in resistance while a counterclockwise rotation produces a decrease.

4.9-7A   Taper

Taper is a term common to variable resistors. It is the percent of resistance change compared to the percent of shaft rotation in a clockwise direction. It is the left to right when viewing from the front normal shaft end. There are three tapers you will encounter. These are:

(a) *left-hand logarithmic taper* (slang term: left-hand). It is common in audio circuitry where the percentage of change is small at the start of rotation.

(b) *Right-hand logarithmic taper* (slang term: reverse audio). It is common in audio circuitry where the percentage of change is large at the start of rotation.

(c) *linear taper* (slang term: linear). It is also common in audio circuitry where the percentage of change is directly proportional to rotational change.

Note: When checking taper via an ohmmeter, attach probes to the center and left terminals when viewing the potentiometer from the front, having terminals pointing down.

When measuring a potentiometer via an ohmmeter, connect the ohmmeter lead across the two outside terminals (terminals #1 and #3 in Figure 4-28). This measures total resistance and saves rotating the pot shaft for measurements; do use either end and the middle terminal when verifying resistance consistency; often you can discover a dirty or worn pot when using the second method.

Caution: Whenever replacing potentiometers, never replace a plastic or nylon shaft with one of metal since a shock hazard may exist.

RESISTORS

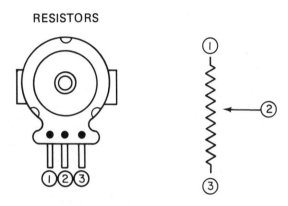

Figure 4-28

Left-handed taper: small change at start of rotation;
Reverse audio taper: large change at start of rotation;
Linear taper: proportional change as rotation is varied.

4.9-7B   Wire-Wound Audio Attenuator

This is often termed balance, stereo level control, L pad attenuator, LL pad attenuator, and T pad attenuator. It has specifications ranging from 4Ω to 400Ω and ten watts to fifty watts. Some useful and common applications are as follows:

Audio Attenuator Application Illustration

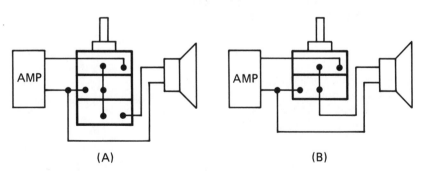

(A)   (B)

Figure 4-29

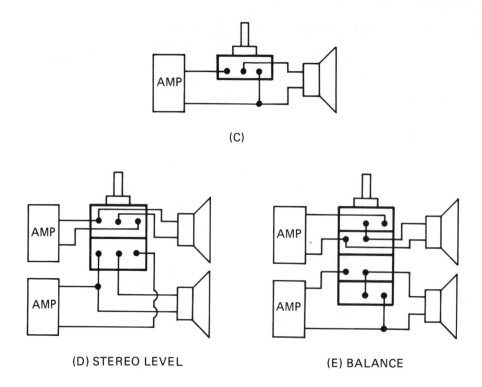

(C)

(D) STEREO LEVEL　　　　　　　　　(E) BALANCE

Figure 4-29 (continued)

4.9-8　KIRCHHOFF'S VOLTAGE LAW—THE IMPLIED MEANING

"The algebraic sum of all the voltages around the circuit is zero." That is, in any complete circuit, all of the voltage applied will be used or consumed. The individual voltage drop across any component or device in the circuit will, when added together, equal the applied voltage.

4.9-9　TOTAL VOLTAGE IN RESISTIVE SERIES CIRCUITS (AC AND DC APPLICATIONS)

E_T = total applied voltage (volts)
R　= resistance (ohms)
E_R = potential difference across
　　　particular resistor (volts)

$$E_T = E_{R1} + E_{R2} + E_{R3} + \ldots$$

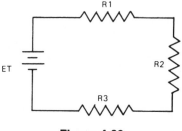

Figure 4-30

4.9-10   VOLTAGE DIVIDER FORMULA

Note: A voltage divider is nothing more than a series circuit from which differing voltages needed are taken at various points in the circuit—all from the same voltage source. The following formulas will help you with voltage dividers. Refer to Figure 4-30.

$$E_{R1} = E_T \left(\frac{R1}{R_T}\right)$$

$$E_{R2} = E_T \left(\frac{R2}{R_T}\right)$$

$$E_{R3} = E_T \left(\frac{R3}{R_T}\right)$$

E_{R1} = voltage developed across R_1
E_{R2} = voltage developed across R_2
E_{R3} = voltage developed across R_3
R_T = circuitry total resistance

4.9-11   TOTAL VOLTAGE IN RESISTIVE PARALLEL CIRCUITS (AC AND DC APPLICATIONS)

E_T = total applied voltage (volts)
R = resistance (ohms)
E_R = potential difference across particular resistor (volts)
$E_T = E_{R1} = E_{R2} = E_{R3}$

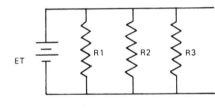

Figure 4-31

4

4.9-12   KIRCHHOFF'S CURRENT LAW—THE IMPLIED MEANING

"The algebraic sum of all the currents at any point in the circuit is zero." That is, in any complete circuit, the total circuit current will not change in value. The current leaving the negative connection of the power source is the total current and will have the same quantity value as the current returning to or entering into the positive power source connection. This total current, which leaves the power source, will simply divide itself into as many smaller values of itself as required by those components or devices connected in the circuit. These individual smaller value portions of the original total current value will regroup at various points throughout the circuit on the way back to the voltage source regardless, whether using theoretical electron current flow (negative to positive) or conventional current flow (positive to negative).

4.9-13 TOTAL CURRENT IN RESISTIVE SERIES CIRCUITS (AC AND DC APPLICATIONS)

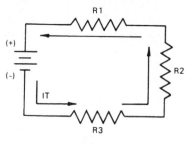

I_T = total current (amperes)
I_R = current flowing through that particular resistor (amperes)
R = resistor's resistance (ohms)

$$I_T = I_{R1} = I_{R2} = I_{R3}$$

Figure 4-32

4.9-14 TOTAL CURRENT IN RESISTIVE PARALLEL CIRCUITS (AC AND DC APPLICATIONS)

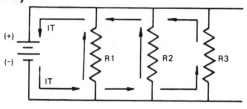

I_T = total current (amperes)
R = resistor's resistance (ohms)
I_R = current flowing through that particular resistor (amperes)

$$I_T = I_{R1} + I_{R2} + I_{R3} + \ldots .$$

Figure 4-33

4.9-15 CURRENT DIVIDER FORMULA

$$I_{R1} = I_T \left(\frac{R_2}{R_1 + R_2} \right)$$

$$I_{R2} = I_T \left(\frac{R_1}{R_1 + R_2} \right)$$

Note: Formulas good for a two-path current divider omit resistor R_3 in Figure 4-33 for application.

4.9-16 TOTAL RESISTANCE IN RESISTIVE SERIES CIRCUITS (AC AND DC APPLICATIONS)

R_T = total resistance (ohms)

R_1-R_4 = individual resistance (ohms)

$$R_T = R_1 + R_2 + R_3 + R_4 + \ldots .$$

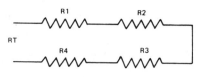

Figure 4-34

4.9-17 TOTAL RESISTANCE IN RESISTIVE PARALLEL CIRCUITS (AC AND DC APPLICATIONS)

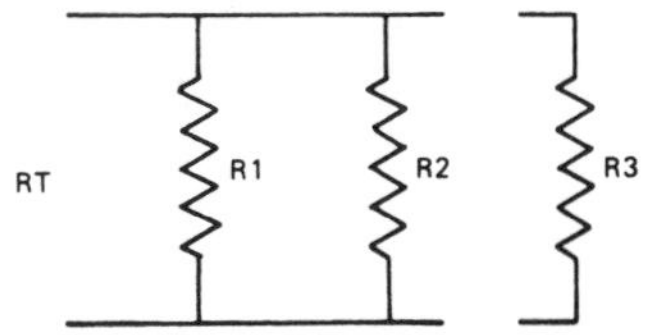

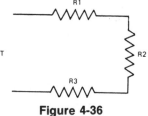

R_T = total resistance (ohms)
R_1-R_3 = individual resistor's resistance

Figure 4-35

A. (for two) $R_T = \dfrac{R_1 \times R_2}{R_1 + R_2}$

B. (finding unknown) $R_2 = \dfrac{R_T \times R_1}{R_1 - R_T}$

C. (for any number) $R_T = \dfrac{1}{\dfrac{1}{R_1} + \dfrac{1}{R_2} + \dfrac{1}{R_3} + \dots}$

Note: Total resistance (R_T) is always less than the smallest resistor's resistance. When two resistors have identical values, the total resistance always equals one-half the value of one resistor's resistance. If there are more than two, identical in value, then divide by the number you have (same valued resistors) into that resistor's resistance. For example, five 10-ohm resistors = $\dfrac{10}{5}$ = 2 ohms for total resistance.

4

4.9-18 TOTAL POWER OF RESISTIVE SERIES CIRCUITS (AC AND DC APPLICATIONS)

P_T = total power (watts)
P_R = wattage of individual resistor
R = resistors used in circuit

$$P_T = P_{R1} + P_{R2} + P_{R3} + \dots$$

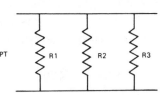

Figure 4-36

4.9-19 TOTAL POWER OF RESISTIVE PARALLEL CIRCUITS (AC AND DC APPLICATIONS)

P_T = total power (watts)
P_R = wattage of individual resistor
R = resistors used in circuit

$$P_T = P_{R1} + P_{R2} + P_{R3} + \dots$$

Figure 4-37

4.9-20   **TOTAL CONDUCTANCE OF RESISTIVE PARALLEL CIRCUITS (AC AND DC APPLICATIONS)**

$$G_T = \frac{1}{R_T} \; or \; S = \frac{1}{R_T}$$

OR

$$G_T = G_1 + G_2 + \ldots.$$
* Replaced by siemens

* G_T = total conductance (mhos)
R_T = circuitry total resistance
* $G_1\text{-}G_2$ = conductance of individual resistors $\left(\dfrac{1}{R_1} + \dfrac{1}{R_2} \right)$

4.10   SILICON CONTROLLED RECTIFIERS
(Refer to Sections 1.10-5, 19, 26, 27, and 48 for Schematic Symbols.)

One solid state in the thyristor family which has fantastic switching capabilities at frequencies near 50 KH$_Z$, no moving parts, and large power control advantages, is the silicon controlled rectifier. The silicon controlled rectifier (SCR) has two possible states of operation: the first is called the *off* state where any currents flowing are negligible; the second is the *on* state. SCRs are normally rated in *on* state maximum forward, RMS current values ranging from about 0.5 amperes to 400 or * 2500 amperes. (* phase control SCRs).

4.10-1   PACKAGING
(Refer to Section 1.9 for Standards)

The packaging styles offer TO-3, TO-5, TO-18, TO-39, TO-48 and 49, TO-64, TO-66, TO-83, TO-92, TO-94, TO-202, TO-220 plus swedge, hexstud, fast pak, or press fits to mention a few. Sometimes various packaging styles tend to be confusing since they may physically look like a three-lead transistor and often begin with the popular 2N prefix.

4.10-2   TESTING

The SCR leads are identified as being a cathode (C), an anode (A), and a gate (G). Most of the time you can tell the difference between a transistor and an SCR by evaluating its resistance. Measure the resistance between the unknown device leads, if it is an SCR, the gate to cathode resistance will be about the same ohmic value even when switching polarity via lead changing. An infinite or nearly infinite resistance will be observed when measuring between the anode and gate or anode and cathode.

4.10-3   RULES/CONDITIONS

The SCR must have certain circuitry criteria to establish conditions suitable for its *on* state operation. There are three: (1) a voltage source — either

AC or DC, (2) a load or something that will use or limit current flow, and (3) some kind of trigger—a gate voltage to force it into the *on* state. The SCR will not or should not conduct when the anode is negative and the cathode positive regardless of the gate voltage potential. This condition is known as "diode action." "Gate action" is a term used when SCR conduction is prevented because the gate voltage is equal to or more negative than the cathode while the anode is positive. The SCR will not or should not conduct and would remain in the *off* state.

SCR *on* state is accomplished when the anode is positive, the cathode negative, and only after a positive potential of sufficient magnitude—a trigger is applied to the gate to establish gate current I_G. Since the SCR is a current-triggered device and not a voltage-triggered device, a constant gate potential need not be used; normally, a pulse of only a few microseconds duration is sufficient to turn it *on*. The SCR once turned *on* remains on even after the trigger voltage or gate pulse has ceased. Now the anode current is limited only by voltage and current rating specifics for the particular SCR employed and the circuitry control features. Once *on*, the SCR behaves like a diode rectifier. The gate potentials applied will have no further use until the SCR is forced back to the *off* state operation.

The *off* state condition is possible when: (1) the DC power source is removed; (2) the DC polarity of the power source is reversed—a polarity change, if AC voltage is the source, is done automatically; (3) the applied voltage potential reduced to a point where the current flowing through the SCR drops below the specified holding current (I_H) value. When any one of these conditions or methods are met or applied, the SCR will turn *off* and will remain *off* until a gate trigger pulse is reapplied.

4

4.10-4   CHARACTERISTICS AND RATING TERMINOLOGY

1. Current commutated turn-off time—t_Q
2. Critical rate applied forward voltage—dv/dt
3. Gate power—P_{GM}
4. Gate trigger current—I_{GT}
5. Gate trigger voltage—V_{GT}
6. Peak off state voltage—V_{DROM}
7. RMS current—$I_{T(RMS)}$
8. Surge current—I_{TSM}
9. *Forward breakover voltage* ($V_{(BR)F}$, V_{BO}, or $V_{F(BO)}$). This is a voltage rating not exceeded in practice and describes the voltage at which the SCR switches from *off* to *on* with no gate signal applied.
10. Holding current (I_H), also known by some as being the latching current value. It is a value describing the minimum value for SCR

current before switching from the *on* to *off*. Any less current value will definitely cause the SCR to stop conducting.

11. *Forward and reverse blocking,* known by some as "diode action" describes an open circuit condition of the SCR, the time current flow is blocked from anode to cathode or vice versa.

12. *Reverse breakdown voltage*. This is a voltage not exceeded in practice and is almost the same as the zener or avalanche region for a semiconductor diode.

4.10-5 ADDITIONAL NOTES: AC VOLTAGE APPLICATIONS

(A) When AC voltage is applied to a single SCR, the SCR will conduct only on that half-cycle which properly biases the anode and cathode.

(B) The voltage delivered to the load is proportional to the SCR conducting time. Output voltage is variable from nearly 0 percent to about 50 percent of the available input power.

(C) For phase control, the SCR may be *on* for a full half-cycle (conduction angle of 180 degrees) or it may be *off* for the full half-cycle (conduction angle of zero degrees).

(D) SCRs may be connected in series or parallel. The capacity and total usefulness for SCR control can be extended.

SCRs may be used in circuitry where fast turn-off time is not a prime requirement, as in AC phase control situations. The packaging variations for these will still tend to confuse us because many appear to be transistor-like structures. SCRs that are categorized for turn-off time, also known as commutation speed, capability, and other speed characteristics, will be used in DC/AC inverter circuitry. Most of these, because of packaging styles, are more easily identified and will lessen the confusion between transistors and triacs.

4.11 TRANSFORMERS

Transformers, being AC devices, have the ability to provide circuitry isolation, signal coupling, impedance-matching, and voltage-current step-up or step-down action. Data and standards of importance concerning audio, IF, and power transformers will be outlined in this section of Chapter 4. The standards for color coding wires are suggested and may or may not be manufactured in accordance with them. When doubt arises, take a continuity check between the wires, pairing or matching primary and secondary leads. Center-tapped leads will require closer resistance checks between the other leads. (Refer to Sections 1.3-33, 34, 35, 36, and 90 for Schematic Symbols.)

4.11-1   AUDIO OUTPUT

The normal frequency of operation is between 20 hertz and 20k hertz. This particular transformer is rated in terms of its primary and secondary winding impedances, plus the wattage rating in watts. The wattage rating describes the maximum power that the secondary can deliver.

When selecting an audio output transformer, three things of importance should be done: (1) match the primary impedance closely to the impedance offered by the circuitry; (2) match the secondary impedance closely to that impedance offered by the speaker; (3) match the transformer power rating with the speaker wattage rating. The recognized audio transformer lead color coding is illustrated in Figure 4-38.

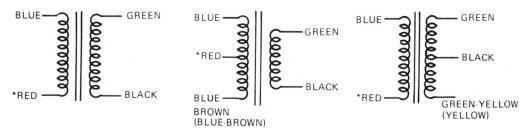

* These leads connect to power source.

Figure 4-38

4.11-2   INTERMEDIATE FREQUENCY

This transformer is designed specifically for operation at a particular frequency. The IF frequencies for standard 540 to 1600k hertz broadcast are 455, 260, and 262.5k hertz; the latter being the vehicular IF assignment. Television sound IF is 41.25 MHz while television picture IF is 45.75 MHz. When VHF is used, a 10.7 MHz IF is required, while for ultra-and super-high frequency equipment, use IF combinations of 30, 60, and 100 MHz.

What all this means is that the IF frequency knowledge is required when replacing these transformers because specific capacitors might be used in parallel with coil windings, thereby producing the desired frequency response. This type of transformer can be checked by verifying schematic resistances of the coils if listed. Adjustments with alignment tools often are possible through top and bottom alignment holes. The repositioning of the tuning slugs peaks the frequency when correct impedance-matching is obtained for that frequency. The intermediate frequency transformer lead colors are illustrated in Figure 4-39, on page 310.

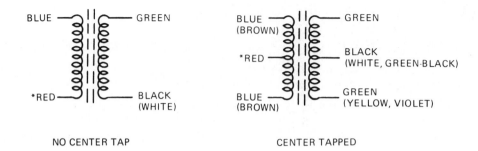

NO CENTER TAP   CENTER TAPPED

*These leads connect to the power source.

Figure 4-39

4.11-3   POWER OR RECTIFIER

Power or rectifier transformers have an operating frequency of 25, 50, 60, or 400 hertz, depending upon the line frequency of the alternating source. This transformer is usually larger physically than audio or IF transformers. The ratings are in terms of the maximum current and voltage delivering capacity of the secondary. An example describing a transformer using 120 volts at 60 hertz might be 520 volts AC at 90mA, 6.3 volts AC at 3.5A, and 5.3 volts AC at 2.5A.

Total wattage normally is not given, but simple calculation can solve this problem. We must first determine the individual winding power ratings and then add them together. The following results when using the previous transformer winding data.

$$
\begin{array}{ll}
520\text{v @ 90mA} \quad 520 \times 0.09 = 46.80 \text{ watts} & P = IE \\
6.3\text{v @ 3.5A} \quad 6.3 \times 3.5 \ = 22.05 \text{ watts} & \\
5.3\text{v @ 2.5A} \quad 5.3 \times 2.5 \ = \underline{13.25 \text{ watts}} & \\
\hphantom{6.3\text{v @ 3.5A} \quad 6.3 \times 3.5 \ } 82.10 \text{ TOTAL WATTAGE} &
\end{array}
$$

The accepted power transformer winding lead color assignments are shown in Figure 4-40.

4.11-4   TRANSFORMER FORMULAS (AC APPLICATIONS ONLY)

Transformers transfer alternating voltage from the primary to secondary and can provide the same voltage on its secondary as on its primary, or the secondary voltage can be stepped-up or down depending upon circuitry requirements. The symbols used in the formulas describing transformer facts are listed first to avoid duplication.

Voltage   Currents

E_p = primary I_p = primary
E_s = secondary I_s = secondary

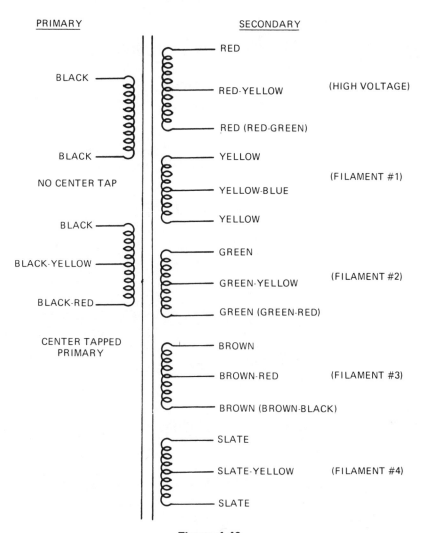

Figure 4-40

Power

Po = output power
PI = input applied
      power

Turns

T = primary to secondary turns ratio
Np = turns of primary
Ns = turns of secondary

Efficiency

Eff = efficiency factor (decimal)
N   = efficiency factor

Impedances

Z_p = primary
Z_s = secondary
Z_a = component in series with primary
Z_b = component in series with secondary
Z_r = ratio

4.11-4A   Transformer Voltage

(A) Primary

$$Ep = \frac{Es\,Np}{Ns} \qquad OR \qquad Ep = \frac{Es\,Is}{Ip}$$

(B) Secondary

$$Es = \frac{Ep\,Ns}{Np} \qquad OR \qquad Es = \frac{Ep\,Ip}{Is}$$

4.11-4B   Transformer Current

(A) Primary

$$Ip = \frac{Es\,Is}{Ep} \qquad OR \qquad Ip = \frac{Ns\,Is}{Np}$$

(B) Secondary

$$Is = \frac{Ep\,Ip}{Es} \qquad OR \qquad Is = \frac{Np\,Ip}{Ns}$$

4.11-4C   Transformer Turns

(A) Primary

$$Np = \frac{Ep\,Ns}{Es} \qquad OR \qquad Np = \frac{Ns\,Is}{Ip}$$

(B) Secondary

$$Ns = \frac{Es\,Np}{Ep} \qquad OR \qquad Ns = \frac{Np\,Ip}{Is}$$

(C) Step-up Turns Ratio

$$T = \frac{Ns}{Np}$$

(D) Step-down Turns Ratio

$$T = \frac{Np}{Ns}$$

4.11-4D   Transformer Impedance

(A) Ratio

$$\frac{Zp}{Zs} = \left(\frac{Np^2}{Ns}\right) \qquad OR \qquad Zp = Zs\,T^2$$

are the following:

(B) Step-up Ratio

$$Zs = Zr\,Zp$$

(C) Step-down Ratio

$$Zs = \frac{Zp}{Zr}$$

(D) Total—looking into primary

$$Zt = Za + Zp - \frac{Zm^2}{Zb + Zs}$$

4.11-4E Transformer Efficiency

(A) General Formula

$$Eff = \frac{Po}{P\imath}$$

(B) Power

$$Po = N\,P\imath \qquad\qquad OR \qquad\qquad Pp = Eff\,P\imath$$

4.11-4F Transformer Voltage, Current, and Turn Relationships

$$\frac{Ep}{Es} = \frac{Np}{Ns} = \frac{Is}{Ip}$$

4

4.12 TRANSISTOR SPECIFICS

Transistors of the junction variety use two basic materials for their construction. The materials used in present day manufacturing are either silicon or germanium. You will find both PNP and NPN transistor types of either material. As a general rule, one can assume a voltage drop across the base-emitter junction to be 0.7 volts for silicon transistors (NPN/PNP) and 0.3 volts for germanium (NPN/PNP) transistors.

The PNP is the complement for the NPN—that is, opposite current direction and opposite voltage polarity. You will hear more solid state devices called complementary something—just remember, it is the same in theory and operation, only different in current direction and voltage references; for example, metal-oxide semiconductors (MOS) or complementary metal-oxide semiconductors (CMOS).

If you hear someone speak of a "small-signal transistor" you should be aware that this term describes those semiconductors of the NPN or PNP variety having low power-wattage ratings of usually less than one watt, and having upper frequency limits of about two to three GHz (gigahertz). It is common practice to use the common-emitter circuitry configuration for small-signal usages. Power transistors, on the other hand, are obviously those PNP and NPN transistors whose wattage ratings are greater than the one-watt value. (Refer to Section 1.9 for Standards and Sections 1.10-1, 2, 3, 7, 12, 13, 17, 18, 21, 22, 24, 29, 31, 33, 37, 38, 41, 44, 52, and 58 for Schematic Symbols.)

4.12-1   MODES OF OPERATION

Transistors of the NPN or PNP variety may be connected in any one of the *three* basic modes of operation or circuitry configurations. These three configurations include (1) the grounded or common base (CB), (2) the grounded collector or emitter follower or common collector (CC), and (3) the grounded or common emitter (CE). The secret of recognition lies in the fact that one of the three transistor elements/leads (emitter, base or collector) is common to both the input and output circuitry. It is upon this mere fact that circuitry reference is made: common base (CB), common collector (CC), and common emitter (CE). For example, picture the following illustration whenever viewing transistor circuitry, and then look for the element common to input and output circuitry.

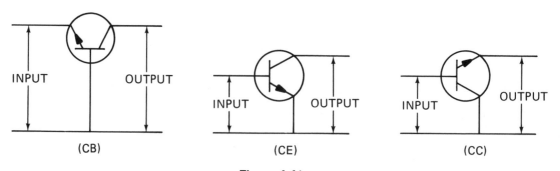

Figure 4-41

These illustrations will provide only basic recognition and will require concentration when analyzing the actual circuitry as you will soon see when biasing voltages and necessary resistors are added to the circuits. But, before going on, you should recognize three basic transistor biasing methods and memorize some very important facts common to all these configurations, regardless of transistor type (silicon/germanium/PNP/NPN). The facts to know are:

1. Emitter current is approximately equal to 100 percent of all current flow.

$$I_E = I_B + I_C$$
(base plus collector current)

2. Base current is approximately equal to 5 percent of all current flow.

$$I_B = I_E - I_C$$
(emitter minus collector current)

3. Collector current is approximately equal to 95 percent of all current flow.

$$I_C = I_E - I_B$$
(emitter minus base current)

The three biasing methods you should recognize, along with these facts are:

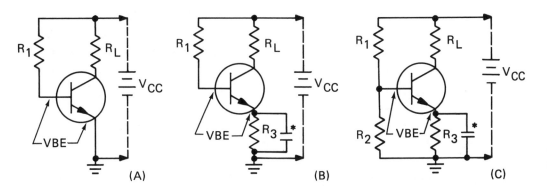

CIRCUIT (A)

$V_{BE} = 0.3v$ germanium   *or*
$V_{BE} = 0.7v$ silicon

$$R_1 = \frac{V_{cc} - V_{BE}}{I_B}$$

$$I_E = I_B + I_C$$

CIRCUIT (B)

$V_{BE} = 0.3v$ germanium
$V_{BE} = 0.7v$ silicon

$$E_{R1} = V_{cc} - E_{R3}$$

$$R_1 = \frac{E_{R1}}{I_B}$$

$$R_1 = \frac{E_{R1}}{I_{R1}}$$

CIRCUIT (C)
(most popular)

$$E_{R2} = R_{R3}$$
$$E_{R1} = V_{cc} - E_{R3}$$
*   *or*
$$E_{R1} = V_{cc} - R_{R2}$$
$$I_{R2} = 10I_B$$

$$R_2 = \frac{E_{R2}}{I_{R2}} \text{ * assume}$$

$$R_1 = \frac{E_{R1}}{I_{R2} + I_B}$$

Figure 4-42

*AC bypass capacitor optional—reduces degeneration

With these lists of information you should be able to look at more realistic circuitry—the kind that exists in real life. It will be noted that biasing method (C) is used in my illustrations (Figures 4-43 to 4-45) and that component number references are given professional names. These names and component numbers are as follows for the CE, CB, and CC circuitry:

$R_1 + R_2$ = voltage divider circuitry
R_1 = base bias resistor (base current flows through it)
R_2 = input signal developing resistor
R_3 = emitter bias/load resistor
R_4 = collector load resistor
C_1 and C_2 = coupling capacitors
C_3 = decoupling capacitor—essentially puts transistor element at ground potential

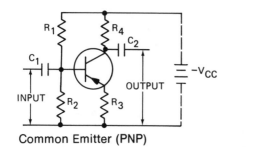 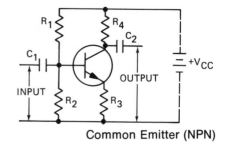

Common Emitter (PNP)   Common Emitter (NPN)

Note: Input and output signals are 180 degrees out of phase.

Figure 4-43

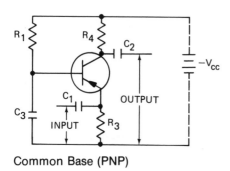 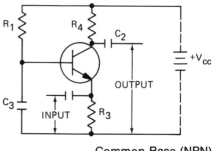

Common Base (PNP)   Common Base (NPN)

Note: Input and output signals are in phase—no signal inversion.

Figure 4-44

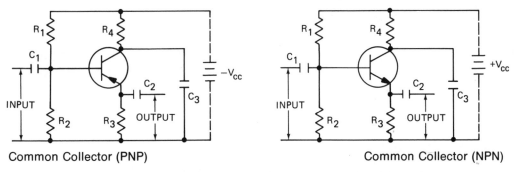

Common Collector (PNP)   Common Collector (NPN)

Note: Input and output signals are in phase—no signal inversion.

Figure 4-45

4.12-2   COMMON EMITTER

The common emitter circuit configuration provides what is called an intermediate input impedance (about 1 kilohm) and an intermediate output impedance (about 50 kilohms). *The input and output signals are 180 degrees out of phase with each other*. This configuration is more frequently used because it offers the greatest gain for all values of load resistance. The current gain for this particular circuit is called Beta (β) and will always be greater than unity; in fact, gains higher than 200 are possible and normal. Although the gain represented by Beta (β) is a ratio between the base and collector currents, is it AC Beta or DC Beta? AC Beta is represented by h_{fe} while DC Beta is h_{FE} in transistor specifications.

4.12-2A   AC Beta

AC Beta is a ratio between a change in collector current and a change in base current *while a fixed collector voltage is applied*.

$$\beta = h_{fe} = \frac{\Delta I_c}{\Delta I_b}$$

ΔI_c = change in collector R_{MS} current

ΔI_b = change in base R_{MS} current

4.12-2B   DC Beta

DC Beta is a ratio between DC base current and the DC collector current.

$$\beta = h_{FE} = \frac{I_C}{I_B}$$

I_C = DC collector current

I_B = DC base current

4.12-2C   Collector Current

OR

$$I_C = \beta I_B$$

$$I_C = I_E - I_B$$

I_C = collector current
β = Beta (current gain)
I_B = base current
I_E = emitter current

4.12-2D   Current Gain

$$* A_I = \frac{\triangle I_C}{\triangle I_B}$$

A_I = current gain
$\triangle I_C$ = collector current change
$\triangle I_B$ = base current change
* Same as AC Beta or h_{fe}

Note: Current gain for the common emitter configuration is almost equal to the common collector's gain, however the CC is a little better.

4.12-2E   DC Load Line

$$V_{cc} = I_c R_c + V_{CE}$$

V_{cc} = collector supply voltage
I_c = collector current
R_c = collector load resistor resistance
V_{CE} = collector-to-emitter voltage

4.12-2F   Emitter Current

OR

OR

$$I_E = I_c + I_B$$

$$I_E = \beta I_B + I_B$$

$$I_E = I_B (\beta + 1)$$

I_E = emitter current
I_c = collector current
I_B = base current
β = Beta

4.12-2G   Input Impedance

$$Z_{ie} = \frac{\triangle V_{BE}}{\triangle I_B}$$

Z_{ie} = input impedance
$\triangle V_{BE}$ = base-to-emitter voltage change
$\triangle I_B$ = base current change

4.12-2H   Output Impedance

$$Z_{oe} = \frac{\Delta V_{CE}}{\Delta I_c}$$

Z_{oe} = output impedance
ΔV_{CE} = collector-to-emitter voltage change
ΔI_C = collector current change

4.12-2I   Power Dissipated

$$P = V_{CE} \times I_C$$

P = power dissipated
V_{CE} = collector-to-emitter voltage
I_C = collector current

4.12-2J   Power Gain

$$A_p = A_I A_V$$

A_p = power gain
A_I = current gain
A_V = voltage gain

4.12-2K   Voltage Gain

$$A = \frac{\Delta V_o}{\Delta V_{in}}$$

OR

$$A = \frac{\Delta V_{CE}}{\Delta V_{BE}}$$

OR

$$A = \frac{\beta_{RL}}{Z_{ie}}$$

A = voltage gain
ΔV_o = output voltage change
ΔV_{in} = input voltage change
ΔV_{CE} = collector-to-emitter voltage change
ΔV_{BE} = base-to-emitter voltage change
β = (Beta) common emitter gain
R_L = collector load resistor resistance
Z_{ie} = input impedance

Note: Voltage gain for a common emitter configuration is almost equal to the voltage gain for a common base. The common emitter, however, is a little better because of higher values of load resistance.

4.12-3   COMMON BASE

The common base is characterized by a low input impedance (about 25-50 ohms) and a high output impedance (about 2k ohms). *The input and output signals are not inverted and remain in phase.* Since the input current is the emitter current, current gains are not possible. Voltage and power gains are possible if the output load resistor is higher in value than the input resistance. The current gain for this type of circuit is called Alpha (α) and is always less than one. There is, however, an AC Alpha and a DC Alpha. The AC Alpha is represented as h_{fb} while DC Alpha is h_{FB}.

4.12-3A   AC Alpha

AC Alpha is the ratio between a change in collector current and a change in emitter current *with a fixed collector voltage*.

$$\alpha = h_{fb} = \frac{\Delta I_c}{\Delta I_e}$$

ΔI_c = change in collector R_{MS} current
ΔI_e = change in emitter R_{MS} current

4.12-3B   DC Alpha

DC Alpha is the ratio between collector DC current and the emitter DC current.

$$\alpha = h_{FB} = \frac{I_C}{I_E}$$

I_C = collector DC current
I_E = emitter DC current

4.12-3C   Collector Current

$$I_C = \alpha I_E$$

OR

$$*I_C = \alpha I_E + I_{co}$$

OR

$$I_C = I_E - I_B$$

I_C = collector current
α = Alpha
I_E = emitter current
I_{co} = collector cutoff current
I_B = base current
* more exact formula

4.12-3D   Collector Current-Saturation

$$I_C \text{ (sat)} = \frac{V_{cc}}{R_c}$$

V_c (sat) = collector saturation current
V_{cc} = collector supply voltage
R_c = collector load resistor resistance

4.12-3E   Current Gain

$$* A_I = \frac{\Delta I_c}{\Delta I_e}$$

A_I = current gain
ΔI_c = collector current R_{MS} change
ΔI_e = emitter current R_{MS} change
* same as AC Alpha or h_{fb}

Note: Current gain for a common base is always less than unity.

4.12-3F   Emitter Current

$$I_E = I_C + I_B$$

I_E = emitter current
I_C = collector current
I_B = base current

4.12-3G   Power Gain

$$A_p = A_I A_V$$

A_p = power gain
A_I = current gain
A_V = voltage gain

4.12-3H   Voltage Gain

$$A_v = \frac{\triangle V_o}{\triangle V_{in}}$$

A_v = voltage gain
$\triangle V_o$ = output voltage change
$\triangle V_{in}$ = input voltage change

Note: Voltage gain for a common base is almost equal to the voltage gain for a common emitter. The common emitter has, however, a higher value because of the higher values of load resistances.

4.12-4   COMMON COLLECTOR

The common collector configuration has been called grounded collector or emitter follower. It is characterized by having high input resistance and low output resistance and *does not invert the input signal —no phase change*. Since the input current is the base current and the emitter current is the sum of both collector and base currents, current gains are possible. However, *there is never a voltage gain greater than one*. The formulas *describing* common collector specifics are:

4.12-4A   Current Gain

$$A_I = \frac{\triangle I_E}{\triangle I_B}$$

OR

$$A_I = \frac{1}{1 - \alpha}$$

* A_I = current gain (α)
$\triangle I_E$ = emitter current change
$\triangle I_B$ = base current change
* output over input

Note: Current gain for the common collector is almost equal to the current gain for the common emitter; the common collector is a bit better.

4.12-4B   Emitter Current

$$I_E = I_C + I_B$$

OR

$$I_E = I_B = \alpha\, I_E$$

OR

$$*I_E = \frac{I_B + I_{co}}{1 - \alpha}$$

I_E = emitter current
I_C = collector current
I_B = base current
α = Alpha (current gain)
I_{co} = collector cutoff current
* more exact formula

4.12-4C   Power Gain

$$A_p = A_I A_V$$

OR

$$A_p = \frac{1}{1 - \alpha}$$

A_p = power gain
A_I = current gain
A_V = voltage gain
α = Alpha (current gain)

4.12-4D   Voltage Gain

$$A_V = \frac{\triangle V_o}{\triangle V_{in}}$$

A_V = voltage gain
$\triangle V_o$ = output voltage change
$\triangle V_{in}$ = input voltage change

Note: The common collector configuration never has a voltage gain greater than one — usually it is less than unity.

4.12-5   GENERAL USE FORMULAS

4.12-5A   Alpha-Beta Relationship

$$\alpha = \frac{\beta}{\beta + 1}$$

$$\beta = \frac{\alpha}{1 - \alpha}$$

α = common base gain
β = common emitter gain

4.12-5B   Current Relationships

$$\alpha = \frac{I_C}{I_E}$$

$$I_E = \frac{I_C}{\alpha}$$

$$I_C = \alpha\, (I_E)$$

$$\beta = \frac{I_C}{I_B}$$

$$I_B = \frac{I_C}{\beta}$$

$$I_C = \beta\, (I_B)$$

$I_E = I_C + I_B = 100\%$
$I_C = I_E - I_B = \quad 95\%$
$I_B = I_E - I_C = \quad \;\; 5\%$

α = Alpha
β = Beta
I_E = emitter current
I_B = base current
I_C = collector current

4.12-5C   Input Resistance

$$Ri = \frac{\Delta Vi}{\Delta Ii}$$

Ri = input resistance
ΔVi = source or input voltage change
ΔIi = input current change

4.12-5D   Output Resistance

$$Ro = \frac{\Delta Vo}{\Delta Io}$$

Ro = output resistance
ΔVo = output voltage change
ΔIo = output current change

4.12-5E   Power Gain

$$Ap = \frac{\Delta Po}{\Delta Pi}$$

Ap = power gain
ΔPo = output power change
ΔPi = input power change

4.12-5F   Voltage Gain

$$A = \frac{\Delta Vc}{\Delta Vb}$$

A   = voltage gain
ΔVc = collector voltage change
ΔVb = base voltage change

4.12-6   GERMANIUM POWER TRANSISTORS

Wattages ranging from about 100 milliwatts to hundreds of watts are obtainable using germanium power transistors. The packaging styles illustrated in Section 1.9-1, vary from TO-3, TO-36, TO-41, TO-66 to various other styles and shapes. Normally, they are grouped according to specific purposes, as drivers, outputs, currents, high voltage, etc. Most manufacturers identify them by assigning 2N prefixes plus numbers. The collector's current maximum value (IC max) is an important factor used when selecting germanium power transistors. Manufacturers normally give this pertinent information when describing their particular transistor. Collector currents from about 1 ampere to 50 and 60 amperes are normal, but currents of 100, 150 and higher are possible when power packages are assembled.

4.12-7   SIGNIFICANCE OF TRANSISTOR LETTER SYMBOLS

Since the development of solid state technology has increased the number of abbreviations, quantity letter subscripts, and symbols often encountered in the field of Electronics, it is both desirable and necessary to use some system to designate circuit parameters. The following general rules conform to the somewhat standardized practice used today.

1. DC values of quantities are indicated by capital letters with capital subscripts (V_{CE}), while direct supply voltages have subscripts repeated (V_{CC}).

2. rms values have capital letters with lower case subscripts (V_{cb}), while time-varying components of currents and voltages have lower case letters with lower case subscripts, (v_{cb}).

3. Instantaneous values are indicated with lower case letters with upper case subscripts (v_{BE}).

4. Maximum or peak values are like rms values but have an additional subscript "m" (E_{bem}).

5. Circuit elements are designated with capital letters (R_{10}) and transistor parameters have lower case symbols (h_{11}).

4.12-7A   Transistor Letter Symbols for Current

MEANING	LETTER SYMBOL
Average output rectified current	I_O
Base current (instantaneous-AC)	i_b
Changing base current (AC-rms)	I_b
Changing collector current (AC)	i_c
Collector current (DC*-between base and emitter)	I_{CEX} * specified circuit
Collector current (rms)	I_c
Collector cutoff DC current (base open)	I_{CEO}
Collector cutoff DC current (base short circuited to emitter)	I_{CES}
Collector cutoff DC current (emitter open)	I_{CBO}
Collector cutoff DC current (specified resistance between base and emitter)	I_{CER}
Collector cutoff DC current (specified voltage between base and emitter)	I_{CEV}
Common base forward current ratio (large signal, short circuit)	H_{Fb}
Common emitter forward current ratio (large signal, short circuit)	H_{Fe}
Common collector forward current ratio (large signal, short circuit)	H_{Fc}
Current amplification with output short circuited	H_{21}
Current gain	A_i
Current stability factor	S_I
DC base current	I_B
DC collector current (maximum continuous)	I_C
Drain current (maximum continuous DC)	I_D
Drain cutoff current	$I_D(off)$
Drain current at zero gate or bias voltage	I_{DSS}

MEANING	LETTER SYMBOL
DC emitter current (total)	I_e
Emitter DC current	I_E
Emitter-collector offset current	$I_{EC(OFS)}$
Emitter current (instantaneous)	i_e
Emitter cutoff DC current (collector open)	I_{EBO}
Emitter cutoff DC current (base short circuited to collector)	I_{ECS}
Forward current (alternating component)	I_f
Forward current (DC)	I_F
Forward current (DC with alternating component)	$I_{F(AV)}$
Forward current (instantaneous)	i_F
Forward current (overload)	$I_{F(OV)}$
Forward current (peak surge)	I_{FSM}
Forward current (peak total value)	I_{FM}
Forward current transfer ratio for common base (static value)	h_{FB}
Forward current transfer ratio for common base (small signal, short circuit)	h_{fb}
Forward current transfer ratio for common collector (static value)	h_{FC}
Forward current transfer ratio for common collector (small signal, short circuit)	h_{fc}
Forward current transfer ratio for common emitter (static value) DC Beta	h_{FE}
Forward current transfer ratio for common emitter (small signal, short circuit) AC Beta	h_{fe}
Gate current (DC)	I_G
Gate current (forward)	I_{GF}
Gate current (reverse)	I_{GR}
Maximum peak collector current	I_{CM}
Peak point current (double-base transistors)	I_P
Regulator current (DC reference)	I_Z
Regulator current-reference current (DC max rated)	I_{ZM}
Regulator current-reference current (DC near breakdown knee)	I_{ZK}
Reverse current (alternating components-rms)	I_r
Reverse current (instantaneous)	i_r
Reverse current (total-rms)	i_R (rms)
Reverse DC current	I_R
Reverse recovery current	i_R (REC)
Source current (zero gate voltage)	I_{SDS}
Valley point current (double base transistors)	I_V

4

4-12-7B   Transistor Letter Symbols for Voltages

MEANING	LETTER SYMBOL
Base-collector DC voltage	V_{BC}
Base-collector voltage (rms)	V_{bc}
Base-collector voltage (instantaneous)	v_{bc}
Base-emitter voltage (rms)	V_{be}
Base supply DC voltage	V_{BB}
Breakdown reverse voltage	BV_R
Breakdown voltage between collector-base (emitter open)	BV_{CBO}, V_{CBO}
Breakdown voltage between collector-emitter (base open)	BV_{CEO}, V_{CEO}
Breakdown voltage between collector-emitter (base short circuited to emitter)	BV_{CES}
Breakdown voltage between emitter-base (collector open) maximum	BV_{EBO}, V_{EBO}
Changing voltage (ac) between base-collector	V_{bc}
Changing voltage (ac) between base-emitter	V_{be}
Changing voltage (ac) between collector-emitter	V_{ce}
Collector DC supply voltage	V_{CC}
Collector to base voltage (rms)	V_{cb}
Collector to base voltage (instantaneous)	v_{cb}
Collector to emitter saturation voltage	$V_{ce(sat)}$
Collector to emitter voltage (instantaneous)	V_{ce}
Emitter to base DC voltage	V_{EB}
Emitter to base voltage (rms)	V_{eb}
Emitter to base voltage (instantaneous)	v_{eb}
Emitter to collector DC voltage	V_{EC}
Emitter to collector voltage (rms)	V_{ec}
Emitter to collector voltage (instantaneous)	v_{ec}
Emitter supply DC voltage	V_{EE}
Fixed base-emitter DC voltage	V_{BE}
Fixed collector-emitter DC voltage	V_{CE}
Forward DC voltage	V_F
Forward voltage (instantaneous)	v_f
Input voltage	E in
Maximum voltage between gate and source	V_{GSS}
Maximum voltage between drain and source	V_{DS}
Output voltage	E out
Reach through voltage	V_{RT}
Reverse DC voltage	V_R
Reverse voltage (instantaneous)	v_r
Reverse voltage transfer ratio for common base (small signal, open circuit)	h_{rb}

MEANING	LETTER SYMBOL
Reverse voltage transfer ratio for common collector (small signal, open circuit)	h_{rc}
Reverse voltage transfer ratio for common emitter (small signal, open circuit)	h_{re}
Saturation voltage	V sat
Source voltage	V_g, V_s
Voltage feedback ratio with input open circuited	H_{12}
Voltage gain	A_v
Voltage stability factor	S_v

4.12-7C   Transistor Resistances Letter Symbols

MEANING	LETTER SYMBOL
AC base resistance	r_b
AC collector resistance	r_c
AC emitter resistance	r_e
Collector-emitter saturation resistance	$r_{CE(sat)}$
Common base input resistance (static value)	h_{IB}
Common collector input resistance (static value)	h_{IC}
Common emitter input resistance (static value)	h_{IE}
Forward transfer resistance with input open	r_{fe}
Input resistance of common base (output short circuited)	h_{ib}
Input resistance of common collector (output short circuited)	h_{ic}
Input resistance of common emitter (output short circuited)	h_{ie}
Input resistance with output open	r_{ie}
Load resistance	R_L
Mutual resistance	r_m
Output resistance with input open	r_{oe}
Reverse transfer resistance with input open	r_{re}

4.12-7D   Transistor Amplification Letter Symbols

MEANING	LETTER SYMBOL
Average power gain of common base (large signal)	G_{PB}
Average power gain of common base (small signal)	G_{pb}
Average power gain of common collector (large signal)	G_{PC}
Average power gain of common collector (small signal)	G_{pc}
Average power gain of common emitter (large signal)	G_{PE}
Average power gain of common emitter (small signal)	G_{pe}

4

4.12-7D   Transistor Amplification Letter Symbols, continued

MEANING	LETTER SYMBOL
Forward short circuit current amplification factor (common base)	α fb
Forward short circuit current amplification factor (common collector)	α fc
Forward short circuit current amplification factor (common emitter)	α fe
Reverse open circuited voltage amplification factor (common base)	μ rb
Reverse common circuited voltage amplification factor (common collector)	μ rc
Reverse open circuited voltage amplification factor (common emitter)	μ re

4.12-7E   Transistor Conductance Letter Symbols

Note: You will find the unit of siemens (s) replacing the unit of mhos (g)

MEANING	LETTER SYMBOL
Base-collector conductance	g_{bc}
Base-emitter conductance	g_{be}
Collector-emitter conductance	g_{ce}
Common base output conductance (open circuit, static value)	h_{OB}
Common collector output conductance (open circuit, static value)	h_{OC}
Common emitter output conductance (open circuit, static value)	h_{OE}
Forward transfer conductance	g_{fe}
Input conductance	g_{ie}
Output conductance	g_{oe}
Output conductance of common base with input open	h_{ob}
Output conductance of common collector with input open	h_{oc}
Output conductance of common emitter with input open	h_{oe}
Reverse transfer conductance	g_{re}

4.12-7F   Transistor Capacitance Letter Symbols

MEANING	LETTER SYMBOL
Common base input capacitance	C_{ib}
Common base input capacitance (open circuit)	C_{ibo}
Common base input capacitance (short circuit)	C_{ibs}
Common base output capacitance	C_{ob}

MEANING	LETTER SYMBOL
Common base output capacitance (open circuit)	C_{obo}
Common base output capacitance (short circuit)	C_{obs}
Common base reverse transfer capacitance (short circuit)	C_{rbs}
Common collector input capacitance	C_{ic}
Common collector output capacitance	C_{oc}
Common collector reverse transfer capacitance (short circuit)	C_{rcs}
Common emitter input capacitance	C_{ie}
Common emitter input capacitance (open circuit)	C_{ieo}
Common emitter input capacitance (short circuit)	C_{ies}
Common emitter output capacitance	C_{oe}
Common emitter output capacitance (open circuit)	C_{oeo}
Common emitter output capacitance (short circuit)	C_{oes}
Common emitter reverse transfer capacitance (short circuit)	C_{res}
Drain source capacitance (gate shorted to source)	C_{oss}
Gate source capacitance (drain shorted to source)	C_{iss}
Interelement capacitance (base-collector)	C_{cb}
Interelement capacitance (base-emitter)	C_{eb}
Interelement capacitance (collector-emitter)	C_{ce}
Reflected capacitance	C_{sp}
Reverse transfer capacitance	C_{rss}

4.12-7G   Transistor Power Letter Symbols

MEANING	LETTER SYMBOL
Base-emitter total power input (DC, average)	P_{BE}
Base-emitter total power input (instantaneous)	p_{BE}
Collector-base total power input (DC, average)	P_{CB}
Collector-base total power input (instantaneous)	p_{CB}
Collector-emitter total power input (DC, average)	P_{CE}
Collector-emitter total power input (instantaneous)	p_{CE}
Common base input power (large signal)	P_{IB}
Common base input power (small signal)	P_{ib}
Common base output power (large signal)	P_{OB}
Common base output power (small signal)	P_{ob}
Common collector input power (large signal)	P_{IC}
Common collector input power (small signal)	P_{ic}
Common collector output power (large signal)	P_{OC}
Common collector output power (small signal)	P_{oc}
Common emitter input power (large signal)	P_{IE}
Common emitter input power (small signal)	P_{ie}
Common emitter output power (large signal)	P_{OE}

4

4.12-7G   Transistor Power Letter Symbols, continued

MEANING	LETTER SYMBOL
Common emitter output power (small signal)	P_{oe}
Emitter-base total power input (DC, average)	P_{EB}
Emitter-base total power input (instantaneous)	p_{ES}
Total average/maximum power dissipated at specified case temperature	P_T, P_D

4.12-7H   Miscellaneous Transistor Letter Symbols

MEANING	LETTER SYMBOL
Ambient temperature	T_A
Base electrode	B, b
Case temperature	T_C
Collector electrode	C, c
Combination of "N" type and "P" type semiconductor	PN
Common base configuration	CB
Common collector configuration	CC
Common emitter configuration	CE
Common emitter input impedance (small signal, short circuited)	h_{ie}
Common base static transconductance	gM^b
Common emitter static transconductance	gM^e
Common collector static transconductance	gM^c
Conversion loss	L_c
Cutoff frequency	$f\alpha$
Emitter electrode	E, e
Fall time	tf
Forward recovery time	tfr
Forward transconductance	g_{fs}
Hybrid	h
Input impedance with output short circuited	H_{11}
Junction temperature	T_j or T_J
Large signal breakdown impedance	BZ
Large signal transconductance (common base)	Gmb
Large signal transconductance (common collector)	Gmc
Large signal transconductance (common emitter)	Gme
Noise figure	NF
Operating temperature	Topr
Output admittance with input open circuited	H_{22}
Pulse average time	tw
Pulse time	tp
Reverse recovery time	trr
Rise time	tr

MEANING	LETTER SYMBOL
Semiconductor with acceptor impurity	P type
Semiconductor with donor impurity	N type
Small-signal breakdown impedance	b_z
Small-signal transconductance (common base)	g_{mb}
Small-signal transconductance (common collector)	g_{mc}
Small-signal transconductance (common emitter)	g_{me}
Storage temperature	T_{stg}
Storage time	ts
Temperature	T
Time delay	td
Total power input (DC, average)	P_T
Total power input (instantaneous)	p_T
Transistor with one N type and two P type semiconductors	PNP
Transistor with one P type and two N type semiconductors	NPN

4.13   TIMERS

Single timers, dual timers, quad timers, long-range and programmable timers or counters are of the monolithic IC variety and have been replacing the outmoded mechanical and electromechanical timing devices. Precise timing pulse rates determined by external resistor and capacitor product values have become widely used and accepted. The 555, in my opinion, was the real beginning to flexible, limitless, and economical pulse generation. The 555, although somewhat standardized in physical size, shape, pin nomenclature, and recognized by three exact numbers, is identified by unique manufacturers' prefixes. Fairchild, for example, uses a *uA* prefix, Intersil, the *NE*, Motorola, *MC*, National, *LM*, Raytheon, *RC*, Signetics, *NE* and Texas Instruments uses *SN72*, to name a few. In each case, timing particulars basically are derived from the product of external timing resistor and capacitor values. Timing intervals can be varied from microseconds to minutes, minutes to days, and days to months.

4.13-1   555 AND 556 DIP STANDARDS

I suspect, with time, that all ICs will be identified by a standardized numbering series and easier direct interchangeability option. Some manufacturers have already begun to eliminate confusion by pin standards, not physical dimension, etc., since they all follow those rules, but standards relating to particular functions assigned to specific IC pins. The 555 and 556 are, for the most part, examples of standardized pin references. The dual in-line plastic and ceramic ICs of the 8-pin (555) and 16-pin (556) varieties are illustrated in Figure 4-46 along with commonly accepted working illustrations for that particular IC timer.

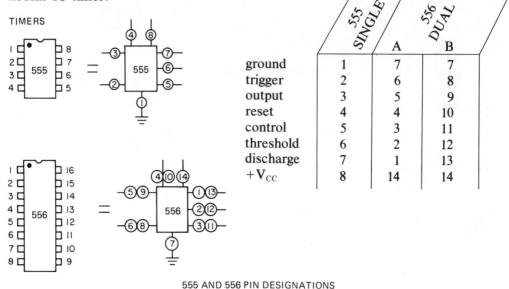

	555 SINGLE	556 DUAL	
		A	B
ground	1	7	7
trigger	2	6	8
output	3	5	9
reset	4	4	10
control	5	3	11
threshold	6	2	12
discharge	7	1	13
$+V_{CC}$	8	14	14

555 AND 556 PIN DESIGNATIONS

Figure 4-46

4.13-2   BASIC OPERATING CATEGORIES

IC timers are classified by operating principles: the "one-shot," also called "single cycle," or "monostable" is one category, while the "multiple cycle," also called "free running" or "astable" is the second category. The "monostable" and "astable" 555 and 556 timers will serve as references in this section. It would be foolish for us to limit any one timer, especially the 555 or 556 to any one mode of operation since these timers basically have limitless possible operating options as evidenced in present day applications.

4.13-2A   Monostable

The monostable timer operation is controlled by the charging action of an external capacitor and the limiting of current action of an external resistor. The resistor and capacitors together form the timing interval for circuitry operation. The product of the resistor-capacitor values dictates the period of time. The monostable, once triggered, will only allow one event or cycle to occur. During the cycle time, the timer will not respond to additional trigger inputs until the normal R-C timing period has elapsed; then it will respond. If, however, you wish to stop the timer during the cycle time, the reset pin (#4) will interrupt the normal R-C timing period and will stay interrupted until the reset is removed and a trigger is then reapplied. When the reset option is not in use, it is common practice to connect it to $+V_{CC}$ until needed.

The monostable timer is generally limited to a range of several microseconds to minutes (hours) and is good for short timing pulses in the microsecond range. Long time delays in the several minute range require large values for external RC but timing accuracy may suffer because of input bias comparator currents, leakage currents of the capacitor, and other characteristics.

The single timer (555) and dual timer (556) monostable schematics illustrated in Figure 4-47 will serve as ready reference for monostable circuitry.

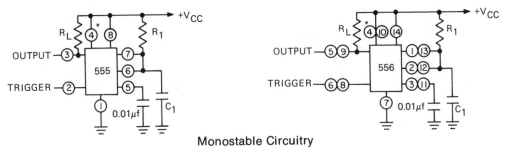

Monostable Circuitry

Note: * Reset
R_L = load
pulse width = $1.1R\ C_1$
Trigger pulse width must be less than $R_1 \times C_1$ timing period.
Negative going trigger activates—provides positive going output.
Can source or sink 150-200 mA

Figure 4-47

4.13-2B   Astable

If you desire a long time duration when time is in excess of the several minute range, then use a multiple cycle timer. The astable timer allows multiple charge or discharge to occur in the external R-C timing circuit. Figure 4-48 illustrates single timer (555) and dual timer (556) astable circuitry. The timing capacitor C_1 charges to approximately $\frac{2}{3}$ the value of V_{CC} through resistors R_1 and R_2 considered to be in parallel. Capacitor C_1 discharges to approximately $\frac{1}{3}$ of the V_{CC} value through resistor R_2. As a result of the capacitor voltage change, from approximately $\frac{1}{3}$ V_{CC} to $\frac{2}{3}$ V_{CC}, an exponential oscillation waveform will be generated. Pin #4 on the 555 or pins #4 and #10 on the 556 serve as on-off control.

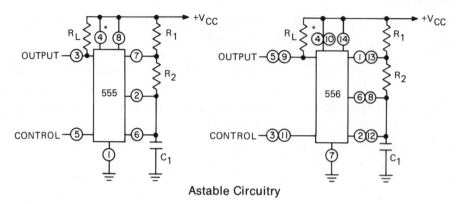

Astable Circuitry

Note: * reset

R_L = load

can sink or source 150-200 mA

charge time = $(0.69)(R_1 + R_2)(C_1)$

discharge time = $(0.69)(R_2)(C_1)$

$$\text{frequency} = \frac{1.46}{(C_1)(R_1 + 2R_2)}$$

$$\text{duty cycle} = \frac{R_2}{R_1 + 2R_2}$$

Figure 4-48

4.14   TRIACS

(Refer to Section 1.10-54 for Schematic Symbols)

The triac, a semiconductor device that utilizes both alternations (full-wave) of the applied AC voltage, has several characteristics similar to SCR semiconductors. In describing the triac, visualize two SCRs placed in parallel, but connected so that current flow will be allowable in either direction. The triac has three leads; two are anodes, and one is a gate. The anodes are identified as being anode number one, also main terminal #1, and anode number two, also known as main terminal #2.

4.14-1   CONTROL FUNCTION

The triac can block voltage. It simply does not allow any current to flow regardless of voltage polarity, until the gate receives a trigger pulse or signal. This gate voltage polarity is usually measured between the gate and anode #1 terminal. At those times when no gate current is present, the triac, regardless of voltage polarity, will not or should not conduct, unless its breakover voltage (V_{BR}) is reached. Naturally, if this point is reached and the triac did conduct without a gate trigger, it would be considered defective since it did not function as intended. The triac's forward direction (forward bias) is usually from anode #2 to anode #1; that is, anode #1 is negative while anode #2 is positive. The triac is assumed to be reverse-biased when anode #1 is positive and anode #2 is negative. In any case, once the triac is turned on by its gate trigger, full conduction is possible and any change in gate potential (positive or negative) has no effect. The triac turns off when its voltage or current drops below its holding point value and will require gate action to turn it back on.

4.14-2   SELECTION PARAMETERS

There are three basic selection parameters common when searching for the ideal triac. These are: (1) voltage, (2) current, and (3) packaging style.

(1) Voltage

Triacs are available with voltage ranges up to 600 volts.

(2) Current

Triacs will normally be rated according to rms forward current values like the SCR except it has a current range from about 1 ampere to 40 and 50 amperes.

(3) Packaging (Refer to Section 1.9 for Standards)

Triac packaging also resembles that of the SCR in that TO-5, TO-48, TO-64, TO-98 and the like are commonly manufactured. These may be press fit, stud mount, isolated stud mount, or even plastic encapsulated (up to 10 amperes).

You will discover that most are identified by the popular SC prefix. If you were to examine the triac via ohmmeter, the resistance measurements you would discover would have a very high reading (infinity or nearly) between either of the two anodes and the gate. Something else you should be aware of is the fact that three electrical descriptive classes for triacs exist. These are: (1) standard, (2) selected gate and (3) 400 Hertz operation.

4.14-3   ELECTRICAL CLASSES OF IMPORTANCE

1. *Standard Triac Class.* This is characterized for gate triggering in three modes of gate triggering:

A. main terminal #2 positive with gate positive
B. main terminal #2 positive with gate negative
C. main terminal #2 negative with gate negative

Commutating and latching currents are normal.

2. *Selected Gate Triac Type*. This is largely used in DC gate triggering and may be used with any of the following modes of gate triggering.

A. main terminal #2 positive with gate positive
B. main terminal #2 positive with gate negative
C. main terminal #2 negative with gate positive
D. main terminal #2 negative with gate negative

Commutating and latching currents are identical to those of the standard class.

4.14-4 SPECIFICATION SHEET TERMINOLOGY

RMS current—$I_{T(RMS)}$
Surge current—I_{TSM}
gate trigger current—I_{GT}
gate trigger voltage—V_{GT}
gate power/wattage—P_{GM}
critical rate applied forward voltage—dv/dt (V/μS)
case style—TO-5, TO-1, TO-48, TO-64, TO-66, TO-98, TO-126, TO-127, TO-220, TO-238

4.15 VACUUM TUBES

Wisdom required for trouble-shooting any electronic device is developed through applied knowledge of three circuits and five components. The three circuits are: (1) series, (2) parallel, and (3) series-parallel. The five components are: (1) resistors, (2) capacitors, (3) inductors (coils, transformers, etc.), (4) solid state devices, and (5) vacuum tubes.

Electronic circuitry having vacuum tubes as its active device may seem easier to work on because you know they must have filament voltage, a negative cathode and a positive plate voltage before they will work as designed. Other plus factors might be that they are easily removed from the circuit for testing or replacement and have uniform, standardized structure-purpose identification traits which are adhered to regardless of manufacturer. The valuable data found within this section of Chapter 4 will contribute to your working knowledge facts which, when applied, will develop trouble-shooting wisdom. (Refer to Section 1.11 for Schematic Symbols.)

4.15-1 PIN NUMBERING AND PHYSICAL LOCATION

Vacuum tube envelopes may be categorized as being either metal or glass. If metal, a ceramic twelvar base (nuvistor type) or small wafer 8 pin (octal type) are common. Glass envelope types are referred to as being: small button 7 pin or 9 pin miniature; small button 9 pin (novar or noval); large button 9 pin (neonoval); small button 12 pin (duodecar); and the 8 pin (octal). The button size terminology refers to the glass indentation (button size) found on the pin side of glass tubes not having base protective-keyed envelope mountings.

Normally, the number of pins extending from the vacuum tube corresponds with the number of electrodes required. Two exceptions are some octal base tubes and some picture tubes. For example, if an octal base tube used as an indirectly heated full-wave rectifier requires two plate electrodes, two filament electrodes and one cathode electrode, a total of five electrodes exists while the tube base normally has 8 pins. Obviously, since the tube and socket are keyed for correct pin alignment, the unused 3 pins can be eliminated. This means that octal based tubes may or may not have all 8 pins protruding from the bottom, but when counting them, missing pin locations must be included. Picture tubes of differing pin counts also exist due to pin-socket alignment techniques.

Tubes not having key type alignment designs use a spacing difference separating pin number 1 from the 7th, 9th, or 12th pin. Pin elimination for the non-keyed base is seldom, if ever, used. The differing tube types, along with standardized pin numbering sequences, are illustrated in Figure 4-49. It must be noted that this relates to the pin protrusion side of the tube or the under side (wired) of the tube socket.

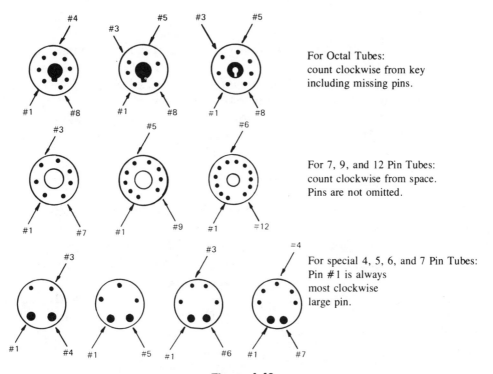

For Octal Tubes:
count clockwise from key
including missing pins.

For 7, 9, and 12 Pin Tubes:
count clockwise from space.
Pins are not omitted.

For special 4, 5, 6, and 7 Pin Tubes:
Pin #1 is always
most clockwise
large pin.

Figure 4-49

4.15-2   TUBE NUMBER-LETTER ARRANGEMENT MEANINGS

Hundreds of thousands of vacuum tubes, differing in type, size, shape, and purpose, presently exist. Some of these tubes have one specific purpose such as diodes, triodes, tetrodes, pentodes, hexodes, or heptodes; some may combine several purposes like dual diode-triode, triode-twin pentode, etc.; and some may be classified as being 7 or 9 pin miniature, 8 pin octal, or 12 pin duodecar types, but regardless of vast differences, a logical, standardized, agency-approved method for vacuum tube purpose and identification is employed. This method is illustrated by the numerical-alphabetical tube identification found on tube price listings, substitution listings, and vacuum tube manual listings. Each tube manufactured has valuable identification data marked, stamped, or etched on the envelope or tube base.

4.15-2A   Filament Voltage Identification

The lowest number used in the standardized vacuum tube identification method begins at zero and progresses numerically by one unit into the thousands. Normally, the digits preceding the alphabetical letters indicate filament voltages, but as in most things, there are some exceptions. These differences are as follows:

1. Vacuum tubes having a zero-something, normally means no filament voltage is required (IE: 0A2 = 105 volt regulator, but a 00A requires 5 volts).

2. Vacuum tubes having a one-something through 117-something, normally indicate the approximate filament voltage (IE: 6BK4 uses 6.3 volts, a 15BD11 uses 14.7 volts, while a 117Z4 uses 117 volts, etc.).

3. Vacuum tubes having only numbers being older tube or industrial coded tube types *cannot* be relied upon for filament voltage requirements, (IE: tube #19 needs 2 volts, tube #78 uses 6.3 volts, while tube #1621 requires 6.3 volts, etc.).

4.15-2B   Alphabetical Letter Identification

Most vacuum tubes have a number-letter-number-letter identification grouping code. The one or two letters following the filament numbers serve as organizational helpers for manufacturers and you and me, since they separate by alphabetically arranged sequence tubes, possibly having the same set of filament numbers. Organization is possible because letters assigned begin with A and go through the alphabet; then a second letter is issued along with the first, thereby making possible combinations of AB, then AC, etc. Common 6-volt filament tubes, each different somewhat, for example, can be identified as being a 6A8G, 6AB5, 6AC6GT, 6AD7G, and so on.

The second number grouping used in tube identification comes close, if not exactly, to the number of active or used elements within the tube. A differing element count from that which is indicated via tube number identification is highly possible unless you observe the following normally true facts. The filaments, although they may require two or more pins, are considered as being one element. An element connected internally to another element is counted only as one element (i.e., suppressor grid to cathode connection).

The last letter combination grouping (tube suffix) may or may not be used since it is related to tube specifics. Tube suffix letters commonly used are as follows:

LETTER	SUFFIX MEANING
G	Octal base, glass envelope
GT	Octal base, smaller than G type glass envelope
A, B, C, D, E, Or F	A indicates first specification modification, while B is the second, C the third, etc. Later modification types *can be* substituted for earlier versions, but not the opposite.
X	Low loss base material
Y	Intermediate loss base material
/	Indicates interchangeability between the tubes

4.15-3   ELECTRODE/ELEMENT NAME AND PURPOSE

Trouble-shooting can be compared to working in the dark or working with light. Working in the dark implies limited or no knowledge of how the device works, while working with light indicates the ability to apply knowledge for symptom analysis. Since the latter trouble-shooting method is preferred, we must acquire knowledge concerning names, purposes, and normal operation traits before we can make educated guesses when trouble-shooting. This section of Chapter 4 will shed some light on vacuum tube electrodes by using Figure 4-50 as a reference. Each numbered electrode illustrated will be examined in building-block fashion, beginning with the diode and progressing through the pentode.

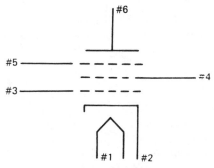

1. Filaments/heater
2. Cathode
3. Control grid
4. Screen grid
5. Suppressor grid
6. Plate/anode

Figure 4-50

4.15-3A Diodes

The diode, a two-electrode tube, requires a positive potential on its plate (#6 of Figure 4-50) plus an electron source called a filament (#1) before plate current (I_b) will exist. When only the filament (#1) and the plate (#6) are used, the diode is termed "directly heated," whereas the term "indirectly heated" is used for diodes having a cathode (#2) inserted between the filament and plate. The filaments in an indirectly heated diode merely heat the cathode thereby supplying electrons, and it is not counted as an electrode.

4.15-3B Triodes

The major current controlling factor of a diode, other than the correct polarity potentials on the plate and cathode, is the amount of plate potential. The higher the attracting plate potential, the more plate current will flow until a point called *saturation* occurs. The major current controlling factor in other tubes is a grid; specifically, a control grid. The triode utilizes the efficient control grid (#3 in Figure 4-50) for signal amplification purposes because small voltages applied to this third electrode can control a comparatively large amount of plate current.

4.15-3C Tetrodes

By adding a second grid to the vacuum tube illustrated in Figure 4-50, a total of four electrodes will exist: the cathode #2, the control grid #3, the screen grid #4, and the plate #6. Such a tube is called a tetrode. The extra grid, operated at a positive voltage which almost equals the plate potential, makes it possible to obtain higher amplification gains than a triode. The tetrode not only allows plate current to be practically independent of plate potentials over a certain range, but also, because of its low grid-plate capacitance, diminishes instability caused by plate-grid feedback.

4.15-3D Pentodes

The name pentode is given to vacuum tubes having five electrodes. The fifth electrode is known as a suppressor grid, identified as #5 in Figure 4-50. This grid usually is connected to the cathode within the tube during manufacturing. As a result of the effects of the suppressor grid, power output pentodes have higher power output capabilities with small grid voltages, while in RF amplifier pentodes, a moderate-plate voltage value will provide high voltage amplification.

4.15-4 TUBE MANUAL TERMINOLOGY

Vacuum tube manual data, if understood and properly applied, can be one of the most useful tube-type circuitry trouble-shooting aids presently available. When situations arise where schematics aren't readily available, reach for your tube manual because voltage and current values, pin electrode positioning, plus application advantages are listed.

In this section of Chapter 4 you will find vacuum tube specifics not only outlined, but also described, and all of them are common to vacuum tube manual data. Potential application, such as class A operation, class C amplifier, sync separator, etc., along with typical construction types like medium mu, triode, pentagrid converter, etc. will be omitted because of the vast number of differing applications and construction types presently manufactured. The data are based upon three generalized rating systems termed as being (1) average values, (2) maximum values, and (3) absolute maximum values. Each of the three rating systems concerns itself with conditions that might affect component values, control positioning, signals, supply potentials, temperature, plus other possible important variables. In most tube manual data, average and maximum values are those suggested as normal for that particular tube.

4.15-4A Amperage

4.15-4A1 Filaments Current—The current values for filaments, also known as heaters are for average tube operation. The first number/numbers written on the tube usually indicate the filament voltage.

4.15-4A2 Plate Current—The values listed for plate current, (Ib) usually in milliamperes, are average. Special markings, sometimes used with audio output tubes, signify the plate current was measured without a control grid signal applied. Maximum values—with a signal—are normally higher in value.

4.15-4A3 Screen Current—Like the plate current values, this current is subject to the conditions of other related potential data. Extra symbols are employed in audio output tubes indicating listed current values measured without a control grid signal, etc.

4.15-4B Amplification Factor

Mu (μ), the amplification factor for specific tubes, relates by number the ratio of small plate current changes to small grid voltage changes when plate current and other electrode voltages are kept constant.

4.15-4C Capacitance

Normally, all capacitance values are average values; special symbols are employed to denote variations possible while measuring. These values are in picofarads (pF), formerly termed micromicrofarads (mmF).

4.15-4C1 Grid to Plate—This capacitance is measured from the control grid to the plate while all other electrodes are grounded out.

4.15-4C2 Input—This capacitive value relates the capacitance measured from the control grid to all electrodes except for the plate, which is connected to ground.

4.15-4C3 Output—The capacitive values listed here are those measured from the plate to all electrodes except for the control grid which is grounded out.

4.15-4D   Power

Each vacuum tube used for amplification has its own power dissipation (wattage) curve. Plate, screen, and output wattage values differ from tube to tube and from application to application. To illustrate this, maximum plate dissipation occurs at zero signal conditions for class A operations, at about sixty-five percent of maximum signal amplitude for class B operations, and at a zero signal level in a mixer or converter stage if it is at the frequency where the oscillator develops minimum bias. Plate wattage, therefore, describes a tube's safe maximum plate dissipation factor.

The screen grid wattage listed is maximum whenever the maximum screen grid voltage is used. Special subscripts or symbols show either average, maximum, or absolute maximum wattage ratings.

Power output wattage describes the average power output obtainable for the given operating conditions. This almost always is less circuit losses or plate dissipation minus input plate power effects. All power factors listed in the tube manual place the tube in the safe-nondestruct regions of the tube characteristics, as long as the operating potentials are observed.

4.15-4E   Resistances

Two resistive values listed in tube manuals are plate resistance (R_p) and sometimes suggested load resistance (R_L).

4.15-4E1   Plate Resistance—The R_p of vacuum tubes is actually an application of Ohm's Law since it is a ratio of E (voltage) divided by I (current). The E is the small change in plate voltage, while I is the corresponding change in plate current when all other electrodes are held constant.

4.15-4E2   Load Resistance—Power amplifier stage vacuum tubes normally have suggested load resistances listed to insure maximum wattage utilization at average or maximum value operation.

4.15-4F   Voltages

The voltages listed in tube manual data are pretty much matter of fact values since tube characteristics were taken into consideration. The data strongly suggested for plate and screen voltage are either average or maximum values and should not be exceeded. This, therefore, means that other values for plate voltages may be used as long as maximum plate voltage ratings are not exceeded, and other screen grid potentials may be used provided the maximum voltage is not exceeded. Limitations for screen grid current should, however, be observed when maximum plate voltage is employed.

The grid bias or negative grid voltage potentials are so chosen in order to provide plate and screen currents while holding plate and screen dissipations within maximum values, thereby providing satisfactory tube operation.

Filament voltages may be operated with AC or DC voltages unless specifically noted.

4.15-5   GETTER SPOTS

If you observe a black or dark silver blob inside the vacuum tube (or on the top or side) DO NOT discard the tube believing it to be defective. This is the end result of burning any oxygen that may have remained trapped inside the tube during manufacturing. The so-called blob is the getter spot and is quite normal.

4.15-6   STANDARDIZED LETTER NOTATION

The standardized notation system for the vacuum tube proposed by the Institute of Radio Engineers has lessened the probable confusion that may have existed when defining voltages and currents. Because of this system, we now know whether the specified voltage or current is the supply, the value between the grid and cathode, with a signal or without a signal applied, peak, rms, or instantaneous value. The following is included as a handy reference for those of us who have forgotten just what represents and means what.

All capital E's and I's designate voltage and currents for static conditions; they refer to the peak, rms, or DC values. All small e's and i's designate the instantaneous values: Subscripts b, c and 1 refer to total voltages between designated tube element points and the cathode. The subscripts g, p, and z indicate the alternating components present at these same corresponding reference points. Figure 4-51 illustrates typical circuitry applications.

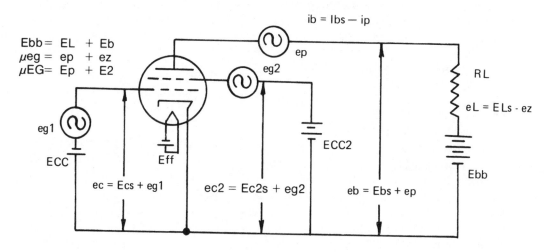

Figure 4-51

4.15-6A   Vacuum Tube Electrode Letters

MEANING	LETTER SYMBOL
Cathode	K
Control grid	C_1, G, G_1
Heater/filament	H, F
Plate/anode	P
Screen grid	C_2, G_2
Suppressor grid	C_3, G_3

4.15-6B   Vacuum Tube Letters for Currents

MEANING	LETTER SYMBOL
Average control grid current (with signal)	I_{cs}
Average load current (with signal)	I_{ls}
Average plate current (with signal)	I_{bs}
Average/quiescent value of grid current	I_{gl}
Average/quiescent value of plate current	I_p
Average screen grid current (with signal)	I_{g2s}
Alternating control grid current (rms value)	I_g
Alternating control grid current (peak value)	I_{gm}
Alternating control grid current (instantaneous value)	i_g
Alternating load current (instantaneous value)	i_z
Alternating load current (peak value)	I_{zm}
Alternating load current (rms value)	I_z
Alternating plate current (instantaneous value)	i_p
Alternating plate current (peak value)	I_{pm}
Alternating plate current (rms value)	I_p
Alternating screen grid current (instantaneous value)	I_{g2}
Alternating screen grid current (peak value)	I_{g2m}
Alternating screen grid current (rms value)	I_{g2}
Control grid current (no signal)	I_c
Filament/heater current	I_f
Instantaneous control grid current	i_c
Instantaneous load current	i_l
Instantaneous plate current	i_b
Instantaneous screen grid current	i_{c2}
Load current (no signal)	I_l
Plate current (no signal)	I_b
Screen grid current	I_{c2}

4.15-6C   Vacuum Tube Letters for Voltages

MEANING	LETTER SYMBOL
Average control grid to cathode voltage (with signal)	E_{cs}
Average control grid voltage	E_c
Average plate to cathode voltage (with signal)	E_{bs}
Average plate voltage	E_b
Average screen grid to cathode voltage (with signal)	E_{c2s}
Average voltage drop across load (with signal)	E_{ls}
Alternating component across load (instantaneous value)	e_z
Alternating component on control grid (instantaneous value)	e_g
Alternating component on plate (instantaneous value)	e_p
Alternating component on screen grid (instantaneous value)	e_{g2}
Alternating voltage across load (peak value)	E_{zm}
Alternating voltage across load (rms value)	E_z
Alternating voltage on control grid (peak value)	E_{gm}
Alternating voltage on control grid (rms value)	E_g
Alternating voltage on plate (peak value)	E_{pm}
Alternating voltage on plate (rms value)	E_p
Alternating voltage on screen grid (peak value)	E_{g2m}
Alternating voltage on screen grid (rms value)	E_{g2}
Control grid supply voltage	E_{cc}
Control grid to cathode voltage (no signal)	E_c
Heater/filament supply voltage	E_{ff}, E_f
Instantaneous control grid to cathode voltage	e_c
Instantaneous plate to cathode voltage/ instantaneous total plate voltage	e_b
Instantaneous screen grid to cathode voltage	e_{c2}
Instantaneous voltage across load	e_L
Plate supply voltage	E_{bb}, B, B+ E source
Plate to cathode voltage (no signal)	E_b
Screen grid supply voltage	E_{cc2}
Screen grid to cathode voltage (no signal)	E_{c2}
Voltage drop across load (no signal)	E_L

4.15-6D   Vacuum Tube Resistance Letters

MEANING	LETTER SYMBOL
Plate resistance (AC)	r_p
Plate resistance (DC)	R_P

4.15-7   VACUUM TUBE AMPLIFIER SPECIFICS

Amplifiers can be classified in three general ways. The first classification involves frequency of operation plus the necessary coupling circuitry. Amplifiers found within this group include DC, audio, video, and RF amplifiers. The second classification separates vacuum tube circuitry into three groups: voltage, current, and power amplifiers. The third classification describes the output-reproduced signal. Examples of this classification include class A, AB, B, and C amplifiers.

4.15-7A   Characteristic Curves

Each vacuum tube has its own set of curves which denote important factors during circuitry design steps. Two such curves are illustrated in Figures 4-52A and 4-52B. Curve A (Ip illustrates grid voltages to plate current relationships. This particular curve results when no plate load resistor is employed and when the plate voltage is held constant during the individual plate voltage curve values. The Ep-Ip curve shown in 4-52B results when the grid voltage is held constant during individual grid voltage curve values.

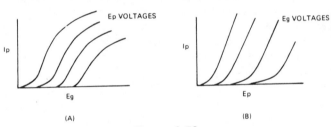

Figure 4-52

4.15-7B   Load Lines

Before selecting the amount of bias necessary to make the vacuum tube amplifier circuitry a particular class of operation, a DC load line must be drawn. The three things required to do this are a set of Ep-Ip curves for the tube, knowledge of plate voltage value, and the amount of plate load resistance to be used.

To demonstrate this concept we will say B+ is 300 volts, R$_L$ is 50,000 ohms, and the family of Ep-Ip curve for the tube resembles the one shown in Figure 4-53.

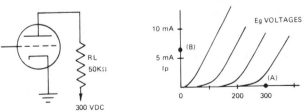

Figure 4-53

First: Determine Ip (point B)

$$Ip = \frac{Es}{RL}$$

$$Ip = \frac{300V}{50K\,\Omega}$$

$$Ip = 6\ mA$$

Ip = plate current (maximum value)
Es = source or applied voltage
RL = value of load resistor
*assume tube has no resistance

Second: Assume no voltage drop across plate load resistor. Point A represents this potential of 300 volts. The DC load line is constructed by drawing a straight line between point B (maximum current) and point A (maximum voltage). The grid voltage lines crossing the load line serve as a reference for tube biasing.

4.15-7C   Classes of Bias

4.15-7C1   Class A, A_1, or A_2

This classification means the vacuum tube is biased in the linear portion of the family curve, thereby providing the highest possible fidelity. Subscript 1 indicates no grid current flowing; subscript 2 means the biasing is the same as for A_1 but grid current flows.

4.15-7C2   Class AB

Biasing is midpoint between class A and class B, just above the cutoff point which is not on the linear portion of the curve. If AB_1 or AB_2 were indicated, then grid current flow would be the same as indicated in the class A explanation.

4.15-7C3   Class B

Biasing is at the cutoff point. Grid current flows.

4.15-7C4   Class C

Biasing is well below the cutoff point. Grid current flow is normally indicated by the C_2 designation.

4.15-7C5   Amplifier Classification Summary (Figure 4-54) (See page 348.)

4.15-8   AMPLIFICATION FACTOR

(A) $\mu = (Gm)(r_p)$

μ = amplification factor
Eb, Ep = plate voltage
Eg, Ec = grid voltage

Class	Input	Output	Conduction Percentage	Efficiency	Fidelity
A	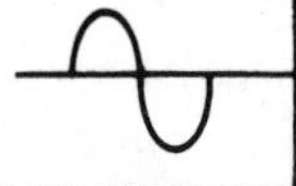	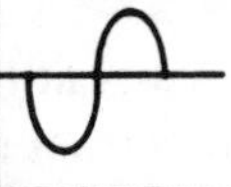	100%	Low	High
AB	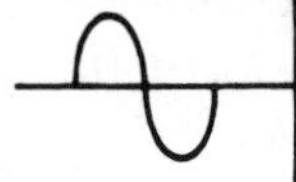	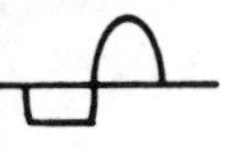	Less than 100% More than 50%	Medium	Medium
B	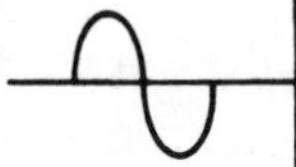		50%	High	Low
C	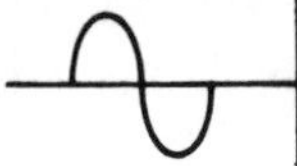		Less than 50%	Highest	Lowest

Figure 4-54

(B) $\mu = \dfrac{\Delta Eb}{\Delta Ec}$ with Ib constant   Ip, Ib = plate current
Gm = transconductance
rp = plate resistance (dynamic)
(C) $\mu = \dfrac{\Delta Ep}{\Delta Eg}$ with Ip constant Δ = change

4.15-9   TRANSCONDUCTANCE

(A) $Gm = \dfrac{\mu}{rp}$

(B) $Gm = \dfrac{\Delta Ip}{\Delta Eg}$

* Gm = transconductance (mutual conductance)
μ = amplification factor
rp = AC plate resistance
Ip = plate current
Eg = grid voltage
Δ = change
* Tells ease with which current flows; measured in siemens (s), formerly mhos.

4.15-10   PLATE RESISTANCE

(A) *DC Resistance*

$Rp = \dfrac{Eb}{Ib}$

Rp = DC plate resistance
Eb = plate to cathode voltage (no signal)
Ib = plate current (no signal)

(B) *AC Resistance*

$$rp = \frac{\Delta Ep}{\Delta Ip} \text{ with eg constant}$$

* rp $\;=$ AC (dynamic) plate resistance
Ep $\;=$ alternating plate voltage
Ip $\;=$ alternating plate current
eg $\;=$ instantaneous grid voltage
Δ $\;=$ change

* Computed from several readings — grid voltage held constant

4.15-11   CATHODE RESISTOR

(A) $Rk = \dfrac{Zo \; rp}{rp - Zo \, (\mu + 1)}$

Rk $\;=$ cathode resistor
Zo $\;=$ output impedance
rp $\;\;=$ AC plate resistance
μ $\;\;=$ amplification factor
Eg $\;=$ grid voltage
Ik $\;\;=$ cathode current

(B) $Rk = \dfrac{Eg}{Ik}$

4.15-12   OUTPUT IMPEDANCE

(A) *Cathode Follower Tube*

$$Zo = \frac{Rk \; rp}{rp + Rk \, (\mu + 1)}$$

Zo $\;=$ output impedance
Rk $\;=$ cathode resistance
rp $\;\;=$ AC plate resistance
μ $\;\;=$ amplification factor

(B) *High-mu tube*

$$Zo = \frac{Rk}{1 + Rk \; Gm}$$

Zo $\;=$ output impedance
Rk $\;=$ cathode resistor
Gm $=$ transconductance

4.15-13   GAIN

(A) *General*

$$A = \frac{Eout}{Ein} = \frac{Eo}{eg}$$

OR

$$A = \frac{\mu \; Rk}{rp + Rk \, (\mu + 1)}$$

OR

$$A = \frac{\mu \; Z_L}{rp + Z_L}$$

A $\;\;=$ vacuum tube gain
Eo $\;=$ output voltage
eg $\;=$ input signal voltage
μ $\;\;=$ amplification factor
rp $\;\;=$ AC plate resistance
Rk $\;=$ cathode resistor
Z_L $\;=$ equivalent load impedance/plate load

(B) *Current in dB*

$$dB = 20 \text{ Log} \frac{Io}{Ii}$$

dB = decibel
Io = output current
Ii = input current

(C) *Voltage in dB*

$$dB = 20 \text{ Log} \frac{Eo}{Ei}$$

dB = decibel
Eo = output voltage
Ei = input voltage

(D) *Power in dB*

$$dB = 10 \text{ Log} \frac{Po}{Pi}$$

dB = decibel
Po = output power
Pi = input power

(E) *Stages in cascade*

$$A_T = A_1 \times A_2 \times A_3$$

OR

$$dB_T = dB_1 + dB_2 + dB_3$$

A_T = total voltage gain
A_1-A_3 = individual stage voltage gains
dB_T = total decibel gain
dB_1-dB_3 = individual stage power gains

(F) *Feedback amplifiers*

$$A_T = \frac{Eo}{Ei}$$

OR

$$A_T = \frac{A}{1 - BA}$$

A_T = total gain
Eo = output voltage
Ei = input voltage
A = gain without feedback
B = fraction of output feedback

(G) *High-mu tubes*

$$A = \frac{Rk \, Gm}{1 + Rk \, Gm}$$

OR

$$A = Zo \, Gm$$

A = gain
Rk = cathode resistance
Gm = transconductance
Zo = output impedance

4.15-14   VIDEO AMPLIFIER FREQUENCY BANDS

(A) *High band passed*

$$F_H = \frac{1}{2 \, \pi \, R_L \, Cs}$$

F_H = highest frequency in band passed
R_L = total load resistance
Cs = total shunt capacitance

(B) *Lowest band passed*

$$F_L = \frac{1}{2 \pi \, Rg \, Cc}$$

F_L = lowest frequency in band passed
Rg = grid resistor value
Cc = coupling capacitor value

4.16   ZENER DIODES
(Refer to Sections 1.10-6, 9, and 60 for Schematic Symbols.)

The zener diode has been called many things; to some it is a silicon voltage regulator, voltage regulator, voltage reference diode, backward diode, breakdown diode, or avalanche diode. At any rate, it is designed to operate in its breakdown region via reverse bias. This, therefore, means the cathode, normally negative as diodes go, is connected to the positive voltage point of the circuit, while the anode, normally positive as diodes go, is connected to a point of negative potential. That's correct—positive on the cathode and negative on the anode! If you inadvertently connected the zener backward, or in the forward bias manner rather than the designed reverse bias position, it would *not* function as a voltage regulator. It would not try to keep the voltage constant but would in effect function in the same manner as a forward-biased general purpose diode.

4.16-1   PACKAGING
(Refer to Section 1.9 for Standards.)

The zener diode may or will resemble a regular general purpose diode in size and shape. Packaging styles resemble the DO-4, DO-5, DO-7, DO-13, DO-29, DO-41, TO-3, TO-92 or something quite similar. The cathode end of the zener is polarity marked when packaged in the DO-7 style by a band or color closest to one lead, while the DO-4 and DO-5 may have either end serving as the cathode.

4.16-2   PURCHASING DATA

When purchasing zeners you will need to know the desired voltage and wattage values required. Common voltages range from about 2 volts to 200 volts or higher and wattage ranges obtainable are from 250 milliwatts to 50 watts. They may be, if necessary, connected in series to achieve the desired voltage. If you do connect them in series, the desired voltage total will be a plus or minus voltage tolerance because at each individual zener voltage rating there is a voltage tolerance. If you are in doubt as to its specific tolerance, expect a five percent variation; plan on it in circuitry design. Usually the specific voltage rating of the zener is a part of the zener part number, but not always. Some useful formulas are as follows:

4.16-3 USEFUL GENERAL FORMULAS

4.16-3A Maximum Current

$$I_Z = \frac{P_Z}{E_Z}$$

I_Z = maximum diode current
P_Z = maximum power rating
E_Z = breakdown voltage

4.16-3B Dynamic Impedance

$$Z_T = \frac{\triangle E_Z}{\triangle I_Z}$$

Z_T = dynamic impedance
E_Z = breakdown voltage
I_Z = current at breakdown voltage
$\triangle$ = change

4.16-4 SPECIFICATION SHEET TERMINOLOGY

Pd—power dissipation
V_R, V_Z—breakdown voltage or regulator voltage (+5%)
I_{ZM}, I_R, I_{ZT}—DC test current or regulator current
Z_{ZT}—zener impedance or breakdown impedance

4.16-5 VOLTAGE REGULATOR APPLICATION TERMINOLOGY

This terminology refers to Figure 4-55.

I_{R_1} — current flowing through series dropping resistor "R_1"
E_{in} — unregulated DC voltage applied
E_o — regulated DC voltage out
R_1 — resistance of series dropping resistor
I_{Z_1} — zener diode current at breakdown voltage
I_{RL} — current flowing through the load (resistor)
R_L — load (resistor) resistance
E_{R_1} — voltage developed across Resistor R_1
E_{Z_1} — zener diode breakdown voltage
P_{R_1} — wattage rating for resistor R_1

Note: (a) The value for R_1 must be less than the R_1 max value calculated and must be of sufficient size (wattage) to handle the current. Round off calculations to the next highest standard wattage rating. Round off calculations to the next highest standard resistive value.

(b) I_{Z_1} (max) should *not* exceed 0.9 times the maximum current rating for the zener diode.

(c) I_{Z_1} (min) is usually calculated at 0.1 times the current rating for the zener diode.

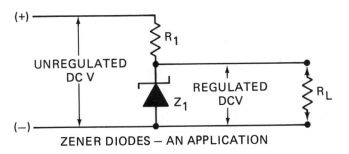

ZENER DIODES – AN APPLICATION

Figure 4-55

4.16-5A Series Dropping Resistor Current

$$I_{R_1} = \frac{E_{in} - E_o}{R_1} \text{ when } E_o = E_{Z1}$$

OR

$$I_{R_1}(max) = I_{Z1}(min) + I_{R_L}(max)$$

4.16-5B Zener Diode Current

$$I_{Z_1} = I_{R_1} - I_{R_L}$$

OR

$$I_{Z_1}(max) = I_{R_1} - I_{R_L}(min)$$

4.16-5C Load Current

$$I_{R_L} = \frac{E_o}{R_L}$$

OR

$$I_{R_L}(max) = I_{R_1} - I_{Z_1}(min)$$

4.16-5D Series Dropping Resistor Voltage

$$E_{R_1} = E_{in} - E_{Z_1}$$

OR

$$E_{R_1} = I_{R_1} \times R_1$$

4.16-5E Series Dropping Resistor Value

$$R_1(max) = \frac{E_{in}(min) - E_o}{I_{R_L}(max)}$$

OR

$$R_1 = \frac{E_{R_1}}{I_{R_1}}$$

4.16-5F Series Dropping Resistor Wattage

$$P_{R_1} = E_{R_1} \times I_{R_1}$$

OR

$$P_{R_1} = \frac{(E_{R_1})^2}{R_1}$$

4.16-5G Zener Diode Wattage Rating

$$P_{Z_1} = E_{Z_1} \times I_{Z_1}(max)$$

4.16-5H Load Resistor Value

$$R_L(min) = \frac{E_{Z_1}}{I_{R_L}(max)}$$

4

5   Time-Saving Tables, Measurements, and Service Data

5.1   ALPHA-BETA RELATIONSHIPS (TRANSISTOR)

The common PNP and NPN alpha-beta gain relationships may seem confusing to those of us who have not yet realized that this relationship portrays current gains for two different circuitry configurations.

The first circuit configuration is called a grounded or common base and is characterized by a low input impedance and a high output impedance. The current gain for this type of circuit and also the common collector circuit is called alpha (α) and is always less than one.

The second circuit configuration, called a grounded or common emitter, provides what is called an intermediate input impedance (about 1 kilohm) and an intermediate output impedance (about 50 kilohm). The current gain for this particular circuit is called beta (β) and will always be greater than unity; in fact, gains higher than 200 are possible and normal.

Most transistor literature hints as to circuitry configuration when telling the current gain for a specific transistor. The current gain value is normally listed under the letters HFE or under the heading Direct Current Gain. These values simply relate a number obtained by ratios of collector and base currents for a common emitter configuration or by ratios of collector and emitter currents for a common base configuration. In essence it tells the ability of the transistor to amplify currents flowing through its elements.

Since alpha and beta have formulas indicating their relationship:

$$\alpha = \frac{\beta}{1+\beta} \quad \text{AND} \quad \beta = \frac{\alpha}{1-\alpha}$$

you could calculate one or the other, if one were known. If you found a number less than one under a transistor's current gain (alpha) or a number greater than one (beta), the other value could be obtained using the formulas, if circuitry demanded. Most of these common alpha-beta relationship values are shown here to lessen your calculation time.

BETA	ALPHA	BETA	ALPHA	BETA	ALPHA
1	0.5000	41	0.9762	81	0.9878
2	0.6666	42	0.9767	82	0.9880
3	0.7500	43	0.9773	83	0.9881
4	0.8000	44	0.9778	84	0.9882
5	0.8333	45	0.9783	85	0.9884
6	0.8571	46	0.9787	86	0.9885
7	0.8750	47	0.9792	87	0.9886
8	0.8889	48	0.9796	88	0.9888
9	0.9000	49	0.9800	89	0.9889
10	0.9091	50	0.9804	90	0.9890
11	0.9167	51	0.9808	91	0.9891
12	0.9231	52	0.9811	92	0.9892
13	0.9286	53	0.9815	93	0.9894
14	0.9333	54	0.9818	94	0.9895
15	0.9375	55	0.9821	95	0.9896
16	0.9412	56	0.9825	96	0.9897
17	0.9444	57	0.9828	97	0.9898
18	0.9474	58	0.9831	98	0.9899
19	0.9500	59	0.9833	99	0.9900
20	0.9524	60	0.9836	100	0.9901
21	0.9545	61	0.9839	110	0.9910
22	0.9565	62	0.9841	120	0.9917
23	0.9583	63	0.9844	130	0.9924
24	0.9600	64	0.9846	140	0.9929
25	0.9615	65	0.9848	150	0.9934
26	0.9630	66	0.9851	160	0.9938
27	0.9643	67	0.9853	170	0.9942
28	0.9655	68	0.9855	180	0.9945
29	0.9667	69	0.9857	190	0.9948
30	0.9677	70	0.9859	200	0.9950
31	0.9688	71	0.9861	210	0.9953
32	0.9697	72	0.9863	220	0.9955
33	0.9706	73	0.9865	230	0.9957
34	0.9714	74	0.9867	240	0.9959
35	0.9722	75	0.9868	250	0.9960
36	0.9730	76	0.9870	260	0.9962
37	0.9737	77	0.9872	270	0.9963
38	0.9744	78	0.9873	280	0.9964
39	0.9750	79	0.9875	290	0.9966
40	0.9756	80	0.9877	300	0.99667

5

5.2   AMERICAN WIRE GAGE BARE WIRE SPECIFICATIONS

The American Wire Gage (AWG) is also known as the Brown and Sharpe (B&S) wire gage. If your work involves wire data, a good fact to know is that the wire resistance is cut approximately in half when gage numbers decrease by each three gage unit steps. For example, number 20 wire has 10.15 ohms per each 1000 feet while number 17 has 5.064 ohms per each 1000 feet. The area is doubled but the resistance is divided by two.

Wire Size (AWG) (B+S)	Nominal Diameter in Mils $\left(\frac{1}{1000} \text{ of inch}\right)$	*Diameter in MM.	Circular Mil-Area	OHMS Per 1000 Ft. @ 68° F (20° C)	Current Carrying Capacity @ 700 CM/AMP
0000	460.0	11.684	211,600	0.0490	302.3
000	409.6	10.404	167,800	0.0618	239.7
00	364.8	9.266	133,100	0.0779	190.1
0	324.9	8.252	105,500	0.0983	150.9
1	289.3	7.348	83,690	0.1239	119.6
2	257.6	6.543	66,370	0.1563	94.8
3	229.4	5.827	52,640	0.1970	75.2
4	204.3	5.189	41,740	0.2485	59.6
5	181.9	4.620	33,100	0.3133	47.3
6	162.0	4.115	26,250	0.3951	37.5
7	144.3	3.665	20,820	0.4982	29.7
8	128.5	3.264	16,510	0.6282	23.6
9	114.4	2.906	13,090	0.7921	18.7
10	101.9	2.588	10,380	0.9989	14.8
11	90.74	2.305	8,234	1.260	11.8
12	80.81	2.053	6,530	1.588	9.33
13	71.96	1.828	5,178	2.003	7.40
14	64.08	1.628	4,107	2.525	5.87
15	57.07	1.450	3,257	3.184	4.65
16	50.82	1.291	2,583	4.016	3.69
17	45.26	1.150	2,048	5.064	2.93
18	40.30	1.024	1,624	6.385	2.32
19	35.89	0.912	1,288	8.051	1.84
20	31.96	0.812	1,022	10.15	1.46
21	28.46	0.723	810.1	12.80	1.16
22	25.35	0.644	642.4	16.14	0.918
23	22.57	0.573	509.5	20.36	0.728
24	20.10	0.511	404.0	25.67	0.577
25	17.90	0.455	320.4	32.37	0.458
26	15.94	0.405	254.1	40.81	0.363

Wire Size (AWG) (B+S)	Nominal Diameter in Mils ($\frac{1}{1000}$ of inch)	*Diameter in MM.	Circular Mil-Area	OHMS Per 1000 Ft. @ 68° F (20° C)	Current Carrying Capacity @ 700 CM/AMP
27	14.20	0.361	201.5	51.47	0.288
28	12.64	0.321	159.8	64.90	0.228
29	11.26	0.286	126.7	81.83	0.181
30	10.03	0.255	100.5	103.2	0.144
31	8.928	0.227	79.70	130.1	0.114
32	7.950	0.202	63.21	164.1	0.090
33	7.080	0.180	50.13	206.9	0.072
34	6.305	0.160	39.75	260.9	0.057
35	5.615	0.143	31.52	329.0	0.045
36	5.000	0.127	25.00	414.8	0.036
37	4.453	0.113	19.83	523.1	0.028
38	3.965	0.101	15.72	659.6	0.022
39	3.531	0.090	12.47	831.8	0.018
40	3.145	0.080	9.89	1049.0	0.014

*Rounded off to third significant digit using 0.0254 as the conversion factor.

5.3   DECIBELS

GAIN

LOSS

Decibel	E/I Ratios	Power Ratios	Decibel	E/I Ratios	Power Ratios
0	1.000	1.000	0	1.0000	1.0000
0.2	1.023	1.047	−0.2	0.9772	0.9550
0.4	1.047	1.096	−0.4	0.9550	0.9120
0.6	1.072	1.148	−0.6	0.9333	0.8710
0.8	1.096	1.202	−0.8	0.9120	0.8318
1.0	1.122	1.259	−1.0	0.8913	0.7943
1.2	1.148	1.318	−1.2	0.8710	0.7586
1.4	1.175	1.380	−1.4	0.8511	0.7244
1.6	1.202	1.445	−1.6	0.8318	0.6918
1.8	1.230	1.514	−1.8	0.8128	0.6607
2.0	1.259	1.585	−2.0	0.7943	0.6310
2.2	1.288	1.660	−2.2	0.7762	0.6026
2.4	1.318	1.738	−2.4	0.7586	0.5754
2.6	1.349	1.820	−2.6	0.7413	0.5495

5

5.3   DECIBELS, continued

GAIN				LOSS		
Decibel	E/I Ratios	Power Ratios		Decibel	E/I Ratios	Power Ratios
2.8	1.380	1.905		−2.8	0.7244	0.5248
3.0	1.413	1.995		−3.0	0.7079	0.5012
3.2	1.445	2.089		−3.2	0.6918	0.4786
3.4	1.479	2.188		−3.4	0.6761	0.4571
3.6	1.514	2.291		−3.6	0.6607	0.4365
3.8	1.549	2.399		−3.8	0.6457	0.4169
4.0	1.585	2.512		−4.0	0.6310	0.3981
4.2	1.622	2.630		−4.2	0.6166	0.3802
4.4	1.660	2.754		−4.4	0.6026	0.3631
4.6	1.698	2.884		−4.6	0.5888	0.3467
4.8	1.738	3.020		−4.8	0.5754	0.3311
5.0	1.778	3.162		−5.0	0.5623	0.3162
5.2	1.820	3.311		−5.2	0.5495	0.3020
5.4	1.862	3.467		−5.4	0.5370	0.2884
5.6	1.905	3.631		−5.6	0.5248	0.2754
5.8	1.950	3.802		−5.8	0.5129	0.2630
6.0	1.995	3.981		−6.0	0.5012	0.2512
6.2	2.042	4.169		−6.2	0.4898	0.2399
6.4	2.089	4.365		−6.4	0.4786	0.2291
6.6	2.138	4.571		−6.6	0.4677	0.2188
6.8	2.188	4.786		−6.8	0.4571	0.2089
7.0	2.239	5.012		−7.0	0.4467	0.1995
7.2	2.291	5.248		−7.2	0.4365	0.1905
7.4	2.344	5.495		−7.4	0.4266	0.1820
7.6	2.399	5.754		−7.6	0.4169	0.1738
7.8	2.455	6.026		−7.8	0.4074	0.1660
8.0	2.512	6.310		−8.0	0.3981	0.1585
8.2	2.570	6.607		−8.2	0.3890	0.1514
8.4	2.630	6.918		−8.4	0.3802	0.1445
8.6	2.692	7.244		−8.6	0.3715	0.1380
8.8	2.754	7.586		−8.8	0.3631	0.1318
9.0	2.818	7.943		−9.0	0.3548	0.1259
9.2	2.884	8.318		−9.2	0.3467	0.1202
9.4	2.951	8.710		−9.4	0.3388	0.1148
9.6	3.020	9.120		−9.6	0.3311	0.1096
9.8	3.090	9.550		−9.8	0.3236	0.1047
10.0	3.162	10.00		−10.0	0.3162	0.1000
10.2	3.236	10.47		−10.2	0.3090	0.0955
10.4	3.311	10.96		−10.4	0.3020	0.0912
10.6	3.388	11.48		−10.6	0.2951	0.0871
10.8	3.467	12.02		−10.8	0.2884	0.0832

GAIN

Decibel	E/I Ratios	Power Ratios
11.0	3.548	12.59
11.2	3.631	13.18
11.4	3.715	13.80
11.6	3.802	14.45
11.8	3.890	15.14
12.0	3.981	15.85
12.2	4.074	16.60
12.4	4.169	17.38
12.6	4.266	18.20
12.8	4.365	19.05
13.0	4.467	19.95
13.2	4.571	20.89
13.4	4.677	21.88
13.6	4.786	22.91
13.8	4.898	23.99
14.0	5.012	25.12
14.2	5.129	26.30
14.4	5.248	27.54
14.6	5.370	28.84
14.8	5.495	30.20
15.0	5.623	31.62
15.2	5.754	33.11
15.4	5.888	34.67
15.6	6.026	36.31
15.8	6.166	38.02
16.0	6.310	39.81
16.2	6.457	41.69
16.4	6.607	43.65
16.6	6.761	45.71
16.8	6.918	47.86
17.0	7.079	50.12
17.2	7.244	52.48
17.4	7.413	54.95
17.6	7.586	57.54
17.8	7.762	60.26
18.0	7.943	63.10
18.2	8.128	66.07
18.4	8.318	69.18
18.6	8.511	72.44
18.8	8.710	75.86
19.0	8.913	79.43
19.2	9.120	83.18
19.4	9.333	87.10

LOSS

Decibel	E/I Ratios	Power Ratios
−11.0	0.2818	0.0794
−11.2	0.2754	0.0759
−11.4	0.2692	0.0724
−11.6	0.2630	0.0692
−11.8	0.2570	0.0661
−12.0	0.2512	0.0631
−12.2	0.2455	0.0603
−12.4	0.2399	0.0575
−12.6	0.2344	0.0550
−12.8	0.2291	0.0525
−13.0	0.2239	0.0501
−13.2	0.2188	0.0479
−13.4	0.2138	0.0457
−13.6	0.2089	0.0437
−13.8	0.2042	0.0417
−14.0	0.1995	0.0398
−14.2	0.1950	0.0380
−14.4	0.1905	0.0363
−14.6	0.1862	0.0347
−14.8	0.1820	0.0331
−15.0	0.1778	0.0316
−15.2	0.1738	0.0302
−15.4	0.1698	0.0288
−15.6	0.1660	0.0275
−15.8	0.1622	0.0263
−16.0	0.1585	0.0251
−16.2	0.1549	0.0240
−16.4	0.1514	0.0229
−16.6	0.1479	0.0219
−16.8	0.1445	0.0209
−17.0	0.1413	0.0199
−17.2	0.1380	0.0191
−17.4	0.1349	0.0182
−17.6	0.1318	0.0174
−17.8	0.1288	0.0166
−18.0	0.1259	0.0159
−18.2	0.1230	0.0151
−18.4	0.1202	0.0145
−18.6	0.1175	0.0138
−18.8	0.1148	0.0132
−19.0	0.1122	0.0126
−19.2	0.1096	0.0120
−19.4	0.1072	0.0115

5

5.3   DECIBELS, continued

GAIN

Decibel	E/I Ratios	Power Ratios
19.6	9.550	91.20
19.8	9.772	95.50
20.0	10.00	100.00
25.0	17.78	316.2
30.0	31.62	1000.0
35.0	56.23	3162.0
40.0	100.00	10,000.0
45.0	177.8	31,620.0
50.0	316.2	100,000.0

LOSS

Decibel	E/I Ratios	Power Ratios
−19.6	0.1047	0.0110
−19.8	0.1023	0.0105
−20.0	0.1000	0.0100
−25.0	0.0562	0.00316
−30.0	0.0316	0.00100
−35.0	0.0178	3.162×10^{-4}
−40.0	0.0100	1×10^{-4}
−45.0	0.0056	3.162×10^{-5}
−50.0	0.0032	1×10^{-5}

5.4   DRILL, TAP, AND MACHINE SCREW SPECIFICS PLUS DECIMAL EQUIVALENTS

Tap Drill	Drill Diameter	Machine Screw	Tap Drill	Drill Diameter	Machine Screw
97	0.0059	———	77	0.0180	———
96	0.0063	———	76	0.0200	———
95	0.0067	———	75	0.0210	———
94	0.0071	———	74	0.0225	———
93	0.0075	———	73	0.0240	———
92	0.0079	———	72	0.0250	———
91	0.0083	———	71	0.0260	———
90	0.0087	———	70	0.0280	———
89	0.0091	———	69	0.0292	———
88	0.0095	———	68	0.0310	———
87	0.0100	———	1/32	0.0313	———
86	0.0105	———	67	0.0320	———
85	0.0110	———	66	0.0330	———
84	0.0115	———	65	0.0350	———
83	0.0120	———	64	0.0360	———
82	0.0125	———	63	0.0370	———
81	0.0130	———	62	0.0380	———
80	0.0135	———	61	0.0390	———
79	0.0145	———	60	0.0400	———

Tap Drill	Drill Diameter	Machine Screw	Tap Drill	Drill Diameter	Machine Screw
1/64	0.0156	———	59	0.0410	———
78	0.0160	———	58	0.0420	———
57	0.0430	———	28	0.1405	8-40
56	0.0465	———	9/64	0.1406	11/64-32
3/64	0.0469	0-80	27	0.1440	9-30
		1/16-64	26	0.1470	9-32, 3/16-24
		1/16-72	25	0.1495	10-24
55	0.0520	———	24	0.1520	———
54	0.0550	1-56	23	0.1540	10-28
53	0.0595	1-64	5/32	0.1562	———
		1-72	22	0.1570	10-30, 3/16-32
1/16	0.0625	5/64-60	21	0.1590	10-32
52	0.0635	5/64-72	20	0.1610	13/64-24
51	0.0670	———	19	0.1660	———
50	0.0700	2-56, 2-64	18	0.1695	———
49	0.0730	3/32-48	11/64	0.1719	———
		3/32-50	17	0.1730	———
48	0.0760	———	16	0.1770	12-24,
5/64	0.0781	———			7/32-24
47	0.0785	3-48	15	0.1800	———
46	0.0810	———	14	0.1820	12-28
45	0.0820	3-56, 4-32	13	0.1850	12-32
44	0.0860	4-36	3/16	0.1875	———
43	0.0890	4-40, 7/64-48	12	0.1890	7/32-32
42	0.0935	4-48	11	0.1910	———
3/32	0.0938	1/8-32	10	0.1935	14-20
41	0.0960	———			15/64-24
40	0.0980	5-36	9	0.1960	———
39	0.0995	———	8	0.1990	———
38	0.1015	5-40, 1/8-40	7	0.2010	14-24, ¼-20
37	0.1040	5-44	13/64	0.2031	———
36	0.1065	6-32	6	0.2040	———
7/64	0.1094	———	5	0.2055	———
35	0.1100	———	4	0.2090	¼-24
34	0.1110	6-36	3	0.2130	16-18, ¼-27
					¼-28
33	0.1130	6-40	7/32	0.2188	16-20, ¼-32
32	0.1160	9/64-40	2	0.2210	16-22
31	0.1200	7-30, 7-32	1	0.2280	———
1/8	0.1250	7-36, 5/32-32	A	0.2340	———
30	0.1285	8-30, 5/32-36			
			15/64	0.2344	———

5

Tap Drill	Drill Diameter	Machine Screw	Tap Drill	Drill Diameter	Machine Screw
29	0.1360	8-32, 8-36, 9-24	B	0.2380	18-18
C	0.2420	————	7/16	0.4375	————
D	0.2460	18-20	29/64	0.4531	½-20
					½-24
E, ¼	0.2500	————	15/32	0.4688	½-27
F	0.2570	5/16-18	31/64	0.4844	9/16-12
G	0.2610	20-16	1/2	0.5000	————
17/64	0.2656	20-18, 5/16-20	33/64	0.5156	9/16-18
H	0.2660	————	17/32	0.5312	9/16-27
I	0.2720	20-20, 5/16-24			5/8-11
J	0.2770	5/16-27	35/64	0.5469	5/8-12
			9/16	0.5625	————
K	0.2810	————	37/64	0.5781	5/8-18
9/32	0.2812	22-16, 5/16-32	19/32	0.5938	5/8-27
L	0.2900	22-18			11/16-11
M	0.2950	————	39/64	0.6094	————
19/64	0.2969	————	5/8	0.6250	11/16-16
N	0.3020	————	41/64	0.6406	————
5/16	0.3125	24-16, 3/8-16	21/32	0.6562	3/4-10
0	0.3160	24-18	43/64	0.6719	3/4-12
			11/16	0.6875	3/4-16
P	0.3230	————	45/64	0.7031	————
21/64	0.3281	26-14, 3/8-20	23/32	0.7188	3/4-27
Q	0.3320	3/8-24			13/16-10
R	0.3390	26-16	47/64	0.7344	————
		3/8-27	3/4	0.7500	————
11/32	0.3438	————	49/64	0.7656	7/8-9
S	0.3480	————	25/32	0.7812	————
T	0.3580	28-14	51/64	0.7969	7/8-12
23/64	0.3594	28-16			
U	0.3680	7/16-14	13/16	0.8125	7/8-14
3/8	0.3750	————	53/64	0.8281	7/8-18
V	0.3770	30-14			15/16-9
W	0.3860	————	27/32	0.8438	7/8-27
25/64	0.3906	30-16,	55/64	0.8594	————
		7/16-20	7/8	0.8750	1-8
X	0.3970	7/16-24	57/64	0.8906	————
Y	0.4040	7/16-27	29/32	0.9062	————
13/32	0.4062	————			
Z	0.4130	————	59/64	0.9219	1-12
27/64	0.4219	½-12	15/16	0.9375	1-14
		½-13	61/64	0.9531	————

Tap Drill	Drill Diameter	Machine Screw
31/32	0.9688	1-27
63/64	0.9844	——
1	1.000	——

5.5   DECIMAL, MILLIMETER, FRACTIONAL UNIT OF AN INCH EQUIVALENTS

FRACTION			DECIMAL*	MILLIMETER
		1/64	0.015625	0.3969
	1/32		0.03125	0.7938
		3/64	0.046875	1.1906
1/16			0.0625	1.5875
		5/64	0.078125	1.9844
	3/32		0.09375	2.3813
		7/64	0.109375	2.7781
1/8			0.125	3.1750
		9/64	0.140625	3.5719
	5/32		0.15625	3.9688
		11/64	0.171875	4.3656
3/16			0.1875	4.7625
		13/64	0.203125	5.1594
	7/32		0.21875	5.5563
		15/64	0.234375	5.9531
1/4			0.250	6.3500
		17/64	0.265625	6.7469
	9/32		0.28125	7.1438
		19/64	0.296875	7.5406
5/16			0.3125	7.9375
		21/64	0.328125	8.3344
	11/32		0.34375	8.7313
		23/64	0.359375	9.1281
3/8			0.375	9.5250
		25/64	0.390625	9.9219
	13/32		0.40625	10.3188
		27/64	0.421875	10.7156

*Using internationally agreed conversion factor of 25.4 and rounding off last digit if equaling 5 or greater.

FRACTION			DECIMAL*MILLIMETER	
7/16			0.4375	11.1125
		29/64	0.453125	11.5094
	15/32		0.46875	11.9063
		31/64	0.484375	12.3031
1/2			0.500	12.7000
		33/64	0.515625	13.0969
	17/32		0.53125	13.4938
		35/64	0.546875	13.8906
9/16			0.5625	14.2875
		37/64	0.578125	14.6844
	19/32		0.59375	15.0813
		39/64	0.609375	15.4781
5/8			0.625	15.8750
		41/64	0.640625	16.2719
	21/32		0.65625	16.6688
		43/64	0.671875	17.0656
11/16			0.6875	17.4625
		45/64	0.703125	17.8594
	23/32		0.71875	18.2563
		47/64	0.734375	18.6531
3/4			0.750	19.0500
		49/64	0.76525	19.4469
	25/32		0.78125	19.8438
		51/64	0.796875	20.2406
13/16			0.8125	20.6375
		53/64	0.828125	21.0344
	27/32		0.843750	21.4313
		55/64	0.859375	21.8281
7/8			0.875	22.2250
		57/64	0.890625	22.6219
	29/32		0.90625	23.0188
		59/64	0.921875	23.4156
15/16			0.9375	23.8125
		61/64	0.953125	24.0938
	31/32		0.96875	24.6063
		63/64	0.984375	25.0031
1			1.000	25.4000

* Using internationally agreed conversion factor of 25.4 and rounding off last digit if equaling 5 or greater

5.6   dBmV CONVERSION TABLE

(Reference Level: 0 dBmV = 1000 μV = 1mV)

dBmV	micro-volt (μV)	dBmV	millivolt (mV)	dBmV	millivolt (mV)
−40	10.00	0	1.000	41	112.20
−39	11.22	1	1.122	42	125.90
−38	12.59	2	1.259	43	141.30
−37	14.13	3	1.413	44	158.50
−36	15.85	4	1.585	45	177.80
−35	17.78	5	1.778	46	199.50
−34	19.95	6	1.995	47	223.90
−33	22.39	7	2.239	48	251.20
−32	25.12	8	2.512	49	281.80
−31	28.18	9	2.818	50	316.20
−30	31.62	10	3.162	51	354.80
−29	35.48	11	3.548	52	398.10
−28	39.81	12	3.981	53	446.70
−27	44.67	13	4.467	54	501.20
−26	50.12	14	5.012	55	562.30
−25	56.23	15	5.623	56	631.00
−24	63.10	16	6.310	57	707.90
−23	70.79	17	7.079	58	794.30
−22	79.43	18	7.943	59	891.30
−21	89.13	19	8.913	60	1,000.00
−20	100.0	20	10.000	61	1,122.00
−19	112.2	21	11.220	62	1,259.00
−18	125.9	22	12.590	63	1,413.00
−17	141.3	23	14.130	64	1,585.00
−16	158.5	24	15.850	65	1,778.00
−15	177.8	25	17.780	66	1,995.00
−14	199.5	26	19.950	67	2,239.00
−13	223.9	27	22.390	68	2,512.00
−12	251.2	28	25.120	69	2,818.00
−11	281.8	29	28.180	70	3,162.00
−10	316.2	30	31.620	71	3,548.00
−9	354.8	31	35.480	72	3,981.00
−8	398.1	32	39.810	73	4,467.00
−7	446.7	33	44.670	74	5,012.00
−6	501.2	34	50.120	75	5,632.00
−5	562.3	35	56.230	76	6,310.00
−4	631.0	36	63.100	77	7,079.00
−3	707.9	37	70.790	78	7,943.00
−2	794.3	38	79.430	79	8,913.00
−1	891.3	39	89.130	80	10,000.00
0	1,000.0	40	100.00		

5

5.7   GAS-FILLED LAMPS

The following neon, argon, and circuit glow lamps arranged according to their normal working voltage range show the current ratings, series resistance, if any required, and their popular lamp number. Some of them have two identification numbers illustrated. The second group shows the American Standards Association (ASA) number. When ordering, any listed number may be used.

Some of the similar lamp base style terminology common to gas-filled and miniature lamps is provided in Figure 5-1 for your reference.

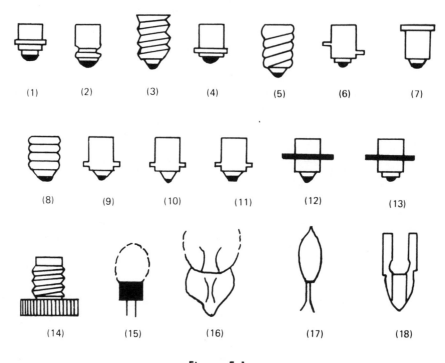

Figure 5-1

1. Submidget flanged
2. Midget grooved
3. Midget screw
4. Midget flanged
5. Candelabra
6. Double contact bayonet index
7. Miniature flange
8. Miniature screw
9. Miniature bayonet
10. Single contact bayonet
11. Double contact bayonet
12. Single contact prefocus
13. Double contact prefocus
14. Knurled screw
15. Bi-pin
16. Wedge
17. Wire terminal
18. Telephone slide

Voltage Range	Lamp Number	Current Rating (mA)	Series Resistance	Base
55-90 volts	NE-3 (8AA)	0.3 mA	—	tel. slide
	NE-67 (6AC)	0.2 mA	—	min bay
	NE-86 (5AJ)	1.5 mA	—	wire term
	5AJA	1.5 mA	—	wire term
60-65 volts	NE-83 (5AH)	10 mA	—	wire term
60-80 volts	3AGA	0.4 mA	—	wire term
	5AB-A	0.3 mA	—	wire term
60-85 volts	5AH-A	10 mA	—	wire term
60-90 volts	NE-4 (8AB)	0.3 mA	—	tel. slide
	NE-23 (5AB)	0.3 mA	—	wire term
	NE-68 (5AC)	0.3 mA	—	wire term
	3AG	0.4 mA	—	wire term
60-100 volts	8AE	10 mA	—	tel. slide
62-72 volts	5AB-B	0.3 mA	—	wire term.
64-80 volts	NE-81 (5AG)	0.1 mA	—	wire term.
65-73 volts	3AG-B	0.4 mA	—	wire term.
67-87 volts	NE-16 (7AA)	1.5 mA	—	D.C. bay.
68-76 volts	NE-76 (5AG-A)	0.4 mA	—	wire term.
	3AG-C	0.4 mA	—	wire term.
68-78 volts	5AB-C	0.3 mA	—	wire term.
70-90 volts	5AJ-B	1.5 mA	—	wire term.
75-85 volts	5AH-B	10 mA	—	wire term.
75-100 volts	5AH-C	10 mA	—	wire term.
75-135 volts	3AH	2 mA	—	wire term.
105-125 volts	NE-2 (A1A)	0.5 mA	150k ohms	wire term.
	A1B	0.3 mA	220k ohms	wire term.
	A1C	0.8 mA	68k ohms	wire term.
	NE-2A (A2A)	0.3 mA	220k ohms	wire term.
	NE-2D (C7A)	0.7 mA	100k ohms	S.C. midget-flg.
	NE-2E (A9A)	0.7 mA	100k ohms	wire term.
	NE-2H (C2A)	1.9 mA	30k ohms	wire term.
	NE-2J (C9A)	1.9 mA	30k ohms	S.C. midget-flg.
	NE-2V (A2B)	0.7 mA	100k ohms	wire term.
	NE-7 (B4A)	2.0 mA	30k ohms	wire term.
	NE-17 (B5A)	2.0 mA	30k ohms	D.C. bay.
	NE-21 (B6A)	2.0 mA	30k ohms	S.C. bay.
	NE-30 (J5A)	12.0 mA	4.8k ohms	med. scr.
	NE-32(L6A)(L5A)	12.0 mA	7.5k ohms	D.C. bay.
	NE-45 (B7A)	2.0 mA	30k ohms	cand. scr.
	NE-47 (B8A)	2.0 mA	30k ohms	S.C. bay.
	NE-48 (B9A)	2.0 mA	30k ohms	D.C. bay.

5

Voltage Range	Lamp Number	Current Rating (mA)	Series Resistance	Base
	NE-51 (B1A)	0.3 mA	220k ohms	min. bay.
	NE-51H (B2A)	1.2 mA	47k ohms	min. bay.
	NE-54 (F2A)	2.0 mA	30k ohms	wire term.
	NE-57 (F3A)	2.0 mA	30k ohms	cand. scr.
	NE-66	1.0 mA	3.6k ohms	cand. scr.
	NE-79	12.0 mA	7.5k ohms	bay.
	(J2A)(AR3)	3.5 mA	15k ohms	cand. scr.
	(J3A)(AR4)	3.5 mA	15k ohms	D.C. bay.
110-125 volts	AR1	18 mA	—	med. scr.
	AR3	3.5 mA	—	cand. scr.
	AR4	3.5 mA	15k ohms	D.C. bay.
	NE-34	18 mA	—	med. scr.
	NE-40	30 mA	—	med. scr.
110-140 volts	NE-97 (4AC)	0.5 mA	—	wire term.
120-150 volts	NE-96 (4AB)	0.5 mA	—	wire term.
	NE-5 (8AC)	0.5 mA	—	tel. slide
210-250 volts	NE-56 (J9A)	5 mA	30k ohms	med. scr.
	NE-58 (F4A)	2 mA	100k ohms	cand. scr.
220-300 volts	AR1	18 mA	10k ohms	med. scr.
	AR3	3.5 mA	68k ohms	cand. scr.
	AR4	3.5 mA	82k ohms	D.C. bay.
	NE-2	3 mA	750k ohms	wire term.
	NE-2A	3 mA	750k ohms	wire term.
	NE-17	2 mA	110k ohms	D.C. bay.
	NE-30	12 mA	10k ohms	med. scr.
	NE-32	12 mA	18k ohms	D.C. bay.
	NE-34	18 mA	9.1k ohms	med. scr.
	NE-40	30 mA	6.2k ohms	med. scr.
	NE-45	2 mA	82k ohms	cand. scr.
	NE-48	2 mA	110k ohms	D.C. bay.
	NE-51	0.3 mA	750k ohms	min. bay.
	NE-57	2 mA	82k ohms	cand. scr.
300-375 volts	AR1	18 mA	18k ohms	med. scr.
	AR3	3.5 mA	9.1k ohms	cand. scr.
	AR4	3.5 mA	100k ohms	D.C. bay.
	NE-2	3 mA	1M ohms	wire term.
	NE-2A	3 mA	1M ohms	wire term.
	NE-17	2 mA	150k ohms	D.C. bay.
	NE-30	12 mA	20k ohms	med. scr.
	NE-32	12 mA	27k ohms	D.C. bay.

Voltage Range	Lamp Number	Current Rating (mA)	Series Resistance	Base
	NE-34	18 mA	13k ohms	med. scr.
	NE-40	30 mA	8.2k ohms	med. scr.
	NE-45	2 mA	120k ohms	cand. scr.
	NE-48	2 mA	150k ohms	D.C. bay.
	NE-51	0.3 mA	1M ohms	min. bay.
	NE-57	2 mA	120k ohms	cand. scr.
375-450 volts	AR1	18 mA	24k ohms	med. scr.
	AR3	3.5 mA	150k ohms	cand. scr.
	AR4	3.5 mA	160k ohms	D.C. bay.
	NE-2	3 mA	1.2M ohms	wire term.
	NE-2A	3 mA	1.2M ohms	wire term.
	NE-17	2 mA	180k ohms	D.C. bay.
	NE-30	12 mA	24k ohms	med. scr.
	NE-32	12mA	33k ohms	D.C. bay.
	NE-34	18 mA	16k ohms	med. scr.
	NE-40	30 mA	11k ohms	med. scr.
	NE-45	2mA	150k ohms	cand. scr.
	NE-48	2 mA	180k ohms	D.C. bay.
	NE-51	0.3 mA	1.2M ohms	min. bay.
	NE-57	2 mA	150k ohms	cand. scr.
450-600 volts	AR1	18 mA	30k ohms	med. scr.
	AR3	3.5 mA	160k ohms	Cand. scr.
	AR4	3.5 mA	180k ohms	D.C. bay.
	NE-2	3 mA	1.6M ohms	wire term.
	NE-2A	3 mA	1.6M ohms	wire term.
	NE-17	2 mA	240k ohms	D.C. bay.
	NE-30	12 mA	36k ohms	med. scr.
	NE-32	12 mA	43k ohms	D.C. bay.
	NE-34	18 mA	22k ohms	med. scr.
	NE-40	30 mA	16k ohms	med. scr.
	NE-45	2 mA	200k ohms	cand. scr.
	NE-48	2 mA	240k ohms	D.C. bay.
	NE-51	0.3 mA	1.6M ohms	min. bay.
	NE-57	2 mA	200k ohms	cand. scr.

5.8   MINIATURE LAMP DATA

Throughout the field of electronics one will often find the common miniature lamps used as indicating devices. The word miniature might be mis-

5

leading; it does not relate to a specific range of sizes, but does usually mean its operating voltage is under 60 volts.

Miniature lamp size, shape, base type, and number-letter combination have, for the most part, become standardized. The following letter and number bulb identification tells us from the letter the shape of the bulb, while the number indicates the approximate bulb diameter in eighths of an inch. For example:

Miniature lamp manufacturers make several different styles and sizes of bases for their lamps. Twenty-two different base types are listed throughout the following organized miniature lamp data. The base types referred to are:

Bulb Shape	Number-Letter Combination	Approximate Diameter
(B)	B-3½	7/16
	B-6	3/4
Figure 5-2		
	G-2	1/4
	G-3½	7/16
Figure 5-3	G-4½	9/16
	G-5	5/8
	G-5½	3/4
	G-6	3/4
(G)	G-8	1
	G-16½	2 1/16
Figure 5-4	R-12	1½
(R)		
	RP-11	1 3/8
Figure 5-5		
(RP)	S-8	1
	S-11	1 3/8
Figure 5-6	T-3/4	3/32
	T-1	1/8
(S)	T-1¼	5/32
	T-1 3/4	7/32
	T-2	1/4
	T-3	3/8
Figure 5-7	T-3¼	13/32
	T-4	1/2
(T)	T-4½	9/16
	T-5	5/8

HOW TO USE THE DATA

In the following lamp data, each lamp number has been grouped under its specific operating voltage range. The current, maximum overall length (MOL), bulb type, and base type or style have also been listed to aid you in finding or substituting miniature lamps to suit your immediate needs. Each bulb number will have its manufacturer's specific letter combination assigned to it when you buy its brand. For example, if General Electric were bought, then it would have GE-47, Chicago miniature would have CM-47, etc. However, technical data remains as shown here.

VOLTAGE	LAMP #	CURRENT	MOL	BULB TYPE	BASE
1.15v	8712	0.90A	0.187	T-¾	wire term
1.25v	123	0.30A	0.940	G-3½	min scr
	136	0.60A	1.060	G-4½	min scr
	423	0.60A	1.060	G-4½	min bay
	7244	0.012A	0.375	T-1	sub midget flg
	7252	0.012A	0.380	T-1	Bi pin
	8798	0.012A	0.250	T-1	wire term
1.3v	131	0.100A	0.940	G-3½	min scr
	2135	0.030A	0.460	T-1¼	wire term
	7301	0.030A	0.546	T-1¼	knurled scr
	7302	0.030A	0.500	T-1¼	special midget scr
	7303	0.030A	0.550	T-1¼	special scr
	7306	0.030A	0.600	T-1¼	Bi pin
1.35v	331	0.060A	0.625	T-1¾	midget flg
	359	0.060A	0.940	G-3½	min scr
	698	0.060A	0.625	T-1¾	midget groove
	1728	0.060A	0.520	T-1¾	wire term
	1800	0.060A	1.190	T-3¼	min scr
	7245	0.220A	0.375	T-1	sub midget flg
	7253	0.220A	0.380	T-1	Bi pin
	7636	0.060A	0.600	T-1¼	Bi pin
	7931	0.060A	0.625	T-1¾	Bi pin
	8631	0.060A	0.460	T-1¼	wire term
	8636	0.060A	0.500	T-1¼	special midget flg
	8641	0.060A	0.550	T-1¼	special scr
	8647	0.060A	0.546	T-1¼	knurled scr
	8669	0.060A	0.688	T-1¾	midget scr
	8910	0.220A	0.250	T-1	wire term

5

VOLTAGE	LAMP #	CURRENT	MOL	BULB TYPE	BASE
1.5v	3225	0.010A	0.380	T-1	Bi pin
	3810	0.015A	0.300	T-¾	micro midget flg
	3811	0.015A	0.300	T-¾	micro midget flg
	7100	0.015A	0.187	T-¾	wire term
	7101	0.015A	0.187	T-¾	wire term
	7200	0.010A	0.250	T-1	wire term
	7201	0.015A	0.250	T-1	wire term
	7203	0.075A	0.250	T-1	wire term
	7225	0.010A	0.375	T-1	sub midget flg
	7226	0.015A	0.375	T-1	sub midget flg
	7254	0.015A	0.380	T-1	Bi pin
	7255	0.075A	0.380	T-1	Bi pin
	8102	0.075A	0.375	T-1	sub midget flg
2v	48	0.060A	1.190	T-3¼	min scr
	49	0.060A	1.190	T-3¼	min bay
	352	0.060A	0.940	G-3½	min scr
	1809	0.060A	1.190	T-3¼	min bay
2.33v	PR-4	0.270A	1.250	B-3½	S.C. min flg
	233	0.270A	0.940	B-3½	min scr
2.35v	PR-5	0.350A	1.250	B-3½	S.C. min flg
2.38v	PR-2	0.500A	1.250	B-3½	S.C. min flg
2.4v	1491	0.800A	1.750	G-8	D.C. bay
2.46v	245	0.500A	0.940	G-3½	min scr
2.47v	PR-6	0.300A	1.250	B-3½	S.C. min flg
	14	0.300A	0.940	G-3½	min scr
	354	0.300A	0.940	G-3½	min bay
2.5v	10	0.500A	0.940	G-3½	min 2 pin
	35	0.800A	1.250	G-5½	min scr
	41	0.500A	1.190	T-3¼	min scr
	43	0.500A	1.190	T-3¼	min bay
	248	0.800A	1.250	G-5½	min scr
	266	0.350A	0.625	T-1¾	midget groove
	268	0.350A	0.625	T-1¾	midget flg
	326	0.400A	0.546	T-1¼	knurled scr
	329	0.400A	0.550	T-1¼	special scr
	343	0.400A	0.625	T-1¾	midget flg
	368	0.200A	0.625	T-1¾	midget flg
	1492	1.500A	2.000	S-8	D.C. bay
	1769	0.200A	0.688	T-1¾	midget scr
	1783	0.200A	0.520	T-1¾	wire term
	2169	0.350A	0.520	T-1¾	wire term
	7121	0.110A	0.300	T-¾	micro midget flg
	7246	0.015A	0.375	T-1	sub midget flg
	7247	0.100A	0.375	T-1	sub midget flg

VOLTAGE	LAMP #	CURRENT	MOL	BULB TYPE	BASE
2.5v	7248	0.320A	0.375	T-1	sub midget flg
(continued)	7256	0.015A	0.380	T-1	Bi pin
	7257	0.320A	0.380	T-1	Bi pin
	7307	0.400A	0.600	T-1¼	Bi pin
	7312	0.350A	0.688	T-1¾	midget scr
	7357	0.400A	0.625	T-1¾	Bi pin
	7732	0.100A	0.380	T-1	Bi pin
	7868	0.350A	0.625	T-1¾	Bi pin
	7968	0.200A	0.625	T-1¾	Bi pin
	8534	0.110A	0.187	T-¾	wire term
	8601	0.015A	0.250	T-1	wire term
	8655	0.400A	0.460	T-1¼	wire term
	8656	0.400A	0.500	T-1¼	special midget flg
	8663	0.400A	0.520	T-1¾	wire term
	8671	0.400A	0.688	T-1¾	midget scr
	8699	0.200A	0.625	T-1¾	midget groove
	8703	0.400A	0.625	T-1¾	midget groove
	8711	0.320A	0.250	T-1	wire term
	8732	0.100A	0.250	T-1	wire term
2.7v	PR-9	0.150A	1.250	B-3½	S.C. min flg
	338	0.060A	0.625	T-1¾	midget flg
	1738	0.060A	0.525	T-1¾	wire term
	7838	0.060A	0.625	T-1¾	Bi pin
	8693	0.060A	0.688	T-1¾	midget scr
	8704	0.060A	0.625	T-1¾	midget groove
3v	323	0.190A	0.546	T-1¼	knurled scr
	324	0.190A	0.460	T-1¼	wire term
	325	0.190A	0.550	T-1¼	special scr
	375	0.015A	0.625	T-1¾	midget flg
	390	0.015A	0.625	T-1¾	midget flg
	679	0.0125A	0.375	T-1	sub midget flg
	2128	0.0125A	0.250	T-1	wire term
	2156	0.030A	0.520	T-1¾	wire term
	2158	0.015A	0.520	T-1¾	wire term
	3229	0.015A	0.380	T-1	Bi pin
	7205	0.015A	0.250	T-1	wire term
	7207	0.060A	0.250	T-1	wire term
	7208	0.120A	0.250	T-1	wire term
	7229	0.015A	0.375	T-1	sub midget flg
	7231	0.060A	0.375	T-1	sub midget flg
	7232	0.120A	0.375	T-1	sub midget flg
	7249	0.008A	0.375	T-1	sub midget flg
	7258	0.008A	0.380	T-1	Bi pin
	7259	0.0125A	0.380	T-1	Bi pin

5

VOLTAGE	LAMP #	CURRENT	MOL	BULB TYPE	BASE
3v	7260	0.060A	0.380	T-1	Bi pin
(continued)	7261	0.120A	0.380	T-1	Bi pin
	7313	0.150A	0.688	T-1¾	midget scr
	7314	0.030A	0.688	T-1¾	midget scr
	7329	0.030A	0.625	T-1¾	midget flg
	7343	0.030A	0.625	T-1¾	midget groove
	7358	0.030A	0.625	T-1¾	Bi pin
	7375	0.015A	0.625	T-1¾	Bi pin
	7637	0.190A	0.600	T-1¼	Bi pin
	8637	0.190A	0.500	T-1¼	special midget flg
	8846	0.008A	0.250	T-1	wire term
3.2v	45	0.350A	1.190	T-3¼	min bay
	1490	0.160A	1.190	T-3¼	min bay
3.57v	PR-3	0.500A	1.250	B-3½	S.C. min flg
3.69v	365	0.500A	0.940	G-3½	min scr
3.7v	PR-7	0.300A	1.250	B-3½	S.C. min flg
	13	0.300A	0.940	G-3½	min scr
	1874	2.750A	1.750	T-5	S.C. bay
3.8v	1438	0.430A	0.940	G-3½	min scr
4v	4A	0.190A	1.688	T-2	telephone slide
	4ES	0.040A	0.700	T-2	wire term
	4ESB	0.040A	0.915	T-2	short slide
	403	0.300A	0.940	G-3½	min scr
	1804	0.060A	1.190	T-3¼	min bay
4.5v	30	0.021A	0.187	T-¾	wire term
	673	0.285A	0.550	T-1¼	special scr
	1021	1.250A	2.250	RP-11	S.C. prefocus
	2171	0.120A	0.520	T-1¾	wire term
	3102	0.022A	0.187	T-¾	wire term
	7304	0.285A	0.546	T-1¼	knurled scr
	7305	0.285A	0.500	T-1¼	special midget flg
	7308	0.285A	0.600	T-1¼	Bi pin
	7315	0.120A	0.688	T-1¾	midget scr
	7331	0.120A	0.625	T-1¾	midget flg
	7345	0.120A	0.625	T-1¾	midget groove
	7359	0.120A	0.625	T-1¾	Bi pin
	8816	0.285A	0.500	T-1¼	wire term
4.75v	PR-13	0.500A	1.250	B-3½	S.C. min flg
4.82v	PR-15	0.500A	1.250	B-3½	S.C. min flg
4.9v	27	0.300A	1.060	G-4½	min scr
	407	0.300A	1.060	G-4½	min scr
	408	0.300A	1.060	G-4½	min bay
5v	2	0.021A	0.187	T-¾	wire term
	5ES	0.040A	0.700	T-2	wire term
	5ESB	0.040A	0.915	T-2	short slide
	425	0.500A	1.060	G-4½	min scr
	515	0.115A	0.460	T-1¼	wire term

VOLTAGE	LAMP #	CURRENT	MOL	BULB TYPE	BASE
5v———————	580	0.060A	0.460	T-1¼	wire term
(continued)	583	0.060A	0.460	T-1¼	wire term
	680	0.060A	0.250	T-1	wire term
	682	0.060A	0.375	T-1	sub midget flg
	683	0.060A	0.250	T-1	wire term
	685	0.060A	0.375	T-1	sub midget flg
	713	0.075A	0.250	T-1	wire term
	714	0.075A	0.375	T-1	sub midget flg
	715	0.115A	0.250	T-1	wire term
	718	0.115A	0.375	T-1	sub midget flg
	1651	0.600A	2.000	S-8	S.C. bay
	1850	0.090A	1.190	T-3¼	min bay
	2022	0.021A	0.145	T-1	wire term
	2200	0.060A	0.520	T-1¾	wire term
	2203	0.115A	0.520	T-1¾	wire term
	2950	0.017A	0.688	T-1¾	midget scr
	3022	0.021A	0.187	T-1	wire term
	3149	0.060A	0.625	T-1¾	Bi pin
	3150	0.060A	0.625	T-1¾	midget flg
	3151	0.060A	0.525	T-1¾	wire term
	3152	0.060A	0.625	T-1¾	midget groove
	3153	0.060A	0.688	T-1¾	midget scr
	3211	0.115A	0.187	T-1	wire term
	3515	0.115A	0.550	T-1¼	special scr
	3516	0.115A	0.546	T-1¼	knurled scr
	3518	0.115A	0.500	T-1¼	special midget flg
	3580	0.060A	0.550	T-1¼	special scr
	3581	0.060A	0.546	T-1¼	knurled scr
	3582	0.060A	0.500	T-1¼	special midget flg
	3583	0.060A	0.550	T-1¼	special scr
	3584	0.060A	0.546	T-1¼	knurled scr
	3585	0.060A	0.500	T-1¼	special midget flg
	3950	0.017A	0.520	T-1¾	wire term
	6022	0.021A	0.250	T-1	wire term
	6150	0.060A	0.250	T-1	wire term
	6151	0.060A	0.187	T-1	wire term
	6152	0.060A	0.145	T-1	wire term
	6153	0.060A	0.187	T-¾	wire term
	6180	0.060A	0.375	T-1	sub midget flg
	6183	0.060A	0.300	T-¾	micro midget flg
	6211	0.080A	0.187	T-1	wire term
	6212	0.080A	0.145	T-1	wire term
	6801	0.060A	0.187	T-1	wire term
	6802	0.060A	0.145	T-1	wire term
	6803	0.060A	0.187	T-¾	wire term
	6831	0.060A	0.187	T-1	wire term
	6832	0.060A	0.145	T-1	wire term

5

VOLTAGE	LAMP #	CURRENT	MOL	BULB TYPE	BASE
5v ————	6833	0.060A	0.187	T-¾	wire term
(continued)	6950	0.017A	0.625	T-1¾	midget groove
	7022	0.021A	0.380	T-1	Bi pin
	7102	0.115A	0.187	T-¾	wire term
	7112	0.021A	0.325	T-¾	Bi pin
	7113	0.060A	0.325	T-¾	Bi pin
	7114	0.060A	0.325	T-¾	Bi pin
	7115	0.060A	0.325	T-¾	Bi pin
	7116	0.075A	0.325	T-¾	Bi pin
	7117	0.080A	0.325	T-¾	Bi pin
	7118	0.115A	0.325	T-¾	Bi pin
	7119	0.115A	0.325	T-¾	Bi pin
	7122	0.021A	0.300	T-¾	micro midget flg
	7123	0.115A	0.300	T-¾	micro midget flg
	7131	0.075A	0.187	T-1	wire term
	7132	0.075A	0.145	T-1	wire term
	7133	0.075A	0.187	T-¾	wire term
	7151	0.115A	0.187	T-1	wire term
	7152	0.115A	0.145	T-1	wire term
	7153	0.115A	0.187	T-¾	wire term
	7210	0.030A	0.250	T-1	wire term
	7211	0.080A	0.250	T-1	wire term
	7212	0.115A	0.145	T-1	wire term
	7213	0.115A	0.250	T-1	wire term
	7216	0.125A	0.250	T-1	wire term
	7234	0.030A	0.375	T-1	sub midget flg
	7235	0.080A	0.375	T-1	sub midget flg
	7236	0.115A	0.375	T-1	sub midget flg
	7239	0.125A	0.375	T-1	sub midget flg
	7250	0.045A	0.375	T-1	sub midget flg
	7251	0.145A	0.375	T-1	sub midget flg
	7262	0.017A	0.380	T-1	Bi pin
	7263	0.030A	0.380	T-1	Bi pin
	7264	0.045A	0.380	T-1	Bi pin
	7265	0.060A	0.380	T-1	Bi pin
	7266	0.080A	0.380	T-1	Bi pin
	7267	0.115A	0.380	T-1	Bi pin
	7268	0.125A	0.380	T-1	Bi pin
	7269	0.145A	0.380	T-1	Bi pin
	7316	0.060A	0.688	T-1¾	midget scr
	7317	0.190A	0.688	T-1¾	midget scr
	7318	0.060A	0.688	T-1¾	midget scr
	7319	0.115A	0.688	T-1¾	midget scr
	7332	0.060A	0.625	T-1¾	midget flg
	7333	0.060A	0.625	T-1¾	midget flg
	7334	0.190A	0.625	T-1¾	midget flg
	7335	0.115A	0.625	T-1¾	midget flg

VOLTAGE	LAMP #	CURRENT	MOL	BULB TYPE	BASE
5v———	7346	0.060A	0.625	T-1¾	midget groove
(continued)	7347	0.060A	0.625	T-1¾	midget groove
	7348	0.115A	0.625	T-1¾	midget groove
	7350	0.190A	0.625	T-1¾	midget groove
	7360	0.060A	0.625	T-1¾	Bi pin
	7361	0.060A	0.625	T-1¾	Bi pin
	7362	0.115A	0.625	T-1¾	Bi pin
	7363	0.190A	0.625	T-1¾	Bi pin
	7515	0.115A	0.600	T-1¼	Bi pin
	7538	0.015A	0.325	T-¾	Bi pin
	7580	0.060A	0.600	T-1¼	Bi pin
	7583	0.060A	0.600	T-1¼	Bi pin
	7680	0.060A	0.380	T-1	Bi pin
	7683	0.060A	0.380	T-1	Bi pin
	7714	0.075A	0.380	T-1	Bi pin
	7715	0.115A	0.380	T-1	Bi pin
	7950	0.017A	0.625	T-1¾	Bi pin
	8022	0.021A	0.375	T-1	sub midget flg
	8096	0.145A	0.250	T-1	wire term
	8175	0.125A	0.145	T-1	wire term
	8179	0.125A	0.187	T-1	wire term
	8270	0.115A	0.300	T-¾	micro midget flg
	8383	0.080A	0.300	T-¾	micro midget flg
	8537	0.150A	0.187	T-¾	wire term
	8538	0.015A	0.300	T-¾	micro midget flg
	8587	0.060A	0.300	T-¾	micro midget flg
	8605	0.017A	0.375	T-1	sub midget flg
	8666	0.800A	0.187	T-¾	wire term
	8729	0.045A	0.250	T-1	wire term
	8784	0.190A	0.520	T-1¾	wire term
	8805	0.060A	0.520	T-1¾	wire term
	8828	0.075A	0.300	T-¾	micro midget flg
	8913	0.060A	0.300	T-¾	micro midget flg
	8950	0.017A	0.625	T-1¾	midget flg
5.1v———	502	0.150A	1.060	G-4½	min scr
	503	0.150A	1.060	G-4½	min bay
5.4v———	1611	1.860A	2.000	S-8	S.C. bay
5.5v———	958	2.000A	3.000	G-16½	D.C. bay
	1183	6.250A	2.250	RP-11	S.C. bay
	1184	6.250A	2.250	RP-11	D.C. bay
	1188	6.180A	2.250	RP-11	D.C. bay
5.95v———	PR-12	0.500A	1.250	B-3½	S.C. min flg
	1501	6.360A	2.250	RP-11	S.C. prefocus
	1503	6.530A	2.250	RP-11	S.C. prefocus
	2530	6.530A	2.250	RP-11	D.C. prefocus
6v———	6A	0.140A	1.688	T-2	telephone slide
	6B	0.290A	1.688	T-2	telephone slide

5

VOLTAGE	LAMP #	CURRENT	MOL	BULB TYPE	BASE
6v——————	6C	0.040A	1.688	T-2	telephone slide
(continued)	6ES	0.040A	0.700	T-2	wire term
	6ESB	0.040A	0.915	T-2	short slide
	6PS	0.140A	0.857	T-2	wire term
	6PSB	0.140A	1.115	T-2	short slide
	6MB	0.140A	1.187	T-2	min bay
	30	0.450A	1.119	T-3¼	min scr
	60	5.500A	2.380	RP-11	S.C. bay
	316	0.700A	1.190	T-3¼	min bay
	328	0.200A	0.625	T-1¾	midget flg
	337	0.200A	0.625	T-1¾	midget groove
	342	0.040A	0.688	T-1¾	midget scr
	345	0.040A	0.625	T-1¾	midget flg
	371	0.060A	0.550	T-1¼	special scr
	634	0.200A	0.460	T-1¼	wire term
	1025	2.350A	2.250	RP-11	S.C. prefocus
	1482	0.450A	1.060	G-4½	min scr
	1483	0.040A	1.060	G-4½	min scr
	1730	0.040A	0.520	T-1¾	wire term
	1768	0.200A	0.688	T-1¾	midget scr
	1784	0.200A	0.520	T-1¾	wire term
	2114	0.060A	0.460	T-1¼	wire term
	7309	0.060A	0.600	T-1¼	Bi pin
	7328	0.200A	0.625	T-1¾	Bi pin
	7336	0.200A	0.625	T-1¾	midget flg
	7364	0.200A	0.625	T-1¾	Bi pin
	7628	0.200A	0.600	T-1¼	Bi pin
	7660	0.040A	0.600	T-1¼	Bi pin
	7945	0.040A	0.625	T-1¾	Bi pin
	8541	0.060A	0.500	T-1¼	special midget flg
	8543	0.060A	0.546	T-1¼	knurled scr
	8628	0.200A	0.500	T-1¼	special midget flg
	8639	0.200A	0.546	T-1¼	knurled scr
	8645	0.200A	0.550	T-1¼	special scr
	8657	0.040A	0.546	T-1¼	knurled scr
	8660	0.040A	0.500	T-1¼	special midget flg
	8661	0.040A	0.460	T-1¼	wire term
	8662	0.040A	0.550	T-1¼	special scr
	8664	0.200A	0.520	T-1¾	wire term
	8687	0.200A	0.688	T-1¾	midget scr
	8705	0.040A	0.625	T-1¾	midget flg
	8706	0.200A	0.625	T-1¾	midget groove
6.15v——————	31	0.300A	1.060	G-4½	min scr
	605	0.500A	1.060	G-4½	min scr
	1209	4.100A	2.250	RP-11	S.C. prefocus
	1763	4.100A	2.38	S-11	S.C. prefocus

VOLTAGE	LAMP #	CURRENT	MOL	BULB TYPE	BASE
6.2v	1000	3.870A	2.250	RP-11	D.C. bay
	1133	3.910A	2.250	RP-11	S.C. prefocus
	1134	3.910A	2.250	RP-11	D.C. bay
	1323	4.130A	2.250	RP-11	S.C. prefocus
	1724	4.500A	2.380	S-11	D.C. bay
	2330	4.230A	2.250	RP-11	D.C. prefocus
6.3v	12	0.150A	0.940	G-3½	min 2 pin
	40	0.150A	1.190	T-3¼	min scr
	44	0.250A	1.190	T-3¼	min bay
	46	0.250A	1.190	T-3¼	min scr
	47	0.150A	1.190	T-3¼	min bay
	130	0.150A	0.940	G-3½	min bay
	137	0.250A	0.940	G-3½	min bay
	219	0.250A	0.940	G-3½	min bay
	239	0.360A	1.190	T-3¼	min bay
	240	0.360A	1.190	T-3¼	min bay
	349	0.200A	0.625	T-1¾	midget flg
	350	0.150A	0.625	T-1¾	midget flg
	377	0.075A	0.625	T-1¾	midget flg
	378	0.200A	0.688	T-1¾	midget scr
	379	0.200A	0.625	T-1¾	midget groove
	380	0.040A	0.625	T-1¾	midget flg
	381	0.200A	0.625	T-1¾	midget flg
	398	0.200A	0.625	T-1¾	midget groove
	755	0.150A	1.190	T-3¼	min bay
	1739	0.075A	0.520	T-1¾	wire term
	1775	0.075A	0.688	T-1¾	midget scr
	1810	0.400A	1.190	T-3¼	min bay
	1830	0.150A	1.190	T-3¼	min bay
	1847	0.150A	1.190	T-3¼	min bay
	1855	0.800A	1.380	T-4½	S.C. min bay
	1866	0.250A	1.190	T-3¼	min bay
	2112	0.200A	0.520	T-1¾	wire term
	2180	0.040A	0.520	T-1¾	wire term
	2181	0.200A	0.520	T-1¾	wire term
	7310	0.200A	0.600	T-1¼	Bi pin
	7320	0.040A	0.688	T-1¾	midget scr
	7321	0.150A	0.688	T-1¾	midget scr
	7323	0.200A	0.688	T-1¾	midget scr
	7349	0.200A	0.625	T-1¾	Bi pin
	7351	0.040A	0.625	T-1¾	midget groove
	7352	0.150A	0.625	T-1¾	midget groove
	7368	0.150A	0.625	T-1¾	Bi pin
	7377	0.075A	0.625	T-1¾	Bi pin
	7380	0.040A	0.625	T-1¾	Bi pin
	7381	0.200A	0.625	T-1¾	Bi pin

5

VOLTAGE	LAMP #	CURRENT	MOL	BULB TYPE	BASE
6.3v	8350	0.150A	0.520	T-1¾	wire term
(continued)	8551	0.200A	0.500	T-1¼	special midget flg
	8552	0.200A	0.550	T-1¼	special scr
	8553	0.200A	0.546	T-1¼	knurled scr
	8610	0.200A	0.460	T-1¼	wire term
	8708	0.075A	0.625	T-1¾	midget groove
6.4v	6	3.000A	2.000	S-8	D.C. bay
	1129	2.630A	2.000	S-8	S.C. bay
	1130	2.600A	2.000	S-8	D.C. bay
	1154	2.630A	2.000	S-8	D.C. index
	1158	2.630A	2.000	S-8	D.C. bay
	1618	2.800A	2.000	S-8	D.C. bay
6.5v	81	1.020A	1.440	G-6	S.C. bay
	81K	1.020A	1.38	G-6	cand scr
	82	1.050A	1.440	G-6	D.C. bay
	209	1.780A	1.750	B-6	S.C. bay
	210	1.780A	1.750	B-6	D.C. bay
	455	0.500A	1.060	G-4½	min bay
	707	1.880A	1.700	B-6	D.C. bay
	808	1.880A	1.280	B-6	wire term
	1489	2.750A	1.750	T-5	S.C. bay
	1493	2.800A	2.000	S-8	D.C. bay
	1630	2.750A	2.000	S-8	D.C. prefocus
	1811	0.400A	1.190	T-3¼	min bay
	1884	1.540A	1.750	T-5	S.C. bay
6.7v	1619	1.900A	2.000	S-8	S.C. bay
6.8v	87	1.910A	2.000	S-8	S.C. bay
	88	1.900A	2.000	S-8	D.C. bay
	88L	2.000A	2.000	S-8	D.C. bay
7.0v	15	0.400A	1.060	G-4½	min 2 pin
	55	0.410A	1.060	G-4½	min bay
	63	0.630A	1.440	G-6	S.C. bay
	63K	0.630A	1.380	G-6	cand scr
	64	0.630A	1.440	G-6	D.C. bay
	162	0.630A	0.550	G-2	midget scr
	1888	0.500A	1.190	T-3¼	min bay
7.2v	PR-18	0.550A	1.250	B-3½	S.C. min flg
7.5v	50	0.220A	0.940	G-3½	min scr
	51	0.220A	0.940	G-3½	min bay
8v	8	2.200A	2.000	S-8	D.C. bay
	8A	0.900A	1.688	T-2	telephone slide
	426	0.250A	1.060	G-4½	min scr
	1648	2.000A	2.000	S-8	D.C. bay
8.63v	PR-20	0.500A	1.250	B-3½	S.C. min flg
10v	10A	0.110A	1.688	T-2	telephone slide
	10B	0.250A	1.688	T-2	telephone slide

VOLTAGE	LAMP #	CURRENT	MOL	BULB TYPE	BASE
10v ———————	10AS	0.010A	0.700	T-2	wire term
(continued)	10ASB	0.010A	0.915	T-2	short slide
	10CS	0.017A	0.700	T-2	wire term
	10CSB	0.017A	0.915	T-2	short slide
	10ES	0.040A	0.700	T-2	wire term
	10ESB	0.040A	0.915	T-2	short slide
	240	1.020A	0.940	T-3	wire term
	344	0.014A	0.625	T-1¾	midget flg
	367	0.040A	0.625	T-1¾	midget flg
	389	0.040A	0.688	T-1¾	midget scr
	397	0.040A	0.625	T-1¾	midget groove
	709	0.014A	0.625	T-1¾	midget groove
	755	0.450A	0.550	T-3	wire term
	1869	0.014A	0.520	T-1¾	wire term
	2107	0.040A	0.520	T-1¾	wire term
	7218	0.027A	0.250	T-1	wire term
	7240	0.027A	0.375	T-1	sub midget flg
	7311	0.014A	0.600	T-1¼	Bi pin
	7344	0.014A	0.625	T-1¾	Bi pin
	7367	0.040A	0.625	T-1¾	Bi pin
	8095	0.027A	0.380	T-1	Bi pin
	8606	0.014A	0.550	T-1¼	special scr
	8607	0.014A	0.546	T-1¼	knurled scr
	8608	0.014A	0.460	T-1¼	wire term
	8609	0.014A	0.500	T-1¼	special midget flg
	8691	0.014A	0.688	T-1¾	midget scr
11v ———————	7325	0.022A	0.688	T-1¾	midget scr
	7338	0.022A	0.625	T-1¾	midget flg
	7353	0.022A	0.625	T-1¾	midget groove
	7369	0.022A	0.625	T-1¾	Bi pin
	8946	0.022A	0.520	T-1¾	wire term
12v ———————	12A	0.100A	1.688	T-2	telephone slide
	12B	0.350A	1.688	T-2	telephone slide
	12C	0.170A	1.688	T-2	telephone slide
	12ES	0.040A	0.700	T-2	wire term
	12ESB	0.040A	0.915	T-2	short slide
	12PS	0.070A	0.857	T-2	wire term
	12PSB	0.170A	1.115	T-2	short slide
	12MB	0.170A	1.187	T-2	min bay
	32	0.060A	0.375	T-1	sub midget flg
	394	0.040A	0.625	T-1¾	midget flg
	1446	0.200A	0.940	G-3½	min scr
	1471	0.260A	1.380	G-6	cand scr
	2174	0.040A	0.520	T-1¾	wire term
	7219	0.060A	0.250	T-1	wire term
	7326	0.040A	0.688	T-1¾	midget scr

5

VOLTAGE	LAMP #	CURRENT	MOL	BULB TYPE	BASE
12 v—————	7354	0.040A	0.625	T-1¾	midget groove
(continued)	7371	0.040A	0.625	T-1¾	Bi pin
	8097	0.060A	0.380	T-1	Bi pin
12.5v—————	PR-16	0.250A	1.250	B-3½	S.C. min flg
	428	0.250A	1.060	G-4½	min scr
	1124	1.920A	2.250	RP-11	D.C. bay
	1143	2.000A	2.250	RP-11	S.C. bay
	1144	2.000A	2.250	RP-11	D.C. bay
	1195	3.000A	2.250	RP-11	S.C. bay
	1196	3.000A	2.250	RP-11	D.C. bay
	1507	3.000A	2.250	RP-11	S.C. prefocus
	2336	2.230A	2.250	RP-11	D.C. prefocus
12.8v—————	93	1.040A	2.000	S-8	S.C. bay
	94	1.000A	2.000	S-8	D.C. bay
	1003	0.940A	1.750	B-6	S.C. bay
	1004	0.940A	1.750	B-6	S.C. bay
	1005	1.260A	2.000	S-8	D.C. bay
	1011	2.080A	2.250	RP-11	S.C. prefocus
	1016	1.340A	2.000	S-8	D.C. index
	1026	2.180A	2.250	RP-11	D.C. prefocus
	1034	1.800A	2.000	S-8	D.C. index
	1044	1.850A	2.250	RP-11	D.C. prefocus
	1073	1.800A	2.000	S-8	S.C. bay
	1076	1.800A	2.000	S-8	D.C. bay
	1141	1.440A	2.000	S-8	S.C. bay
	1142	1.440A	2.000	S-8	D.C. bay
	1156	2.100A	2.000	S-8	S.C. bay
	1157	2.100A	2.000	S-8	D.C. index
	1176	1.340A	2.000	S-8	D.C. bay
	1327	2.080A	2.250	RP-11	S.C. prefocus
13v—————	78	0.370A	1.380	G-5	D.C. bay
	89	0.580A	1.380	G-6	S.C. bay
	89K	0.530A	1.380	G-6	cand scr
	90	0.580A	1.440	G-6	D.C. bay
	1816	0.330A	1.190	T-3¼	min bay
13.5v—————	67	0.590A	1.440	G-6	S.C. bay
	67K	0.410A	1.380	G-6	cand scr
	67M	0.410A	1.310	G-6	min scr
	68	0.590A	1.440	G-6	D.C. bay
	1155	0.590A	1.440	G-6	S.C. bay
14v—————	57	0.240A	1.060	G-4½	min bay
	57X	0.240A	1.060	G-4½	min bay
	163	0.065A	0.550	G-2	midget scr
	257	0.270A	1.060	G-4½	min bay
	258	0.270A	1.060	G-4½	min scr
	330	0.080A	0.625	T-1¾	midget flg
	336	0.080A	0.625	T-1¾	midget groove

VOLTAGE	LAMP #	CURRENT	MOL	BULB TYPE	BASE
14v	363	0.200A	0.940	G-3½	min bay
(continued)	373	0.080A	0.688	T-1¾	midget scr
	382	0.080A	0.625	T-1¾	midget scr
	386	0.080A	0.625	T-1¾	midget groove
	393	0.100A	0.625	T-1¾	midget groove
	431	0.250A	1.060	G-4½	min bay
	631	0.630A	1.440	G-6	S.C. bay
	756	0.080A	1.190	T-3¼	min bay
	1074	0.510A	2.250	RP-11	D.C. prefocus
	1247	0.480A	1.440	G-6	S.C. bay
	1449	0.200A	0.940	G-3½	min scr
	1474	0.170A	1.250	T-3	min scr
	1479	0.170A	1.500	T-4	cand scr
	1487	0.200A	1.190	T-3¼	min scr
	1488	0.150A	1.190	T-3¼	min bay
	1705	0.080A	0.520	T-1¾	wire term
	1815	0.200A	1.190	T-3¼	min bay
	1889	0.270A	1.190	T-3¼	min bay
	1891	0.240A	1.190	T-3¼	min bay
	1893	0.330A	1.190	T-3¼	min bay
	1895	0.270A	1.060	G-4½	min bay
	2162	0.100A	0.520	T-1¾	wire term
	2182	0.080A	0.520	T-1¾	wire term
	7330	0.080A	0.625	T-1¾	Bi pin
	7646	0.080A	0.600	T-1¼	Bi pin
	7373	0.100A	0.625	T-1¾	Bi pin
	7382	0.080A	0.625	T-1¾	Bi pin
	8098	0.065A	0.380	T-1	Bi pin
	8111	0.065A	0.250	T-1	wire term
	8112	0.065A	0.375	T-1	sub midget flg
	8162	0.100A	0.688	T-1¾	midget scr
	8362	0.080A	0.688	T-1¾	midget scr
	8640	0.080A	0.460	T-1¼	wire term
	8644	0.080A	0.550	T-1¼	special scr
	8646	0.080A	0.500	T-1¼	special midget flg
	8654	0.080A	0.546	T-1¼	knurled scr
	8918	0.100A	0.625	T-1¾	midget flg
14.4v	19	0.100A	0.940	G-3½	min 2 pin
	52	0.100A	0.940	G-3½	min scr
	53	0.120A	0.940	G-3½	min bay
	53X	0.120A	0.940	G-3½	min bay
	1813	0.100A	1.190	T-3¼	min bay
	1892	0.120A	1.190	T-3¼	min bay
16v	16A	0.100A	1.688	T-2	telephone slide
	16B	0.290A	1.688	T-2	telephone slide
	16CS	0.017A	0.700	T-2	wire term
	16CSB	0.017A	0.915	T-2	short slide

5

VOLTAGE	LAMP #	CURRENT	MOL	BULB TYPE	BASE
16v ————	16ES	0.040A	0.700	T-2	wire term
(continued)	16ESB	0.040A	0.915	T-2	short-slide
18v ————	18A	0.040A	1.688	T-2	telephone slide
	18B	0.100A	1.688	T-2	telephone slide
	18ES	0.040A	0.700	T-2	wire term
	18ESB	0.040A	0.915	T-2	short slide
	346	0.040A	0.625	T-1¾	midget groove
	370	0.040A	0.625	T-1¾	midget flg
	432	0.250A	1.060	G-4½	min scr
	433	0.250A	1.060	G-4½	min bay
	1445	0.150A	0.940	G-3½	min bay
	1447	0.150A	0.940	G-3½	min scr
	1456	0.250A	1.190	G-5	min bay
	1476	0.170A	1.250	T-3	min scr
	1480	0.170A	1.500	T-4	cand scr
	1826	0.150A	1.190	T-3¼	min bay
	2102	0.040A	0.520	T-1¾	wire term
	7220	0.026A	0.250	T-1	wire term
	7241	0.026A	0.375	T-1	sub midget flg
	7370	0.040A	0.625	T-1¾	Bi pin
	8099	0.026A	0.380	T-1	Bi pin
	8536	0.040A	0.688	T-1¾	midget scr
20v ————	20C	0.034A	1.688	T-2	telephone slide
	1458	0.250A	1.190	G-5	min bay
22v ————	71	0.180A	1.440	G-6	S.C. bay
	71K	0.180A	1.380	G-6	cand scr
	71M	0.180A	1.310	G-6	min scr
	72	0.180A	1.440	G-6	D.C. bay
	457	0.040A	0.625	T-1¾	midget groove
	459	0.040A	0.625	T-1¾	midget flg
	1464	0.250A	1.190	G-5	min bay
	7459	0.040A	0.625	T-1¾	Bi pin
	8425	0.040A	0.520	T-1¾	wire term
	8437	0.040A	0.688	T-1¾	midget scr
24v ————	24A	0.030A	1.688	T-2	telephone slide
	24B	0.040A	1.688	T-2	telephone slide
	24C	0.072A	1.688	T-2	telephone slide
	24CS	0.017A	0.700	T-2	wire term
	24CSB	0.017A	0.915	T-2	short slide
	24D	0.100A	1.688	T-2	telephone slide
	24E	0.035A	1.688	T-2	telephone slide
	24ES	0.040A	0.700	T-2	wire term
	24ESB	0.040A	0.915	T-2	short slide
	24F	0.090A	1.688	T-2	telephone slide
	24MB	0.073A	1.187	T-2	min bay
	24PS	0.073A	0.857	T-2	wire term
	24PSB	0.073A	1.115	T-2	short slide

VOLTAGE	LAMP #	CURRENT	MOL	BULB TYPE	BASE
24v——————24X	0.035A	1.688	T-2	telephone slide	
(continued)	509	0.180A	1.440	G-6	S.C. bay
	509K	0.180A	1.380	G-6	cand scr
	530	0.170A	1.380	G-6	cand scr
	1448	0.035A	0.940	G-3½	min scr
	1477	0.170A	1.250	T-3	min scr
	1818	0.170A	1.190	T-3¼	min bay
	1841	0.170A	1.500	T4	cand scr
	2176	0.050A	0.520	T-1¾	wire term
	7001	0.050A	0.625	T-1¾	Bi pin
	8176	0.050A	0.625	T-1¾	midget flg
	8177	0.050A	0.625	T-1¾	midget groove
	8178	0.050A	0.688	T-1¾	midget scr
25.6v——————1271	1.340A	2.250	RP-11	S.C. prefocus	
26v——————1047	2.700A	2.250	RP-11	S.C. bay	
28v——————28ES	0.040A	0.700	T-2	wire term	
	28ESB	0.040A	0.915	T-2	short slide
	28PS	0.040A	0.857	T-2	wire term
	28PSB	0.040A	1.115	T-2	short slide
	28MB	0.040A	1.187	T-2	min bay
	301	0.170A	1.380	G-5	S.C. bay
	302	0.170A	1.380	G-5	D.C. bay
	303	0.300A	1.440	G-6	S.C. bay
	304	0.300A	1.440	G-6	D.C. bay
	305	0.560A	2.000	S-8	S.C. bay
	306	0.510A	2.000	S-8	D.C. bay
	307	0.660A	2.000	S-8	S.C. bay
	308	0.670A	2.000	S-8	D.C. bay
	309	0.900A	2.380	S-11	S.C. bay
	310	0.920A	2.380	S-11	D.C. bay
	311	1.290A	2.380	S-11	S.C. bay
	313	0.170A	1.190	T-3¼	min bay
	315	0.900A	2.000	S-8	S.C. bay
	327	0.040A	0.625	T-1¾	midget flg
	334	0.040A	0.625	T-1¾	midget groove
	335	0.040A	0.688	T-1¾	midget scr
	336	0.170A	0.940	G-3½	min bay
	376	0.060A	0.625	T-1¾	midget flg
	385	0.040A	0.625	T-1¾	midget flg
	387	0.040A	0.625	T-1¾	midget flg
	388	0.040A	0.625	T-1¾	midget groove
	399	0.040A	0.688	T-1¾	midget scr
	623	0.370A	1.440	G-6	S.C. bay
	1203	0.700A	2.000	S-8	S.C. bay
	1204	0.700A	2.000	S-8	D.C. bay
	1251	0.230A	1.440	G-6	S.C. bay
	1252	0.230A	1.440	G-6	D.C. bay

5

VOLTAGE	LAMP #	CURRENT	MOL	BULB TYPE	BASE
28v (continued)	1309	0.520A	1.750	B-6	S.C. bay
	1495	0.300A	1.380	T-4½	S.C. min bay
	1666	0.680A	2.000	S-8	D.C. bay
	1683	1.020A	2.000	S-8	S.C. bay
	1691	0.610A	2.000	S-8	S.C. bay
	1692	0.610A	2.000	S-8	D.C. bay
	1696	0.420A	2.000	S-8	D.C. bay
	1764	0.040A	0.520	T-1¾	wire term
	1819	0.040A	1.190	T-3¼	min bay
	1820	0.100A	1.190	T-3¼	min bay
	1821	0.170A	1.190	T-3¼	min scr
	1829	0.070A	1.190	T-3¼	min bay
	1864	0.170A	1.190	T-3¼	min bay
	2185	0.040A	0.520	T-1¼	wire term
	2187	0.040A	0.520	T-1¾	wire term
	6838	0.024A	0.250	T-1	wire term
	6839	0.024A	0.375	T-1	sub midget flg
	7327	0.040A	0.625	T-1¾	Bi pin
	7341	0.065A	0.625	T-1¾	midget flg
	7355	0.040A	0.625	T-1¾	midget groove
	7356	0.065A	0.625	T-1¾	midget groove
	7374	0.040A	0.625	T-1¾	Bi pin
	7376	0.065A	0.615	T-1¾	Bi pin
	7387	0.040A	0.625	T-1¾	Bi pin
	7632	0.040A	0.600	T-1¼	Bi pin
	7839	0.024A	0.380	T-1	Bi pin
	7876	0.060A	0.625	T-1¾	Bi pin
	8361	0.065A	0.520	T-1¾	wire term
	8369	0.065A	0.688	T-1¾	midget scr
	8623	0.040A	0.546	T-1¼	knurled scr
	8627	0.040A	0.460	T-1¼	wire term
	8632	0.040A	0.500	T-1¼	special midget flg
	8635	0.040A	0.550	T-1¼	special scr
32v	1054	0.740A	2.250	RP-11	D.C. bay
	1056	1.150A	2.250	RP-11	D.C. bay
	1224K	0.160A	1.380	G-6	cand scr
	1226	0.210A	1.750	G-8	D.C. bay
	1230	0.530A	2.250	RP-11	D.C. bay
	1238	3.500A	3.000	G-16½	D.C. bay
	1240	3.500A	3.000	G-16½	D.C. prefocus
34v	1223	0.160A	1.440	G-6	S.C. bay
	1224	0.160A	1.440	G-6	D.C. bay
	1228	0.450A	2.000	S-8	D.C. bay

VOLTAGE	LAMP #	CURRENT	MOL	BULB TYPE	BASE
44v————	44A	0.072A	1.688	T-2	telephone slide
	109	0.170A	2.000	S-8	S.C. bay
	110	0.170A	2.000	S-8	D.C. bay
	1150	0.470A	2.250	RP-11	D.C. bay
45v————	536	0.200A	1.440	G-6	D.C. bay

5.9   RADIO FREQUENCY CABLE SPECIFICS

Impedance	RG/U#	Diameters Inch	Millimeter	Maximum Operating Voltage
25 ohms—————	191	1.460	37.084	15,000 vrms
35 ohms—————	83	0.405	10.287	—
48 ohms—————	25	0.565	14.351	8,000 V peak
	25A	0.505	12.827	10,000 V peak
	25B	0.750	19.050	15,000 V peak
	26	0.525	13.335	8,000 V peak
	26A	0.505	12.827	10,000 V peak
	27	0.675	17.145	15,000 V peak
	27A	0.670	17.018	15,000 V peak
	28	0.805	20.447	15,000 V peak
	28B	0.750	19.050	15,000 V peak
	64	0.495	12.573	8,000 V peak
	64A	0.475	12.065	10,000 V peak
	77	0.414	10.516	—
	78	0.385	9.779	—
	88	0.515	13.081	10,000 Vrms
50 ohms—————	5A	0.328	8.331	—
	9B	0.420	10.668	—
	55B	0.206	5.232	1,900 Vrms
	58A	0.195	4.953	—
	58C	0.195	4.959	1,900 Vrms
	60	0.425	10.795	—
	87	0.425	10.795	—
	115	0.375	9.525	—
	117	0.730	18.542	—
	119	0.470	11.938	—
	122	0.160	4.064	—
	126	0.290	7.366	—
	141	0.195	4.953	—
	141A	0.190	4.826	—

5

Impedance	RG/U#	Diameters Inch	Millimeter	Maximum Operating Voltage
50 ohms———	142	0.206	5.232	—
(continued)	142B	0.195	4.953	—
	143	0.325	8.255	—
	156	0.540	13.716	10,000 Vrms
	157	0.725	18.415	15,000 Vrms
	158	0.725	18.415	15,000 Vrms
	174	0.100	2.540	—
	178B	0.075	1.905	1,000 Vrms
	179B	0.105	2.667	1,200 Vrms
	188A	0.102	2.591	—
	190	0.700	17.780	15,000 Vrms
	196A	0.080	2.032	1,000 Vrms
	211A	0.730	18.542	7,000 Vrms
	212	0.332	8.433	3,000 Vrms
	213	0.405	10.287	5,000 Vrms
	214	0.425	10.795	5,000 Vrms
	215	0.405	10.287	5,000 Vrms
	217	0.545	13.843	7,000 Vrms
	218	0.870	22.098	11,000 Vrms
	219	0.603	15.316	11,000 Vrms
	220	1.120	28.448	14,000 Vrms
	221	1.195	30.353	14,000 Vrms
	223	0.216	5.486	1,900 Vrms
	224	0.615	15.621	7,000 Vrms
	225	0.430	10.922	5,000 Vrms
	226	0.500	12.700	7,000 Vrms
	227	0.490	12.446	5,000 Vrms
	228A	0.795	20.193	7,000 Vrms
	301	0.245	6.223	3,000 Vrms
	303	0.170	4.318	1,900 Vrms
	304	0.280	7.112	3,000 Vrms
	316	0.102	2.591	1,200 Vrms
51 ohms———	9	0.420	10.668	4,000 Vrms
	9A	0.420	10.668	4,000 Vrms
	33	0.470	11.938	—
	8	0.405	10.287	4,000 Vrms
	8A	0.405	10.287	—
	10	0.475	12.065	4,000 Vrms
	14	0.545	13.843	5,500 Vrms
	16	0.630	16.002	—
	17	0.870	22.098	11,000 Vrms
	18	0.945	24.003	11,000 Vrms
	19	1.120	28.448	14,000 Vrms
	20	1.195	30.353	14,000 Vrms
	74	0.615	15.621	5,500 Vrms

Impedance	RG/U#	Diameters Inch	Millimeter	Maximum Operating Voltage
52 ohms	212	0.332	8.433	—
(continued)	213	0.405	10.287	—
	217	0.545	13.843	—
	218	0.870	22.098	—
	219	0.945	24.003	—
	220	1.120	28.448	—
52.5 ohms	5	0.332	8.433	3,000 Vrms
53 ohms	21	0.332	8.433	2,700 Vrms
53.5 ohms	55	0.206	5.232	1,900 Vrms
	55B	0.206	5.232	—
	58	0.195	4.953	1,900 Vrms
58 ohms	54A	0.245	6.223	3,000 Vrms
67.5 ohms	41	0.425	10.795	3,000 Vrms
69.0 ohms	36	1.180	29.972	—
71 ohms	34	0.625	15.875	5,200 Vrms
	35	0.945	24.003	10,000 Vrms
72 ohms	144	0.395	10.033	—
73 ohms	59	0.242	6.147	2,300 Vrms
	140	0.242	6.147	—
74 ohms	13	0.420	10.668	4,000 Vrms
	216	0.425	10.795	—
75 ohms	6A	0.332	8.433	2,700 Vrms
	11	0.405	10.287	4,000 Vrms
	11A	0.412	10.465	5,000 Vrms
	12A	0.475	12.065	5,000 Vrms
	34B	0.630	16.002	6,500 Vrms
	35B	0.945	25.003	10,000 Vrms
	59B	0.242	6.147	2,300 Vrms
	84A	1.000	25.400	10,000 Vrms
	85A	1.565	39.751	10,000 Vrms
	101	0.588	14.935	—
	164	0.870	22.098	10,000 Vrms
	179A	0.100	2.540	—
	187	0.110	2.794	1,200 Vrms
	216	0.425	10.795	5,000 Vrms
	302	0.206	5.232	2,300 Vrms
	307	0.270	6.858	400 Vrms
	144	0.410	10.414	5,000 Vrms
76 ohms	6	0.332	8.433	2,700 Vrms
	6A	0.332	8.433	—
	15	0.545	13.843	5,000 Vrms
	108	0.245	6.223	—
78 ohms	42	0.342	8.687	2,700 Vrms
93 ohms	62A	0.242	6.147	750 Vrms
	62B	0.242	6.147	750 Vrms

5

Impedance	RG/U#	Diameters Inch	Millimeter	Maximum Operating Voltage
95 ohms———71	71	0.250	6.350	750 Vrms
(continued)	71B	0.250	6.350	750 Vrms
	22	0.405	10.287	1,000 Vrms
	22B	0.420	10.668	1,000 Vrms
	57	0.625	15.875	3,000 Vrms
	57A	0.625	15.875	3,000 Vrms
	65	0.405	10.287	1,000 Vrms
	111A	0.490	12.446	1,000 Vrms
	130	0.625	15.875	8,000 Vrms
	131	0.710	18.034	8,000 Vrms
	180B	0.145	3.683	1,500 Vrms
	195A	0.155	3.937	1,500 Vrms
125 ohms———23	23	0.945	24.003	3,000 Vrms
	63B	0.405	10.287	1,000 Vrms
	79B	0.475	12.065	1,000 Vrms
	181	0.640	16.256	3,500 Vrms
	89	0.632	16.053	—
140 ohms———102	102	1.088	27.635	—
185 ohms———114	114	0.405	10.287	—

5.10 VHF AND UHF TV CHANNEL SPECTRUM

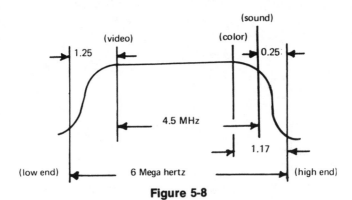

Figure 5-8

Channel Number (Low VHF)	Lower Frequency (MHz)	Picture Carrier (AM) (MHz)	Color Carrier (MHz)	Sound Carrier (FM) (MHz)	Upper Frequency (MHz)
2	54	55.25	58.85	59.75	60
3	60	61.25	64.83	65.75	66
4	66	67.25	70.83	71.75	72

Channel Number	Lower Frequency (MHz)	Picture Carrier (AM) (MHz)	Color Carrier (MHz)	Sound Carrier (FM) (MHz)	Upper Frequency (MHz)
		GOVERNMENTAL, AERONAUTICAL, AND ASTRONOMY ASSIGNMENTS			
5	76	77.25	80.83	81.75	82
6	82	83.25	86.83	87.75	88

FM, GOVERNMENTAL, AERONAUTICAL, TELEMETERING, INDUSTRIAL,
AMATEUR AND MISC. ASSIGNMENTS

(High VHF)

7	174	175.25	178.83	179.75	180
8	180	181.25	184.83	185.75	186
9	186	187.25	190.83	191.75	192
10	192	193.25	196.83	197.75	198
11	198	199.25	202.83	203.75	204
12	204	205.25	208.83	209.75	210
13	210	211.25	214.83	215.75	216

GOVERNMENTAL, TELEMETERING, AMATEUR, AERONAUTICAL,
INDUSTRIAL AND MISC. ASSIGNMENTS

(UHF)

14	470	471.25	474.83	475.75	476
15	476	477.25	480.83	481.75	482
16	482	483.25	486.83	487.75	488
17	488	489.75	492.83	493.75	494
18	494	495.25	498.83	499.75	500
19	500	501.25	504.83	505.75	506
20	506	507.25	510.83	511.75	512
21	512	513.25	516.83	517.75	518
22	518	519.25	522.83	523.75	524
23	524	525.25	528.83	529.75	530
24	530	531.25	534.83	535.75	536
25	536	537.25	540.83	541.75	542
26	542	543.25	546.83	547.75	548
27	548	549.25	552.83	553.75	554
28	554	555.25	558.83	559.75	560
29	560	561.25	564.83	565.75	566
30	566	567.25	570.83	571.75	572
31	572	573.25	576.83	577.75	578
32	578	579.25	582.83	583.75	584
33	584	585.25	587.83	589.75	590
34	590	591.25	594.83	595.75	596
35	596	597.25	600.83	601.75	602

5

Channel Number	Lower Frequency (MHz)	Picture Carrier (AM) (MHz)	Color Carrier (MHz)	Sound Carrier (FM) (MHz)	Upper Frequency (MHz)
36	602	603.25	606.83	607.75	608
37	608	609.25	612.83	613.75	614
38	614	615.25	618.83	619.75	620
39	620	621.25	624.83	625.75	626
40	626	627.25	630.83	631.75	632
41	632	633.25	636.83	637.75	638
42	638	639.25	642.83	643.75	644
43	644	645.25	648.83	649.75	650
44	650	651.25	654.83	655.75	656
45	656	657.25	660.83	661.75	662
46	662	663.25	666.83	667.75	668
47	668	669.25	672.83	673.75	674
48	674	675.25	678.83	679.75	680
49	680	681.25	684.83	685.75	686
50	686	687.25	690.83	691.75	692
51	692	693.25	696.83	697.75	698
52	698	699.25	702.75	703.75	704
53	704	705.25	707.83	709.75	710
54	710	711.25	714.83	715.75	716
55	716	717.25	720.83	721.75	722
56	722	723.25	726.83	727.75	728
57	728	729.25	732.83	733.75	734
58	734	735.25	738.83	739.75	740
59	740	741.25	744.83	745.75	746
60	746	747.25	780.83	751.75	752
61	752	753.25	756.83	757.75	758
62	758	759.25	762.83	763.75	764
63	764	765.25	768.83	769.75	770
64	770	771.25	774.83	775.75	776
65	776	777.25	780.83	781.75	782
66	782	783.25	786.83	787.75	788
67	788	789.25	792.83	793.75	794
68	794	795.25	798.83	799.75	800
69	800	801.25	804.83	805.75	806
70	806	807.25	810.83	811.75	812
71	812	813.25	816.83	817.75	818
72	818	819.25	822.83	823.75	824
73	824	825.25	828.83	829.75	830
74	830	831.25	834.83	835.75	836
75	836	837.25	840.83	841.75	842
76	842	843.25	846.83	847.75	848
77	848	849.25	852.83	853.75	854
78	854	855.25	858.83	859.75	860
79	860	861.25	864.83	865.75	866

Channel Number	Lower Frequency (MHz)	Picture Carrier (AM) (MHz)	Color Carrier (MHz)	Sound Carrier (FM) (MHz)	Upper Frequency (MHz)
80	866	867.25	870.83	871.75	872
81	872	873.25	876.83	877.75	878
82	878	879.25	882.83	883.75	884
83	884	885.25	888.83	889.75	890

5

6 Alphabetized Conversion Factors for Technical Applications

Not too long ago the word electronics meant only radio and television, but in this modern day, electronics is employed one way or another in every imaginable facet of life. The data for calculations, normally used by only a few highly trained individuals, have become the language used by most electronics professional personnel.

It is the intent of this chapter to share with you the "working tool information" for converting from one unit to another simply by multiplying by its conversion factor.

Over 800 units have been alphabetized. If you were working with centimeters and wished to convert into meters, look under the c's for centimeter and then for the conversion factor required to convert into meters.

	TO CONVERT	INTO	MULTIPLY BY
(A)	Abamperes	Amperes	10
	Abamperes	Statamperes	3×10^{10}
	Abamperes/sq. cm.	Amperes/sq. inch	64.52
	Abampere-turns	Ampere-turns	10
	Abampere-turns	Gilberts	12.57
	Abampere-turns/cm.	Ampere-turns/inch	25.40
	Abcoulombs	Coulombs	10
	Abcoulombs	Statcoulombs	3×10^{10}
	Abcoulombs/sq. cm.	Coulombs/sq inch	64.52
	Abfarads	Farads	1×10^9
	Abfarads	Microfarads	1×10^{15}
	Abfarads	Statfarads	9×10^{20}
	Abhenries	Henries	1×10^{-9}
	Abhenries	Millihenries	1×10^{-6}
	Abhenries	Stathenries	$1/_9 \times 10^{-20}$
	Abohms/cm. cube	Microhms/cm. cube	1×10^{-3}
	Abohms/cm. cube	Ohms/mil foot	6.015×10^{-3}
	Abvolts	Statvolts	$1/_3 \times 10^{-10}$
	Abvolts	Volts	1×10^{-8}
	Acres	Square Feet	43,560.00
	Acres	Square meters	4,047.00
	Acres	Square Miles	1.562×10^{-3}
	Acres	Square Yards	4,840.00

TO CONVERT	INTO	MULTIPLY BY
Acre-feet	Cubic-feet	43,560.00
Acre-feet	Gallons	3.259×10^5
Amperes	Abamperes	$^1/_{10}$
Amperes	Microamperes	1×10^6
Amperes	Milliamperes	1×10^3
Amperes	Statamperes	$3' \times 10^9$
Amperes/sq. cm.	Amperes/sq. inch	6.452
Amperes/sq. cm.	Amperes/sq. meter	1×10^4
Amperes/sq. inch	Abamperes/sq.cm.	0.0155
Amperes/sq. inch	Amperes/sq. meter	1,550.00
Amperes/sq. inch	Amperes/sq.cm.	0.1550
Amperes/sq. inch	Statamperes/sq. cm.	4.650×10^8
Amperes/sq. meter	Amperes/sq. cm.	1×10^{-4}
Amperes/sq. meter	Amperes/sq. inch	6.452×10^{-4}
Ampere-hours	Coulombs	3,600.00
Ampere-hours	Faradays	0.03731
Ampere-turns	Abampere-turns	$^1/_{10}$
Ampere-turns	Gilberts	1.257
Ampere-turns/cm.	Ampere-turns/inch	2.540,
Ampere-turns/cm.	Ampere-turns/meter	100.00
Ampere-turns/cm.	Gilberts/cm.	1.257
Ampere-turns/inch	Abampere-turns/cm.	0.03937
Ampere-turns/inch	Ampere-turns/cm.	0.3937
Ampere-turns/inch	Gilberts/cm.	0.4950
Ampere-turns/inch	Ampere-turns/meter	39.37
Ampere-turns/meter	Ampere-turns/cm.	0.01
Ampere-turns/meter	Ampere-turns/inch	0.0254
Ampere-turns/meter	Gilberts/cm.	0.01257
Angstrum units	Inches	3.937×10^{-8}
Angstrum units	Meters	1×10^{-10}
Atmospheres	Cms of mercury	76.00
Atmospheres	Feet of water (@ 4°C)	33.90
Atmospheres	inches of mercury (@ 0° C)	29.92
Atmospheres	Kgs/sq. cm.	1.033
Atmospheres	Kgs/sq. meter	10,332.00
Atmospheres	Pounds/sq. inch	14.70
Atmospheres	Tons/sq. foot	1.058

	TO CONVERT	INTO	MULTIPLY BY
(B)	Barrels (oil)	Gallons (oil)	42.00
	Barns	Sq. cm.	1×10^{-24}
	Bars	Atmospheres	9.870×10^{-7}
	Bars	Dynes/sq. cm.	1×10^6
	Bars	Kgs/sq. meter	1.020×10^4
	Bars	Pounds/sq. ft.	2.089×10^3
	Bars	Pounds/sq. inch	14.50

6

TO CONVERT	INTO	MULTIPLY BY
Btu	Ergs	1.055×10^{10}
Btu	Foot-pounds	778.30
Btu	Gram-calories	252.00
Btu	Horsepower-hrs.	3.927×10^{-4}
Btu	Joules	1,054.00
Btu	Kilogram-calories	0.2520
Btu	Kilogram-meters	107.5
Btu	Kilowatt-hrs.	2.928×10^{-4}
Btu/hour	Ft-lbs/sec	0.2162
Btu/hour	Gram-cal/sec	0.070
Btu/hour	Horsepower-hrs.	3.929×10^{-4}
Btu/hour	Watts	0.2931
Btu/minute	Ft-lbs/sec	12.96
Btu/minute	Horsepower	0.02356
Btu/minute	Kilowatts	0.01757
Btu/minute	Watts	17.57
Btu/sq.ft./minute	Watts/sq. inch	0.1221
Bushels	Cubic foot	1.2445
Bushels	Cubic inch	2,150.400
Bushels	Cubic meters	0.03524
Bushels	Liters	35.24
Bushels	Pecks	4.0
Bushels	Pints (dry)	64.0
Bushels	Quarts (dry)	32.0
(C) Centares	Sq. meters	1.0
Centigrade	Fahrenheit	$(C° \times 9/5) + 32$
Centigrade	Celsius	1.0
Centigrade	Kelvin	$(C° + 273.1)$
Centigrams	Grams	0.01
Centiliters	Liters	0.01
Centimeters	Feet	3.281×10^{-2}
Centimeters	Inches	0.3937
Centimeters	Kilometers	1×10^{-5}
Centimeters	Meters	0.01
Centimeters	Miles	6.214×10^{-6}
Centimeters	Millimeters	10.0
Centimeters	Mils	393.7
Centimeters	Yards	1.094×10^{-2}
Centimeter-dynes	Meter-kilograms	1.020×10^{-8}
Centimeter-dynes	Pound-feet	7.376×10^{-8}
Centimeter-grams	Centimeter-dynes	980.7
Centimeter-grams	Meter-kilograms	1×10^{-5}
Centimeter-grams	Pound-feet	7.233×10^{-5}
Centimeters of mercury	Atmospheres	0.01316
Centimeters of mercury	Feet of water	0.4461
Centimeters of mercury	Kgs/sq. meter	136.0
Centimeters of mercury	Lbs/sq. foot	27.85

TO CONVERT	INTO	MULTIPLY BY
Centimeters of mercury	Lbs/sq. inch	0.1934
Centimeters/second	Feet/min.	1.969
Centimeters/second	Feet/second	0.03281
Centimeters/second	Kilometers/hour	0.036
Centimeters/second	Meters/minute	0.6
Centimeters/second	Miles/hour	0.02237
Centimeters/second	Miles/minute	3.728×10^{-4}
Centimeters/sec/sec	Feet/sec/sec	0.03281
Centimeters/sec/sec	Kilometers/hr/sec	0.036
Centimeters/sec/sec	Miles/hr/sec	0.02237
Centimeters/sec/sec	Meters/sec/sec	0.01
Chains(surveyors)	Feet	66
Circular mils	Sq. centimeters	5.067×10^{-6}
Circular mils	Sq. inches	7.854×10^{-7}
Circular mils	Sq. mils	0.7854
Cord-feet	Cubic feet	4 ft $\times$ 4 ft $\times$ 1 ft
Cords	Cubic feet	8 ft $\times$ 4 ft $\times$ 4 ft
Coulombs	Abcoulombs	1/10
Coulombs	Electrons	6.28×10^{18}
Coulombs	Statcoulombs	3×10^{9}
Coulombs	Faradays	1.036×10^{-5}
Coulombs/sq. inch	Abcoulombs/sq. cm.	0.01550
Coulombs/sq. inch	Coulombs/sq. cm.	0.1550
Coulombs/sq. inch	Statcoulombs/sq. cm.	4.65×10^{8}
Coulombs/sq. inch	Coulombs/sq. meter	1,550.0
Coulombs/sq. cm.	Coulombs/sq. inch	64.52
Coulombs/sq. cm.	Coulombs/sq. meter	1×10^{4}
Coulombs/sq. meter	Coulombs/sq. cm.	1×10^{-4}
Coulombs/sq. meter	Coulombs/sq. inch	6.452×10^{-4}
Cubic centimeters	Cubic feet	3.531×10^{-5}
Cubic centimeters	Cubic inches	6.102×10^{-2}
Cubic centimeters	Cubic meters	1×10^{-6}
Cubic centimeters	Cubic yards	1.308×10^{-6}
Cubic centimeters	Gallons (US liquid)	2.642×10^{-4}
Cubic centimeters	Liters	1×10^{-3}
Cubic centimeters	Pints (liquid)	2.113×10^{-3}
Cubic centimeters	Qts. (liquid)	1.057×10^{-3}
Cubic feet	Bushels (dry)	0.8036
Cubic feet	Cubic cm.	2.832×10^{4}
Cubic feet	Cubic in.	1,728.0
Cubic feet	Cubic meters	0.02832
Cubic feet	Cubic yards	0.03704
Cubic feet	Gals. (liquid US)	7.481
Cubic feet	Liters	28.32
Cubic feet	Pts. (liquid)	59.84
Cubic feet	Qts. (liquid)	29.92
Cubic feet/minute	Cubic cm/sec.	472

6

TO CONVERT	INTO	MULTIPLY BY
Cubic feet/minute	Gallons/sec.	0.1247
Cubic feet/minute	Liters/sec.	0.4720
Cubic feet/minute	Lbs. of water/min.	62.4
Cubic feet/second	Millions gals/day	0.64632
Cubic feet/second	Gals/minute	448.8
Cubic inches	Cubic cm.	16.39
Cubic inches	Cubic ft.	5.787×10^{-4}
Cubic inches	Cubic meters	1.639×10^{-5}
Cubic inches	Cubic yards	2.143×10^{-5}
Cubic inches	Gals. (US liquid)	4.329×10^{-3}
Cubic inches	Liters	1.639×10^{-2}
Cubic inches	Mil-feet	1.061×10^{5}
Cubic inches	Pts. (liquid)	3.463×10^{-2}
Cubic inches	Qts. (liquid)	1.732×10^{-2}
Cubic meters	Bushels (dry)	28.38
Cubic meters	Cubic cm.	1×10^{6}
Cubic meters	Cubic feet	35.31
Cubic meters	Cubic inches	61,023.0
Cubic meters	Cubic yards	1.308
Cubic meters	Gallons	264.2
Cubic meters	Liters	1×10^{3}
Cubic meters	Pts. (liquid)	2,113.0
Cubic meters	Qts. (liquid)	1,057.0
Cubic yards	Cubic cm.	7.646×10^{5}
Cubic yards	Cubic feet	27
Cubic yards	Cubic inches	46,656.0
Cubic yards	Cubic meters	0.7646
Cubic yards	Gallons	202.0
Cubic yards	Liters	764.6
Cubic yards	Pts. (liquid)	1,616.0
Cubic yards	Qts. (liquid)	807.9
Cubic yards/minute	Cubic ft/sec	0.45
Cubic yards/minute	Gals/sec.	3.367
Cubic yards/minute	Liters/sec.	12.74
Cycles/second	Hertz	1.0
(D) Days	Hours	24
Days	Minutes	1,440.0
Days	Seconds	86,400.0
Decigrams	Grams	0.1
Deciliters	Liters	0.1
Decimeters	Meters	0.1
Degrees (angle)	Mils	17.45
Degrees (angle)	Minutes	60
Degrees (angle)	Quadrants	1.111×10^{-2}
Degrees (angle)	Radians	1.745×10^{-2}
Degrees (angle)	Seconds	3,600.0

TO CONVERT	INTO	MULTIPLY BY
Degrees/second	Radians/sec	1.745×10^{-2}
Degrees/second	Revolutions/min.	0.1667
Degrees/second	Revolutions/sec.	2.778×10^{-3}
Dekagrams	Grams	10
Dekaliters	Liters	10
Dekameters	Meters	10
Drams	Grams	1.772
Drams	Grains	27.3437
Drams	Ounces	6.25×10^{-2}
Dynes	Grams	1.02×10^{-3}
Dynes	Joules/cm.	1×10^{-7}
Dynes	Poundals	7.233×10^{-5}
Dynes	Joules/meter	1×10^{-5}
Dynes	Pounds	2.248×10^{-6}
Dynes	Kilogram	1.02×10^{-6}
Dynes/square centimeter	Bars	1×10^{-6}
(E) Ergs	British thermal units	9.486×10^{-11}
Ergs	Dyne-centimeter	1.0
Ergs	Foot-pounds	7.376×10^{-8}
Ergs	Gram-calories	2.389×10^{-8}
Ergs	Gram-centimeter	1.02×10^{-3}
Ergs	Horsepower-hrs.	3.725×10^{-14}
Ergs	Joules	1×10^{-7}
Ergs	Kilogram-calories	2.39×10^{-11}
Ergs	Kilogram-meters	1.02×10^{-8}
Ergs	Kilowatt-hrs.	2.778×10^{-14}
Ergs	Watt-hours	2.778×10^{-11}
Ergs/second	B.T.U./min.	5.692×10^{-9}
Ergs/second	Ft-lbs/min.	4.426×10^{-6}
Ergs/second	Ft/lbs/sec.	7.376×10^{-8}
Ergs/second	Horsepower	1.341×10^{-10}
Ergs/second	Kilogram-cals/min	1.434×10^{-9}
Ergs/second	Kilowatts	1×10^{-10}
(F) Farads	Abfarads	1×10^{-9}
Farads	Microfarads	1×10^{6}
Farads	Picofarads	1×10^{12}
Farads	Statfarads	9×10^{11}
Faradays	Ampere-hours	26.8
Faradays	Coulombs	9.65×10^{4}
Fathoms	Feet	6.0
Feet	Centimeters	30.48
Feet	Inches	12.0
Feet	Kilometers	3.048×10^{-4}
Feet	Meters	3.048×10^{-1}
Feet	Miles (nautical)	1.645×10^{-4}

6

TO CONVERT	INTO	MULTIPLY BY
Feet	Miles (stat)	1.894×10^{-4}
Feet	Millimeters	3.048×10^{2}
Feet	Mils	1.2×10^{4}
Feet	Yards	0.333
Feet of water	Atmospheres	2.95×10^{-2}
Feet of water	Inches of mercury	0.8826
Feet of water	Kilograms/sq. cm.	3.048×10^{-2}
Feet of water	Kilograms/sq. meter	304.8
Feet of water	Lbs/sq. ft.	62.43
Feet of water	Lbs/sq. inch	4.335×10^{-1}
Feet/minute	Cm/sec	0.508
Feet/minute	Feet/sec	0.1667
Feet/minute	Kilometers/hr.	0.01829
Feet/minute	Meters/minute	0.3048
Feet/minute	Miles/hour	0.01136
Feet/second	Cm/second	30.48
Feet/second	Kilometers/hr	1.097
Feet/second	Meters/minute	18.29
Feet/second	Miles/hour	0.6818
Feet/second	Miles/minute	0.01136
Feet/100 feet	Percent grade	1.0
Feet/second per second	Cm/second/second	30.48
Feet/second per second	Kilometers/hr/sec	1.097
Feet/second per second	Meters/sec/sec	0.3048
Feet/second per second	Miles/hr/sec	0.6818
Foot-pounds	B.T.U.	1.286×10^{-3}
Foot-pounds	Ergs	1.356×10^{7}
Foot-pounds	Gram-calories	0.3238
Foot-pounds	Gram-cm	1.383×10^{4}
Foot-pounds	Horsepower hours	5.05×10^{-7}
Foot-pounds	Joules	1.356
Foot-pounds	Kilogram-calories	3.241×10^{-4}
Foot-pounds	Kilogram-meters	0.1383
Foot-pounds	Kilowatt-hours	3.766×10^{-7}
Foot-pounds	Ounce-inches	192
Foot-pounds/minute	B.T.U./minute	1.286×10^{-3}
Foot-pounds/minute	Ft-lbs/sec	0.01667
Foot-pounds/minute	Horsepower	3.03×10^{-5}
Foot-pounds/minute	Kilogram-cals/min	3.24×10^{-4}
Foot-pounds/minute	Kilowatts	2.26×10^{-5}
Foot-pounds/second	B.T.U./hour	4.6263
Foot-pounds/second	B.T.U./minute	0.07717
Foot-pounds/second	Horsepower	1.818×10^{-3}
Foot-pounds/second	Kilogram-cals/min	1.945×10^{-2}
Foot-pounds/second	Kilowatts	1.356×10^{-3}
(G) Gallons	Cubic centimeters	3,785.0

TO CONVERT	INTO	MULTIPLY BY
Gallons	Cubic feet	0.1337
Gallons	Cubic inches	231
Gallons	Cubic meters	3.785×10^{-3}
Gallons	Cubic yards	4.951×10^{-3}
Gallons	Liters	3.785
Gallons	Pints (liquid)	8
Gallons	Quarts (liquid)	4
Gallons of water	Pounds of water	8.3453
Gallons/minute	Cubic ft/second	2.228×10^{-3}
Gallons/minute	Liters/second	0.06308
Gallons/minute	Cubic feet/hr	8.0208
Gausses	Lines/sq. inch	6.452
Gausses	Webers/sq. cm.	1×10^{-8}
Gausses	Webers/sq. inch	6.452×10^{-8}
Gausses	Webers/sq. meter	1×10^{-4}
Gilberts	Abampere-turns	0.07958
Gilberts	Ampere-turns	0.7958
Gilberts/centimeter	Ampere-turns/inch	2.021
Gilberts/centimeter	Ampere/turns/meter	79.58
Gills	Liters	0.1183
Gills	Pints (liquid)	0.25
Grains (troy)	Grains (avdp)	1.0
Grains (troy)	Grams	0.06480
Grains (troy)	Ounces (avdp)	2.0833×10^{-3}
Grains (troy)	Pennyweights (troy)	0.04167
Grains/U.S. gallon	Parts/million	17.118
Grains/U.S. gallon	Lbs/million gal	142.86
Grains/imperial gallon	Parts/million	14.286
Grams	Dynes	980.7
Grams	Grains (troy)	15.43
Grams	Joules/cm.	9.807×10^{-5}
Grams	Joules/meter	9.807×10^{-3}
Grams	Kilograms	1×10^{-3}
Grams	Milligrams	1×10^{3}
Grams	Ounces (avdp)	0.03527
Grams	Ounces (troy)	0.03215
Grams	Poundrals	0.07093
Grams	Pounds	2.205×10^{-3}
Gram-calories	British Thermal units	3.968×10^{-3}
Gram-calories	Ergs	4.1868×10^{7}
Gram-calories	Foot-pounds	3.0880
Gram-calories	Horsepower-hrs.	1.5596×10^{-6}
Gram-calories	Kilowatt-hours	1.1630×10^{-6}
Gram-calories	Watt-hours	1.1630×10^{-3}
Gram-calories/second	BTU/hour	14.286
Gram-centimeters	British Thermal Unit	9.302×10^{-8}
Gram-centimeters	Ergs	980.7

6

TO CONVERT	INTO	MULTIPLY BY
Gram-centimeters	Foot-pounds	7.233×10^{-5}
Gram-centimeters	Joules	9.807×10^{-5}
Gram-centimeters	Kilogram-calories	2.344×10^{-8}
Gram-centimeters	Kilogram-meter	1×10^{-5}
Grams/centimeter	Lbs/inch	5.6×10^{-3}
Grams/cubic centimeter	Lbs/cubic foot	62.43
Grams/cubic centimeter	Lbs/cubic inch	0.03613
Grams/cubic centimeter	Lbs/mil-foot	3.405×10^{-7}
Grams/liter	Grains/gallon	58.417
Grams/liter	Lbs/1000 gallon	8.345
Grams/liter	Lbs/cubic foot	6.243×10^{-2}
Grams/liter	Parts/million	1,000.0
Grams/square centimeter	Lbs/sq. foot	2.0481
(H) Hectares	Acres	2.471
Hectares	Square feet	1.076×10^{5}
Hectograms	Grams	100
Hectoliters	Liters	100
Hectometers	Meters	100
Hectowatts	Watts	100
Hemispheres (solution angle)	Sphere	0.5
Hemispheres (solution angle)	Spherical right angles	4.0
Hemispheres (solution angle)	Steradians	6.283
Henries	Abhenries	1×10^{9}
Henries	Millihenries	1×10^{3}
Henries	Stathenries	$^{1}/_{9} \times 10^{-11}$
Hertz	Kilohertz	1×10^{-3}
Hertz	Megahertz	1×10^{-6}
Horsepower	BTU/minute	42.42
Horsepower	Ft/lb/minute	33,000.0
Horsepower	Ft-1b/second	550.0
Horsepower	Horsepower (metric)	1.014
Horsepower	Kilogram-cal/min	10.7
Horsepower	Kilowatts	0.7457
Horsepower	Watts	745.7
Horsepower (metric)	Horsepower	0.9863
Horsepower (boiler)	BTU/hour	33,520.0
Horsepower (boiler)	Kilowatts	9.804
Horsepower-hours	BTU	2547.0
Horsepower-hours	Ergs	2.6845×10^{13}
Horsepower-hours	Foot-pounds	1.98×10^{6}
Horsepower-hours	Gram-calories	641,190.0
Horsepower-hours	Joules	2.684×10^{6}
Horsepower-hours	Kilogram-calories	641.7
Horsepower-hours	Kilogram-meters	2.737×10^{5}
Horsepower-hours	Kilowatt-hours	0.7457
Hours	Days	4.167×10^{-2}

TO CONVERT	INTO	MULTIPLY BY
Hours	Minutes	60.0
Hours	Seconds	3,600.0
Hours	Weeks	5.952×10^{-3}
(I) Inches	Centimeters	2.54
Inches	Feet	8.333×10^{-2}
Inches	Meters	2.54×10^{-2}
Inches	Miles	1.578×10^{-5}
Inches	Millimeters	25.40
Inches	Mils	1,000.0
Inches	Yards	2.778×10^{-2}
Inches of mercury	Atmospheres	0.03342
Inches of mercury	Feet of water	1.133
Inches of mercury	Kilograms/sq. meter	345.3
Inches of mercury	Kilograms/sq. cm.	3.453×10^{-2}
Inches of mercury	Lbs/sq. ft.	70.73
Inches of mercury	Lbs/sq. inch	0.4912
Inches of water (at 4° C)	Atmospheres	2.458×10^{-3}
Inches of water (at 4° C)	Inches of mercury	7.355×10^{-2}
Inches of water (at 4° C)	Kilograms/sq. cm.	2.54×10^{-3}
Inches of water (at 4° C)	Kilograms/sq. meter	25.40
Inches of water (at 4° C)	Ounces/sq. inch	0.5781
Inches of water (at 4° C)	Lbs/sq. foot	5.204
Inches of water (at 4° C)	Lbs/sq. inch	0.03613
(J) Joules	BTU	9.486×10^{-4}
Joules	Ergs	1×10^{7}
Joules	Foot-pounds	0.7376
Joules	Kilogram-calories	2.389×10^{-4}
Joules	Kilogram-meters	0.102
Joules	Watt-hours	2.778×10^{-4}
Joules/centimeter	Grams	1.02×10^{4}
Joules/centimeter	Dynes	1×10^{7}
Joules/centimeter	Joules/meter (newtons)	100.0
Joules/centimeter	Poundals	723.3
Joules/centimeter	Pounds	22.48
(K) Kilograms	Dynes	980,665.0
Kilograms	Grams	1,000.0
Kilograms	Joules/cm	0.09807
Kilograms	Joules/meter (newtons)	9.807
Kilograms	Poundals	70.93
Kilograms	Pounds (avdp)	2.2046
Kilograms	Tons (long)	9.842×10^{-4}
Kilograms	Tons (short)	1.102×10^{-3}
Kilograms	Tonnes	1×10^{3}
Kilogram-calories	BTU	3.968

TO CONVERT	INTO	MULTIPLY BY
Kilogram-calories	Foot-pounds	3,086.0
Kilogram-calories	Horsepower-hours	1.558×10^{-3}
Kilogram-calories	Joules	4,186.0
Kilogram-calories	Kilogram-meters	426.6
Kilogram-calories	Kilojoules	4.186
Kilogram-calories	Kilowatt-hours	1.62×10^{-3}
Kilogram-calories/minute	Foot pounds/sec	51.43
Kilogram-calories/minute	Horsepower	0.09351
Kilogram-calories/minute	Kilowatts	0.06972
Kilogram-centimeters squared	Lbs-feet squared	2.373×10^{-3}
Kilogram-centimeters squared	Lbs-inches squared	0.3417
Kilogram-meters	BTU	9.302×10^{-3}
Kilogram-meters	Ergs	9.807×10^{7}
Kilogram-meters	Foot-pounds	7.233
Kilogram-meters	Joules	9.807
Kilogram-meters	Kilogram-calories	2.344×10^{-3}
Kilogram-meters	Kilowatt-hours	2.724×10^{-6}
Kilograms/cubic meter	Grams/cubic cm.	1×10^{-3}
Kilograms/cubic meter	Lbs/cubic foot	0.06243
Kilograms/cubic meter	Lbs/cubic inch	3.613×10^{-5}
Kilograms/cubic meter	Lbs/mili-foot	3.405×10^{-10}
Kilograms/meter	Lbs/foot	0.6720
Kilograms/sq. meter	Atmospheres	9.678×10^{-5}
Kilograms/sq. meter	Bars	98.07×10^{-6}
Kilograms/sq. meter	Feet of water	3.281×10^{-3}
Kilograms/sq. meter	Inches of mercury	2.896×10^{-3}
Kilograms/sq. meter	Lbs/sq. foot	0.2048
Kilograms/sq. meter	Lbs/sq. inch	1.422×10^{-3}
Kilograms/sq. millimeter	Kilograms/sq. meter	1×10^{6}
Kilolines	Maxwells	1×10^{3}
Kiloliters	Liters	1×10^{3}
Kilometers	Centimeters	1×10^{5}
Kilometers	Feet	3,281.0
Kilometers	Inches	3.937×10^{4}
Kilometers	Light years	1.0567×10^{-13}
Kilometers	Meters	1×10^{3}
Kilometers	Miles	0.6214
Kilometers	Millimeters	1×10^{6}
Kilometers	Yards	1,093.6
Kilometers/hour	Cm/second	27.78
Kilometers/hour	Feet/minute	54.68
Kilometers/hour	Feet/second	0.9113
Kilometers/hour	Meters/min.	16.67
Kilometers/hour	Miles/hour	0.6214
Kilometers/hour/second	Cm/sec/sec	27.78
Kilometers/hour/second	Feet/sec/sec	0.9113
Kilometers/hour/second	Meters/sec/sec	0.2778

TO CONVERT	INTO	MULTIPLY BY
Kilometers/hour/second	Miles/hr/sec	0.6214
Kilometers/minute	Kilometers/hr.	60.0
Kilowatts	BTU/minute	56.92
Kilowatts	Foot-lbs/minute	4.425×10^4
Kilowatts	Foot-lbs/second	737.6
Kilowatts	Horsepower	1.341
Kilowatts	Kilogram-cals/min	14.34
Kilowatts	Watts	1×10^3
Kilowatts-hours	BTU	3,415.0
Kilowatt-hours	Ergs	3.6×10^{13}
Kilowatt-hours	Foot-pounds	2.655×10^6
Kilowatt-hours	Gram-calories	859,850.0
Kilowatt-hours	Horsepower-hours	1.341
Kilowatt-hours	Joules	3.6×10^6
Kilowatt-hours	Kilogram-cals	860.5
Kilowatt-hours	Kilogram-meters	3.671×10^5
Kilowatt-hours	Watt-hours	1×10^3
(L) Lamberts	Candles/sq. cm.	0.3183
Lamberts	Candles/sq. inch	2.054
League	Miles (approx.)	3.0
Lines/sq. centimeter	Gausses	1.0
Lines/sq. inch	Gausses	0.1550
Lines/sq. inch	Webers/sq. cm.	1.55×10^{-9}
Lines/sq. inch	Webers/sq. inch	1×10^{-8}
Lines/sq. inch	Webers/sq. meter	1.55×10^{-5}
Links	Chains	0.01
Links (engineers)	Inches	12.0
Links (surveyors)	Inches	7.92
Liters	Bushels (US dry)	0.0284
Liters	Cubic cm.	1×10^3
Liters	Cubic feet	0.03531
Liters	Cubic inches	61.02
Liters	Cubic meters	1×10^{-3}
Liters	Cubic yards	1.308×10^{-3}
Liters	Gals (US liquid)	0.2642
Liters	Pts. (US liquid)	2.113
Liters	Quarts (US liquid)	1.057
Liters/minute	Cubic feet/sec	5.885×10^{-4}
Liters/minute	Gals/second	4.403×10^{-3}
Lumens/sq. foot	Foot-candles	1.0
Lux	Foot-candles	0.0929
(M) Maxwells	Kilolines	1×10^{-3}
Maxwells	Megalines	1×10^{-6}
Maxwells	Webers	1×10^{-8}
Megalines	Maxwells	1×10^6

6

TO CONVERT	INTO	MULTIPLY BY
Megmhos/centimeter cube	Abmhos/cm. cube	1×10^{-3}
Megmhos/centimeter cube	Megmhos/inch cube	2.54
Mehmhos/centimeter cube	Mhos/mil foot	0.1662
Megmhos/inch cube	Megmhos/cm. cube	0.3937
Megohms	Ohms	1×10^{6}
Megohms	Microhms	1×10^{12}
Meters	Centimeters	100
Meters	Feet	3.2808
Meters	Inches	39.37
Meters	Kilometers	1×10^{-3}
Meters	Millimeters	1×10^{3}
Meters	Miles (nautical)	5.396×10^{-4}
Meters	Miles (statute)	6.214×10^{-4}
Meters	Yards	1.094
Meter-Kilograms	Centimeter-dynes	9.807×10^{7}
Meter-Kilograms	Centimeter-grams	1×10^{5}
Meter-Kilograms	Pound-feet	7.233
Meters/minute	Cm/sec	1.667
Meters/minute	Ft/minute	3.281
Meters/minute	Ft/second	0.05468
Meters/minute	Kilometers/hr	0.06
Meters/minute	Miles/hr	0.03728
Meters/second	Ft/minute	196.8
Meters/second	Ft/second	3.281
Meters/second	Kilometers/hr	3.6
Meters/second	Kilometers/min	0.06
Meters/second	Miles/hour	2.237
Meters/second	Miles/minute	0.03728
Meters/sec/sec	Cm/sec/sec	100.0
Meters/sec/sec	Ft/sec/sec	3.281
Meters/sec/sec	Kilometers/hr/sec	3.6
Meters/sec/sec	Miles/hr/sec	2.237
Mhos	Micromhos	1×10^{6}
Mhos	Millimhos	1×10^{3}
Microfarads	Abfarads	1×10^{-15}
Microfarads	Farads	1×10^{-6}
Microfarads	Picofarads	1×10^{6}
Microfarads	Statfarads	9×10^{5}
Micrograms	Grams	1×10^{-6}
Microhms	Abohms	1×10^{3}
Microhms	Megohms	1×10^{-12}
Microhms	Ohms	1×10^{-6}
Microhms	Statohms	$^{1}/_{9} \times 10^{-17}$
Microhms/centimeter cube	Abohms/cm cube	1×10^{3}
Microhms/centimeter cube	Microhms/inch cube	0.3937
Microhms/centimeter cube	Ohms/mil foot	6.015
Microhms/inch cube	Microhms/cm cube	2.540

TO CONVERT	INTO	MULTIPLY BY
Microliters	Liters	1×10^{-6}
Microns	Meters	1×10^{-6}
Miles (nautical)	Feet	6,076.103
Miles (nautical)	Kilometers	1.852
Miles (nautical)	Meters	1,852.
Miles (nautical)	Miles (statute)	1.1508
Miles (nautical)	Yards	2,025.4
Miles (statute)	Centimeters	1.609×10^{5}
Miles (statute)	Feet	5,280.0
Miles (statute)	Inches	6.336×10^{4}
Miles (statute)	Kilometers	1.609
Miles (statute)	Light years	1.691×10^{-13}
Miles (statute)	Meters	1,609.0
Miles (statute)	Miles (nautical)	0.8684
Miles (statute)	Yards	1,760.0
Miles/hour	Centimeters/sec	44.7
Miles/hour	Feet/minute	88
Miles/hour	Feet/second	1.467
Miles/hour	Kilometers/hour	1.6093
Miles/hour	Kilometers/minute	0.0268
Miles/hour	Meters/minute	26.82
Miles/hour	Miles/minute	0.01667
Miles/hour/second	Centimeters/sec/sec	44.7
Miles/hr/hr/sec	Feet/sec/sec	1.467
Miles/hr/hr/sec	Kilometers/hr/sec	1.6093
Miles/hr/hr/sec	Meters/sec/sec	0.447
Miles/minute	Centimeters/sec	2682.0
Miles/minute	Feet/second	88
Miles/minute	Kilometers/min	1.6093
Miles/minute	Miles/hour	60
Milliamperes	Microamperes	1×10^{3}
Milliers	Kilograms	1×10^{3}
Milligrams	Grams	1×10^{-3}
Milligrams/liter	Parts/million	1.0
Millihenries	Abhenries	1×10^{6}
Millihenries	Henries	1×10^{-3}
Millihenries	Microhenries	1×10^{3}
Millihenries	Stathenries	$1/9 \times 10^{-14}$
Milliliters	Liters	1×10^{-3}
Millimeters	Centimeters	0.1
Millimeters	Feet	3.281×10^{-3}
Millimeters	Inches	0.03937
Millimeters	Kilometers	1×10^{-6}
Millimeters	Meters	1×10^{-3}
Millimeters	Microns	1×10^{3}
Millimeters	Miles	6.214×10^{-7}
Millimeters	Mils	39.37

TO CONVERT	INTO	MULTIPLY BY
Millimeters	Yards	1.094×10^{-3}
Million gallons/day	Cubic ft/sec	1.54723
Millivolts	Microvolts	1×10^3
Mils	Centimeters	2.54×10^{-3}
Mils	Feet	8.333×10^{-5}
Mils	Inches	1×10^{-3}
Mils	Kilometers	2.54×10^{-8}
Mils	Minutes	3.438
Mils	Yards	2.778×10^{-5}
Miner's inches	Cubic feet/min	1.5
Minutes (angle)	Degrees	0.01667
Minutes (angle)	Quadrants	1.852×10^{-4}
Minutes (angle)	Radians	2.909×10^{-4}
Minutes (angle)	Seconds	60
Months	Days	30.42
Months	Hours	730
Months	Minutes	43,800.0
Months	Seconds	2.628×10^6
Myriagrams	Kilograms	10
Myriameters	Kilometers	10
Myriawatts	Kilowatts	10
(N) Nepers	Decibels	8.686
Newtons	Dynes	1×10^5
Newtons	Pounds (avdp)	0.2248
(O) Ohms	Abohms	1×10^9
Ohms	Ohms (international)	0.99948
Ohms	Megohms	1×10^{-6}
Ohms	Microhms	1×10^6
Ohms	Milliohms	1×10^3
Ohms	Statohms	$\frac{1}{9} \times 10^{-11}$
Ohms/foot	Ohms/meter	0.03048
Ohms/mil foot	Abohms/cm. cube	166.2
Ohms/mil foot	Microhms/cm. cube	0.1662
Ohms/mil foot	Microhms/inch cube	0.06524
Ounces	Drams	8
Ounces	Grains	437.5
Ounces	Grams	28.35
Ounces	Pounds	0.0625
Ounces	Ounces (troy)	0.9115
Ounces	Ton (long)	2.790×10^{-5}
Ounces	Ton (metric)	2.835×10^{-5}
Ounces (fluid)	Cubic inches	1.805
Ounces (fluid)	Liters	0.02957
Ounces (fluid)	Quarts	0.03125
Ounces (troy)	Grains (troy)	480

TO CONVERT	INTO	MULTIPLY BY
Ounces (troy)	Grams	31.10
Ounces (troy)	Ounces (avdp)	1.09714
Ounces (troy)	Pennyweights (troy)	20.0
Ounces (troy)	Pounds (troy)	0.08333
Ounces/square inch	Lbs/sq. inch	0.0625
(P) Parts/million	Grains/U.S. gallon	0.0584.
Parts/million	Grains/imperial gal.	0.07016
Parts/million	Lbs/million gallon	8.345
Pennyweights (troy)	Grains (troy)	24
Pennyweights (troy)	Grams (troy)	1.555
Pennyweights (troy)	Ounces (troy)	0.05
Pennyweights (troy)	Pounds (troy)	4.1667×10^{-3}
Perches (masonry)	Cubic feet	24.75
Picofarad	Micromicrofarad	1.0
Pints (dry)	Cubic inches	33.6
Pints (liquid)	Cubic cm.	473.2
Pints (liquid)	Cubic feet	0.0167
Pints (liquid)	Cubic inches	28.87
Pints (liquid)	Cubic meters	4.732×10^{-4}
Pints (liquid)	Cubic yards	6.189×10^{-4}
Pints (liquid)	Gallons	0.125
Pints (liquid)	Liters	0.4732
Pints (liquid)	Quarts (liquid)	0.5
Poundals	Dynes	13,826.0
Poundals	Grams	14.1
Poundals	Joules/cm.	1.383×10^{-3}
Poundals	Joules/meter	0.1383
Poundals	Kilograms	0.0141
Poundals	Pounds (avdp)	0.03108
Pounds	Drams	256
Pounds	Dynes	44.48×10^{4}
Pounds	Grains	7,000.0
Pounds	Grams	453.59
Pounds	Joules/cm	0.04448
Pounds	Joules/meter	4.448
Pounds	Kilograms	0.4536
Pounds	Ounces	16.0
Pounds	Ounces (troy)	14.5833
Pounds	Poundals	32.17
Pounds	Pounds (troy)	1.2153
Pounds	Tons (short)	5×10^{-4}
Pounds (troy)	Grains	5,760.0
Pounds (troy)	Grams	373.242
Pounds (troy)	Ounces (avdp)	13.157
Pounds (troy)	Ounces (troy)	12.0
Pounds (troy)	Pennyweight (troy)	240

6

TO CONVERT	INTO	MULTIPLY BY
Pounds (troy)	Pounds (avdp)	0.82286
Pounds (troy)	Tons (long)	3.6735×10^{-4}
Pounds (troy)	Tons (metric)	3.7324×10^{-4}
Pounds (troy)	Tons (short)	4.1143×10^{-4}
Pounds of water	Cubic feet	0.01602
Pounds of water	Cubic inches	27.68
Pounds of water	Gallons	0.1198
Pounds of water/minute	Cubic ft/sec	2.67×10^{-4}
Pound-feet	Cm-dynes	1.356×10^{7}
Pound-feet	Cm-grams	13,825.0
Pound-feet	Meter-kilograms	0.1383
Pounds-feet squared	Kilogram-cm. squared	421.3
Pounds-feet squared	Lbs-inches squared	144
Pounds-inches squared	Kilograms-cm squared	2.926
Pounds-inches squared	Pounds-feet squared	6.945×10^{-3}
Pounds/cubic foot	Grams/cubic cm.	0.01602
Pounds/cubic foot	Kilograms/cubic meter	16.02
Pounds/cubic foot	Lbs/cubic inch	5.787×10^{-4}
Pounds/cubic foot	Lbs/mil foot	5.456×10^{-9}
Pounds/cubic inch	Grams/cubic cm	27.68
Pounds/cubic inch	Kilograms/cubic meter	2.768×10^{4}
Pounds/cubic inch	Pounds/cubic foot	1,728.0
Pounds/cubic inch	Pounds/mil foot	9.425×10^{-6}
Pounds/foot	Kilograms/meter	1.488
Pounds/inch	Grams/cm.	178.6
Pounds/mil foot	Grams/cubic cm.	2.306×10^{6}
Pounds/square foot	Atmospheres	4.725×10^{-4}
Pounds/square foot	Feet of water	0.01602
Pounds/square foot	Inches of mercury	0.01414
Pounds/square foot	Kilograms/sq. meter	4.882
Pounds/square foot	Pounds/sq. inch	6.944×10^{-3}
Pounds/square inch	Atmospheres	0.06804
Pounds/square inch	Feet of water	2.307
Pounds/square inch	Inches of mercury	2.036
Pounds/square inch	Kilograms/sq. meter	703.1
Pounds/square inch	Lbs/sq. foot	144
(Q) Quadrants (angle)	Degrees	90
Quadrants (angle)	Minutes	5,400.0
Quadrants (angle)	Radians	1.571
Quadrants (angle)	Seconds	3.24×10^{5}
Quarts (dry)	Cubic inches	67.2
Quarts (liquid)	Cubic cm.	946.4
Quarts (liquid)	Cubic feet	0.03342
Quarts (liquid)	Cubic inches	57.75
Quarts (liquid)	Cubic meters	9.464×10^{-4}
Quarts (liquid)	Cubic yards	1.238×10^{-3}

TO CONVERT	INTO	MULTIPLY BY
Quarts (liquid)	Gallons	0.25
Quarts (liquid)	Liters	0.9463
Quintals	Pounds	100
Quires	Sheets	25
(R) Radians	Degrees	57.3
Radians	Mils	1×10^3
Radians	Minutes	3,438.0
Radians	Quadrants	0.637
Radians	Seconds	2.063×10^5
Radians/second	Degrees/second	57.3
Radians/second	Revolutions/min	9.549
Radians/second	Revolutions/sec	0.1592
Radians/sec/sec	Rev/min/min	573.0
Radians/sec/sec	Rev/min/sec	9.549
Radians/sec/sec	Rev/sec/sec	0.1592
Revolutions	Degrees	360
Revolutions	Quadrants	4
Revolutions	Radians	6.283
Revolutions/minute	Degrees/sec	6
Revolutions/minute	Radians/second	0.1047
Revolutions/minute	Rev/second	0.01667
Revolutions/min/min	Radians/sec/sec	1.745×10^{-3}
Revolutions/min/min	Rev/min/sec	0.01667
Revolutions/min/min	Rev/sec/sec	2.778×10^{-4}
Revolutions/second	Degrees/second	360
Revolutions/second	Radians/second	6.283
Revolutions/second	Rev/minute	60
Revolutions/sec/sec	Radians/sec/sec	6.283
Revolutions/sec/sec	Rev/min/min	3,600.0
Revolutions/sec/sec	Rev/min/sec	60
Rods	Feet	16.5
Rods	Miles	3.125×10^{-3}
Rods	Yards	5.5
(S) Seconds (angle)	Degrees	2.778×10^{-4}
Seconds (angle)	Minutes	0.01667
Seconds (angle)	Quadrants	3.087×10^{-6}
Seconds (angle)	Radians	4.848×10^{-6}
Spheres (solid angle)	Steradians	12.57
Spherical right angles	Hemispheres	0.25
Spherical right angles	Spheres	0.125
Spherical right angles	Steradians	1.571
Square centimeters	Circular mils	1.973×10^5
Square centimeters	Square feet	1.076×10^{-3}
Square centimeters	Square inches	0.155
Square centimeters	Square meters	1×10^{-6}
Square centimeters	Square miles	3.861×10^{-11}

6

TO CONVERT	INTO	MULTIPLY BY
Square centimeters	Square millimeters	100
Square centimeters	Square yards	1.196×10^{-4}
Square feet	Acres	2.296×10^{-5}
Square feet	Circular mils	1.833×10^{8}
Square feet	Square cm.	929
Square feet	Square inches	144
Square feet	Square meters	0.0929
Square feet	Square miles	3.587×10^{-8}
Square feet	Sq. millimeters	9.29×10^{4}
Square feet	Square yards	0.1111
Square ft-ft squared	Sq. inches-inches sq.	2.074×10^{4}
Square inches	Circular mils	1.273×10^{6}
Square inches	Square cm.	6.452
Square inches	Square feet	6.944×10^{-3}
Square inches	Square mils	1×10^{6}
Square inches	Square millimeters	645.2
Square inches	Square yards	7.716×10^{-4}
Square inches-inches squared	Sq. cm-cm squared	41.62
Square inches-inches squared	Sq ft-ft. squared	4.823×10^{-5}
Square kilometers	Acres	247.1
Square kilometers	Sq. centimeters	1×10^{10}
Square kilometers	Square feet	10.76×10^{6}
Square kilometers	Square inches	1.55×10^{9}
Square kilometers	Square meters	1×10^{6}
Square kilometers	Square miles	0.3861
Square kilometers	Square yards	1.196×10^{6}
Square meters	Acres	2.471×10^{-4}
Square meters	Sq. centimeters	1×10^{4}
Square meters	Square feet	10.764
Square meters	Sq. inches	1,555.0
Square meters	Sq. miles	3.861×10^{-7}
Square meters	Sq. millimeters	1×10^{6}
Square meters	Sq. yards	1.196
Square miles	Acres	640
Square miles	Sq. feet	27.88×10^{6}
Square miles	Sq. kilometers	2.59
Square miles	Sq. meters	2.59×10^{6}
Square miles	Sq. yards	3.098×10^{6}
Square millimeters	Circular mils	1.973×10^{3}
Square millimeters	Sq. centimeters	0.01
Square millimeters	Sq. feet	1.076×10^{-5}
Square millimeters	Sq. inches	1.55×10^{-3}
Square mils	Circular mils	1.273
Square mils	Sq. cm.	6.452×10^{-6}
Square mils	Sq. inches	1×10^{-6}
Square yards	Acres	2.066×10^{-4}
Square yards	Sq. cm.	8,361.0
Square yards	Sq. feet	9

TO CONVERT	INTO	MULTIPLY BY
Square yards	Sq. inches	1,926.0
Square yards	Sq. meters	0.8361
Square yards	Sq. miles	3.228×10^{-7}
Square yards	Sq. millimeters	8.361×10^5
Statamperes	Abamperes	$^1/_3 \times 10^{-10}$
Statamperes	Amperes	$^1/_3 \times 10^{-9}$
Statcoulombs	Abcoulombs	$^1/_3 \times 10^{-10}$
Statcoulombs	Coulombs	$^1/_3 \times 10^{-9}$
Statfarads	Abfarads	$^1/_9 \times 10^{-20}$
Statfarads	Farads	$^1/_9 \times 10^{-11}$
Statfarads	Microfarads	$^1/_9 \times 10^{-5}$
Stathenries	Abhenries	9×10^{20}
Stathenries	Henries	9×10^{11}
Stathenries	Millihenries	9×10^{14}
Statohms	Abohms	9×10^{20}
Statohms	Megohms	9×10^5
Statohms	Microhms	9×10^{17}
Statohms	Ohms	9×10^{11}
Statvolts	Abvolts	3×10^{10}
Statvolts	Volts	300
Steradians	Hemispheres	0.1592
Steradians	Spheres	0.07958
Steradians	Spherical right angles	0.6366
Steres	Liters	1×10^3
(T) Tons (long)	Kilograms	1,0160.0
Tons (long)	Pounds	2,240.0
Tons (long)	Tons (short)	1.12
Tons (metric)	Kilograms	1000.0
Tons (metric)	Pounds	2,205.0
Tons (short)	Kilograms	907.2
Tons (short)	Ounces	32,000.0
Tons (short)	Ounces (troy)	29,166.66
Tons (short)	Pounds	2,000.0
Tons (short)	Pounds (troy)	2,430.6
Tons (short)	Tons (long)	0.8928
Tons (short)	Tons (metric)	0.9078
Tons (short)/square foot	Kilograms/sq. meter	9765
Tons (short)/square foot	Lbs/square inch	13.89
Tons (short)/sq. inch	Kilograms/sq. meter	1.406×10^6
Tons (short)/square inch	Lbs/sq. inch	2,000.0
Tons of water/24 hrs.	Lbs of water/hr.	83.333
Tons of water/24 hours	Gallons/min	0.16643
Tons of water/24 hours	Cubic feet/hr	1.3349
(V) Varas	Feet	2.7777
Varas	Inches	33.333

6

TO CONVERT	INTO	MULTIPLY BY
Varas	Miles	5.26×10^{-4}
Varas	Yards	0.9259
Volts	Abvolts	1×10^{8}
Volts	Kilovolts	1×10^{-3}
Volts	Microvolts	1×10^{6}
Volts	Millivolts	1×10^{3}
Volts	Statvolts	1/300
Volts/inch	Abvolts/cm.	3.937×10^{7}
Volts/inch	Statvolts/cm.	1.312×10^{-3}
(W) Watts	BTU/min.	0.05692
Watts	BTU/hr.	3.413
Watts	Ergs/second	1×10^{7}
Watts	Ft-lb/minute	44.26
Watts	Ft-lbs/second	0.7376
Watts	Horsepower	1.341×10^{-3}
Watts	Horsepower (metric)	1.360×10^{-3}
Watts	Kilogram-cals/min	0.01434
Watts	Kilowatts	1×10^{-3}
Watts	Microwatts	1×10^{6}
Watts	Milliwatts	1×10^{3}
Watt-hours	BTU	3.415
Watt-hours	Ergs	3.6×10^{10}
Watt-hours	Foot-pounds	2,655.0
Watt-hours	Gram-cals	859.85
Watt-hours	Horsepower-hrs	1.341×10^{-3}
Watt-hours	Kilogram-cals	0.8605
Watt-hours	Kilogram-meters	367.2
Watt-hours	Kilowatt-hrs	1×10^{-3}
Webers	Maxwells	1×10^{8}
Webers	Kilolines	1×10^{5}
Webers/square inch	Gausses	1.55×10^{7}
Webers/square inch	Lines/sq. inch	1×10^{8}
Webers/square inch	Webers/sq. cm.	0.155
Webers/square inch	Webers/sq. meter	1,550.0
Webers/square meter	Gausses	1×10^{4}
Webers/square meter	Lines/sq. inch	6.452×10^{4}
Webers/square meter	Webers/sq. cm.	1×10^{-4}
Webers/square meter	Webers/sq. inch	6.452×10^{-4}
Weeks	Hours	168
Weeks	Minutes	10,080.0
Weeks	Seconds	604,800.0
(Y) Yards	Centimeters	91.44
Yards	Feet	3.0
Yards	Inches	36.0
Yards	Kilometers	9.144×10^{-4}

TO CONVERT	INTO	MULTIPLY BY
Yards	Meters	0.9144
Yards	Miles (nautical)	4.934×10^{-4}
Yards	Miles (statute)	5.682×10^{-4}
Yards	Millimeters	914.4
Years (common)	Days	365
Years (common)	Hours	8,760.0
Years (leap)	Days	366
Years (leap)	Hours	8,784.0

6

Index

(All references are to section numbers)